D1220921

A CATALOGUE OF THE GREEK AND ROMAN SCULPTURE IN THE FITZWILLIAM MUSEUM CAMBRIDGE

A CATALOGUE OF THE GREEK AND ROMAN SCULPTURE IN THE FITZWILLIAM MUSEUM CAMBRIDGE

BY
LUDWIG BUDDE
AND
RICHARD NICHOLLS

CAMBRIDGE
PUBLISHED FOR
THE FITZWILLIAM MUSEUM
AT THE UNIVERSITY PRESS
1964

PUBLISHED BY
THE SYNDICS OF THE CAMBRIDGE UNIVERSITY PRESS
Bentley House, 200 Euston Road, London, N.W. 1
American Branch: 32 East 57th Street, New York 22, N.Y.
West African Office: P.O. Box 33, Ibadan, Nigeria

Printed in Great Britain at the University Printing House, Cambridge
(Brooke Crutchley, University Printer)

CONTENTS

PREFACE

A grant from the British Council enabled Professor Ludwig Budde, then Dozent in archaeology at the University of Münster, to come to Cambridge in the years 1947–8. He was granted membership of King's College for the period of his stay, which he spent in preparing a catalogue of the Greek and Roman sculpture in the Fitzwilliam Museum. He desires to express his thanks both to the British Council and to the Provost and Fellows of King's for the hospitality which enabled him to undertake the work now published.

The German manuscript was translated, completed and thoroughly revised between 1959 and 1961 by Mr Richard Nicholls, then Senior Assistant Keeper, now Keeper, of the Museum's Department of Antiquities. Mr Nicholls was aided in studying comparative material abroad, particularly in Greece and in Italy, by grants made from the Craven Fund by the University's Faculty Board of Classics.

The catalogue is to be regarded as the joint work of both authors. Mr Nicholls is responsible for its final form, but this and the content of every entry were discussed and agreed upon between him and Professor Budde during a further visit made by the latter to Cambridge in 1961.

The negatives for the illustrations were made by the two authors, and the prints and enlargements used for reproduction have been made, by kind permission of Professor J. D. Boyd, with great care and skill by Mr J. F. Crane, Mr J. A. F. Fozzard, and Mr G. Oakes.

Professor Bernard Ashmole and Professor Jocelyn Toynbee have been so good as to read the text, which has been much improved by their suggestions. Sections of it have also been read and helpfully criticized by Professor R. M. Cook, Professor C. M. Robertson, and the late Dr E. M. W. Tillyard. Professor Budde wishes to record his debt to the late Professor R. Harder and to Mr D. E. L. Haynes for their help in the earlier stages of his work. Mr Nicholls is similarly obliged to Professor E. B. Harrison, Dr E. Paribeni, Dr D. E. Strong, and Professor H. A. Thompson for their courtesy in sparing time to discuss large parts of the material with him at a later stage in the preparation of the catalogue. Dr C. L. Forbes of the Sedgwick Museum of Geology has been so good as to identify the materials in which the sculptures are carved, and thanks are also owed to Mr M. H. Ballance for advice on this subject. Much information about the sculptures was provided by the late Dr Winifred Lamb, who maintained a lively interest in the catalogue, which had been begun while she was still Honorary Keeper of the Museum's Department of Greek and Roman Antiquities.

A special debt is owed to Mr N. C. Rayner, Senior Assistant in the Department of Antiquities, and to other members of the staff, who have helped him to remount many of the sculptures and to free others of inappropriate restorations.

Many scholars have been consulted about specific questions and have helped with advice and information; among these may be named Mrs S. A. Adam, Sir John Beazley, Mr J. Boardman, Mr E. C. Chamberlain, Professor J. M. Cook, Mr M. A. Cook, Professor P. E. Corbett, Dr D. Diringer, Dr F. Eckstein, Dr Nezih Fıratlı, the Reverend H. St J. Hart, Mr H. Honour, Dr L. H. Jeffery, Dr K. V. Karageorghis, Mrs S. Karouzou, Mr J. W. Pope-Hennessy, Dr D. J. de S. Price, Miss J. M. Reynolds, Mrs I. Scott-Ryberg, Professor T. B. L. Webster, and Mr A. G. Woodhead.

To the Council of the Senate of the University the Syndics of the Fitzwilliam Museum express their thanks for a non-recurrent grant which has made the publication of this and of other catalogues possible. Donations generously made by the Faculty Board of Classics and by the Council of the British Academy have been used, with the accumulated income of a fund bequeathed to the Museum in 1935 by the late Mr William Emerton Heitland, as a subsidy to keep the price of the catalogue within the reach of those by whom it is hoped that it will be most used. Thanks are owed finally to Mr Brooke Crutchley, Printer to the University, and to his staff, for the scrupulous attention they have given to the form of the book. The proofs have been read by Miss P. M. Giles and Mr N. C. Rayner.

CARL WINTER

INTRODUCTION

The history of the Fitzwilliam Museum's collection of Greek and Roman sculpture begins in 1818, two years after the Museum's endowment by the bequest of its founder, Richard, seventh Viscount Fitzwilliam of Merrion. In that year it received a Roman statue of the Egyptian god, Bes (**117** in the present catalogue), as a gift from A. E. Gregory of Jesus College. In 1835 Admiral Sir Pulteney Malcolm presented what may well claim to rank as the finest Roman sarcophagus in the country—a work doubly remarkable as being a metropolitan Roman product exported to Greece. This is the so-called Pashley Sarcophagus (**161**), showing the triumphant return of Dionysos from the East. The circumstance that these two works were the only classical sculptures acquired by the Museum in the first half of the nineteenth century is probably attributable to two causes: the slow progress with the building itself, which was not ready to receive the collections until 1848, and the fact that, since 1803, the University's main body of Greek and Roman sculpture had been housed elsewhere, in the University Public Library at the Old Schools.

In 1850 the situation changed dramatically. In that year the Museum was presented by Dr J. Disney with almost all of the collection of marbles which had been gathered over the past century at the Hyde, near Ingatestone, Essex—a gift which alone accounts for almost eighty entries in the present catalogue. The majority of these sculptures had been acquired in Italy between 1748 and 1753 by Thomas Hollis and his friend and heir, Thomas Brand (subsequently renamed Thomas Brand Hollis), although a few items had also been bought in England. Although the collection included a good deal that was spurious, it also contained ancient works of outstanding merit, such as the young satyr or Pan (**83**) and the heads of Ganymedes and Sarapis (**54** and **57**). It included two fine sarcophagi (**162**, **163**), a good range of Imperial Roman portraits (**108** f.) and a varied array of cineraria, one of them (**145**) being of the very highest quality. Not all of the material acquired in Italy had necessarily been found there; the Greek votive reliefs (**35**, **59**, **60**) and the eastern provincial portraits (**110**, **114**, **115**) had doubtless been brought there in comparatively recent times. Some of these sculptures had been mentioned or illustrated in the *Memoirs of Thomas Hollis, Esq.*, published posthumously by his friends in 1780. In 1804 Thomas Brand Hollis had bequeathed the Hyde and the collections it contained to Disney's father, John Disney sr., and in 1807 and 1809 the elder Disney had issued two editions of the first complete catalogue of the objects at the Hyde, the second edition being illustrated with engravings largely derived from the

Hollis *Memoirs*. In 1816 the house and collection had passed to the Museum's benefactor, John Disney jr. In 1817 he had sold a large number of the coins and books and, in the years that followed, he had employed the proceeds in making new purchases, both in England and in Italy. In his choice of ancient marbles Disney had proved little more discerning than his predecessors and added several palpable forgeries to the collection as well as ancient works of major importance, notably a head of Plato (**53**) and a torso of Apollo (**39**—not included in the gift, this last was secured for the Museum by purchase in 1885). In 1824 Disney had completed a manuscript catalogue of his collection and in 1846–9 he had published sections of this, with engravings, under the title *Museum Disneianum*. Finally, following his gift to the Museum in 1850, a short, numbered handlist was issued by the first Disney Professor, described as a *Catalogue of a Collection of Ancient Marbles Presented to the University of Cambridge by John Disney, Esquire, F.R.S., F.S.A.*

In 1853 and 1854 gifts from Vice-Admiral T. A. B. Spratt brought the Museum two sculptures from Crete, an archaic graffito (**25**) and the lid of an Attic sarcophagus (**158**), together with several inscriptions not dealt with in this catalogue. The year 1865 saw the emergence of a balanced collection of both Greek and Roman material. In this year the sculptures and inscriptions lodged since 1803 in the University Public Library were transferred to the Fitzwilliam Museum. The greater part of this collection had been assembled at the beginning of the nineteenth century by Professor E. D. Clarke in the course of the travels he made with J. M. Cripps in eastern Europe, the Aegean and the east Mediterranean. The circumstances under which most of the pieces had been acquired were described by Clarke in his *Travels in Various Countries of Europe, Asia and Africa* (1810 f.). Their provenances are diverse—from the Cimmerian Bosporus, western Asia Minor, Attica, the Greek islands, Cyprus and Egypt. Most remarkable was the colossal female figure from Eleusis (**81**), which had been drawn and described by travellers as early as the seventeenth century. The upper part of one of the two caryatids from the first-century-B.C. Inner Propylaea, it had been interpreted by Clarke as part of the cult statue of Demeter. In 1803 he had published an account of it entitled *Testimonies of Different Authors respecting the Colossal Statue of Ceres, Placed in the Vestibule of the Public Library at Cambridge, July the First, 1803*. Other notable items were a fragment from the Phaidros Bema (**122**), believed by Clarke to be part of a metope of the Parthenon, an Attic decree-heading from Sigeion (**27**) and an Attic votive relief to Asklepios and Hygieia (**123**). The collection had survived shipwreck off Beachy Head and had been brought to Cambridge and presented to the University in its entirety. Other donors had quickly followed suit so that the Clarke marbles had formed the nucleus of a rich and growing collection of Greek sculpture. The Earl of Aberdeen had given a hero-relief from Athens (**36**), the Rev. Bridges Harvey a round altar from Delos (**71**), Capt. G. Clarke part of a base from Pergamon (**75**), John Spencer Smith the splendid Attic grave-lekythos of Hegemon (**29**), the Rev. R. Walpole a torso of Asklepios from Knidos and a relief of a comic mask from Stratonicea (**58** and **121**), and Dr J. Fiott Lee a Hellenistic hero-relief from Asia Minor (**63**). In 1809 Clarke had published a catalogue of this already important collection, entitled *Greek Marbles Brought from the Shores of the Euxine, Archipelago, and Mediterranean, and Deposited in the Vestibule of the Public Library of the University of Cambridge*. Such, then, were the sculptures transferred to the Fitzwilliam Museum in 1865.

In 1874 C. F. Tyrwhitt Drake, joint-author with Sir Richard Burton of *Unexplored Syria*, bequeathed to the Museum a miniature shrine from Ḳanawât in Syria (**126**). This was its most recent accession to be mentioned in Professor A. Michaelis's *Ancient Marbles in Great Britain*, published in Cambridge in 1882. Michaelis had gathered most of his material during visits to England in 1873 and 1877. His account of the sculptures in the Fitzwilliam Museum was by far the most accurate and comprehensive that had existed up to that time (*ibid.* 241 f.). But his work is also to be regarded as marking the culmination of a much longer period of activity by German scholars in England and of their attempts to apply their emergent science of the criticism of ancient art to the Greek and Roman sculpture in this country. With regard to the collections in Cambridge one may instance the earlier assessments of Conze and Huebner (*AA* 1864 169 f., 1866 301).

From 1883 to 1889 the Museum had, in the person of Professor Sir Charles Walston, a classical archaeologist for its Director, and its collection of Greek and Roman sculpture benefited from his activity. Walston himself presented some notable pieces which had been acquired in Greek lands by W. Railton, the architect, during his travels there beginning in 1825. These numbered amongst them an antefix from the Parthenon (**166**) and the Attic grave-stele of Theokles (**30**). Purchases included the figure of a river god (**84**), dredged from his familiar element in the bed of the Tiber, and the Museum's collection of Palmyrene reliefs (**139** f.). A fragment from a Roman decorative relief showing a rural scene (**129**) was presented by Mrs W. H. Thompson and a number of marbles were bequeathed by the Master of Downing College, the Rev. Dr Thomas Worsley. These included a second Delian altar (**72**) and an Attic grave-loutrophoros (**32**). In 1884 the Museum's growing collection of casts of Greek and Roman sculpture was transferred to the newly completed Museum of Classical Archaeology in Little St Mary's Lane, which functioned as a special department of the Fitzwilliam Museum until it achieved autonomy in 1911.

In this period excavations abroad bulked large as a source of new works of classical sculpture. The Fitzwilliam Museum benefited particularly from the investigations at the Greek trading centre at Naukratis in Egypt and from the various activities sponsored by the Cyprus Exploration Fund. The Naukratis excavations were carried out by Petrie and Gardner in 1884–6 on behalf of the Egypt Exploration Fund and continued by Hogarth in 1899 and 1903 under the joint aegis of the Egypt Exploration Fund and the British School at Athens; they yielded most of the archaic limestone sculptures in a mixed Cypriot–East-Greek style (**15** f.), pieces of decorative stucco (**179** f.) and various Hellenistic fragments

(**78** f.). The work undertaken by the Cyprus Exploration Fund at Paphos in 1887–8 produced a number of Hellenistic sculptures now in this Museum, including the statuette dedicated by Artemidoros (**68**) and the little figure of a goddess with Eros hovering behind her (**77**). From their excavations in 1889 on the site of the ancient Marion came a fourth-century-B.C. Attic grave-stele showing an old man (**31**). The exploration of Salamis conducted by the same body in 1890 was even more rewarding. Here an early sanctuary site on the 'Toumba' produced the archaic statuettes, **22** f., together with several others now in the Museum of Classical Archaeology, and the imported East-Greek figure of a god or hero grappling with a lion (**17**). Probes elsewhere in the city, in an area which the recent excavations of Dr K. V. Karageorghis have revealed as the site of a second-century-A.D. gymnasium complex, uncovered three major sculptures now in the Fitzwilliam Museum: a torso of Eros, perhaps copied from the famous Eros of Parion by Praxiteles (**52**), a Sarapis (**56**), and the body of a large Roman figure of Dionysos or Apollo (**98**).

Meanwhile the flow of accessions from other sources was not interrupted. In 1890 Sir W. M. Flinders Petrie gave two Coptic capitals (**176** and **177**). The foundations for a collection of prehistoric Greek sculpture were laid in 1901 by the gift of three Cycladic idols from Professor R. C. Bosanquet (**8**, **10**, **12**) and the purchase of an Early Minoan marble figurine (**14**), followed in 1902 by the Greek Government's presentation of the head of an idol (**9**) from the British excavations at Phylakopi in Melos. But the most valuable acquisition in this field came by gift from Professor R. M. Dawkins in 1909; it was a neolithic statuette from Thessaly representing a fat woman (**1**). In 1902 a curious piece of Roman provincial sculpture in the form of a Lykaonian altar to Zeus and Helios (**124**) was jointly presented by the Rev. H. S. Cronin, Professor W. M. Ramsay and G. A. Wathen. Among a number of works purchased in 1906–7 may be instanced a sun-dial (**185**), a statuette of Artemis of the Rospigliosi type (**89**), and a very careful copy of Bryaxis' Sarapis (**55**). In 1908 came the important gift from the Rev. T. P. A. Fletcher of part of a figure from the Erechtheion frieze (**26**).

In 1898 and 1904 H. A. Chapman, an Assistant on the staff of the Museum, published two editions of his *Handbook to the Collection of Antiquities and Other Objects Exhibited in the Fitzwilliam Museum*. Chapman's assessments of the different sculptures are largely derived from earlier published accounts, in particular that of Michaelis, but he endeavoured to give a detailed factual description and his entries contain much valuable information on matters of provenance. In this period, also, there were issued two major publications of *corpus*-type which included the Museum's Attic grave-monuments and Bosporan stelae: A. Conze's *Attische Grabreliefs* (1893–1922) and G. von Kierseritzky's and C. Watzinger's *Griechische Grabreliefs aus Südrussland* (1909).

In 1912 the bequest of C. B. Marlay gave the Museum two Roman heads, a portrait of Antoninus Pius (**112**) and the idealized likeness of a young man (**90**). Other works of

Roman date were acquired not long afterwards, in 1917 various couch legs from the Hope Collection (**183**), and in 1919 the second-century-A.D. Attic grave-stele of Aphrodisia (**133**), the latter being purchased with funds provided by the Friends of the Fitzwilliam Museum. Even more important was the gift by Lord Carmichael in 1920 of one of the earliest extant Roman marble sarcophagi (**160**). A further fragment from the Erechtheion, this time a piece of moulding probably from the north porch (**167**), was given by Sir John and Lady Sandys in 1919. The lovely Attic statuette of Demeter (**47**) was bequeathed by Professor W. R. Lethaby in 1931. Meanwhile every effort was being made to strengthen the Bronze Age collection. In 1926 a marble statuette of a Minoan goddess or votary (**186**) was purchased from the Marlay Fund. In the following year the late Professor A. J. B. Wace devoted a volume to its description, entitled *A Cretan Statuette in the Fitzwilliam Museum*. The trend of more recent opinion has been to regard this figure as an extremely skilful modern forgery, but it has not yet been possible to reject it outright on technical grounds. Exempt from such doubts are a further Cycladic idol bought in 1924 (**11**) and seven more given by the Friends of the Fitzwilliam Museum between 1933 and 1934 (**2–7, 13**).

The most important large body of Greek and Roman sculpture to reach the Museum in the present century came by bequest in 1937. This was the collection formed by the artists C. S. Ricketts and C. H. Shannon, and jointly bequeathed by them. Its sculptures numbered a few pieces of doubtful authenticity among them, but, for the most part, consisted of ancient works of outstanding merit. Foremost among them are a relief-fragment apparently from a fourth-century-B.C. monumental base (**37**), a Hellenistic head of a girl (**69**), the torso from a very fine copy of the Apollo Sauroktonos of Praxiteles (**51**), and a colossal head of Antinous from Hadrian's Villa (**109**), formerly at Lansdowne House. In view of their importance, it is a regrettable circumstance that all of these sculptures came to the Museum without any record of their original provenance and, save for the Antinous, it is no longer easy to conjecture what their history may have been. Other acquisitions over this period included a miniature Ionic capital from Sicily (**168**) given by Dr C. F. Rogers in 1934 and a remarkable Roman monument of the Cybele-cult (**125**) bequeathed by G. A. Warren in 1938. This last seems to have been a kind of repository in the shape of an altar; it was first made known in an article by Dr E. M. W. Tillyard. In 1948 the Viscountess D'Abernon presented the 'Sir Edgar Vincent head' (**42**)—one of the very finest extant copies of the head of a statue by Polykleitos showing a victorious young athlete and probably to be identified with his Kyniskos at Olympia.

From a variety of causes the Museum is reasonably rich in Greek and Roman sculpture found in Egypt. Recently this tendency has been strengthened by a small number of classical pieces occurring in the very large gifts and bequests of Egyptian material received over the past quarter century. Among these may be numbered a head probably of Dionysos (**93**) presented by G. D. Hornblower in 1936, part of a small capital (**171**) bequeathed by Major

R. G. Gayer-Anderson in 1943, and two statuettes of Aphrodite Anadyomene (**85**, **86**) bequeathed by Sir Robert Greg in 1954.

To reduce overcrowding, in 1947 a number of the Cypriot statuettes hitherto displayed in the Fitzwilliam Museum were transferred to the Museum of Classical Archaeology in Cambridge, together with many of the Cypriot vases and terracottas. The sculptures so transferred are not included in this catalogue. In 1952, in an exchange of material with the Museum of Archaeology and Ethnology in Cambridge, a head probably of Aphrodite (**102**) and two cineraria (**148**, **190**) were formally added to the Museum's collection where they had already figured for several years as loans. In 1959 Dr D. von Bothmer and Dr C. C. Vermeule published Part III. 1 of their *Notes on a New Edition of Michaelis* in Volume LXIII of the *American Journal of Archaeology*. This was one of a series of articles aimed at bringing Michaelis's *Ancient Marbles in Great Britain* up to date and covered, *inter alia*, the sculptures in Cambridge. In anticipation of the present catalogue, only a little space was allocated to the Fitzwilliam Museum, but many of its acquisitions since 1882 were listed and recent bibliography was provided. The latest additions to the collection have been made in 1960 and 1961 by the purchase of two pieces of sculpture from funds provided by Sir William Elderton. These are a Hekateion (**92**) and a late Republican Roman portrait (**82**).

Such, then, is the history of the collection of Greek and Roman sculpture published in this catalogue. The catalogue covers not only the Museum's own material, but also two reliefs lent to it since 1924 (**64** and **134**), which have been included by courtesy of the Master and Fellows of Trinity College, Cambridge, to whom they belong. With negligible exceptions (**5–7**, **179**, **180**), the scope of the catalogue has been limited to sculpture *in stone*. Apart from a few Roman or early medieval pieces in the Egyptian Department (**104**, **171**, **175–7**) and the Trinity College reliefs, the objects published here belong to the Museum's Department of Greek and Roman Antiquities. The sculptures of Renaissance and later date that have come to this Department as supposedly ancient works are briefly listed, without illustrations, in the final section of the catalogue.

In the interests of brevity, two repetitive heads of information have been deliberately suppressed in the catalogue entries. First, the year in which the Museum acquired a given work is not separately stated, since this is already given by the last four digits of the Museum inventory number quoted at the end of the first paragraph of each entry. The few exceptions with a shorter form of inventory serial (**43**, **67**, **87**, **88**, **118**, **165**, **175**, **195**, **198**) represent those objects whose year of acquisition is not recorded. The other deliberate omission has been from the bibliographies given at the end of the catalogue entries, where no reference is made to the *Annual Report of the Fitzwilliam Museum Syndicate* unless it has carried an illustration of the sculpture in question. Normally all of the Museum's acquisitions will also be found briefly listed in the issue of this report covering their year of accession. The report itself has been published independently since 1886, prior to which date it appeared only in the *Cambridge University Reporter*. Among the numerous guide-books issued for the benefit of visitors to the Museum, reference has been mainly confined to the most detailed—the second edition of Chapman's *Handbook* of 1904—and the most recent to date—the *Handbook and Guide* of 1960. The other publications of this nature add little information about the sculptures themselves, but do help one to follow the growth of the collection and the different arrangements made for its display. Of interest from this point of view are various lists issued in 1826, 1833 and 1846, the *Handbook to the Marbles, Casts and Antiquities* of 1855 and the *Visitor's Guide* of 1868. The measurements quoted in the present catalogue are in metres.

It is hoped that this catalogue will make the Greek and Roman sculpture in the Fitzwilliam Museum more accessible to scholars abroad, to students of classical archaeology in Cambridge, and to all interested members of the public.

ABBREVIATIONS

The following have been used in the technical descriptions of the individual sculptures: *D.*: depth; *H.*: height; *L.*: length; *T.*: thickness; *W.*: width; *P.D.*: preserved depth; *P.H.*: preserved height; *P.L.*: preserved length; *P.T.*: preserved thickness; *P.W.*: preserved width; *m.*: metre(s). The principal abbreviations used in citing other publications are listed below, where full details are also given of the rarer works having a special pertinence to the Fitzwilliam Museum collection.

AA *Archäologischer Anzeiger.*

Abh. bay Ak. *Abhandlungen der bayerischen Akademie der Wissenschaften.*

Abh. Heidelberg *Abhandlungen der heidelberger Akademie der Wissenschaften.*

ADelt Ἀρχαιολογικὸν Δελτίον.

AE Ἀρχαιολογικὴ Ἐφημερίς.

AJA *American Journal of Archaeology.*

AM *Mitteilungen des deutschen archäologischen Instituts, Athenische Abteilung.*

Amelung, *Kat. vaticanischen Museums* W. Amelung, *Die Skulpturen des vaticanischen Museums* I–II.

Ann. *Annuario della scuola archeologica di Atene.*

ARW *Archiv für Religionswissenschaft.*

AZ *Archäologische Zeitung.*

BCH *Bulletin de correspondance hellénique.*

Blümel, *Kat. Berlin* C. Blümel, *Staatliche Museen zu Berlin, Katalog der Sammlung antiker Skulpturen.*

BMC *British Museum Catalogue of....*

BMQ *British Museum Quarterly.*

Brunn-Bruckmann *Brunn-Bruckmann's Denkmäler griechischer und römischer Sculptur* (with text by P. Arndt, G. Lippold and others).

BSA *Annual of the British School at Athens.*

BSR *Papers of the British School at Rome.*

Bull. *Bulletin of....*

CAH *Cambridge Ancient History.*

Cat. *Catalogue of....*

Chapman, *Handbook* H. A. Chapman, *A Handbook of the Collection of Antiquities and Other Objects Exhibited in the Fitzwilliam Museum*, first edition, 1898, second edition, 1904.

CIG *Corpus Inscriptionum Graecarum.*

CIL *Corpus Inscriptionum Latinarum.*

Clarke, *Marbles* E. D. Clarke, *Greek Marbles Brought from the Shores of the Euxine, Archipelago, and Mediterranean, and Deposited in the Vestibule of the Public Library of the University of Cambridge*, 1809.

Clarke, *Travels* E. D. Clarke, *Travels in Various Countries of Europe, Asia and Africa*, 1810 f. Reference is given to both the quarto and the octavo editions, which have quite different volume divisions and pagination.

CVA *Corpus Vasorum Antiquorum.*

Disney, J., jr., *MS Cat.* J. Disney, *An Arranged Catalogue of My Marbles at the Hyde, Improved from the Printed Catalogues of 1807 and 1809, with Additions and Corrections*, a manuscript dated 1824, lodged in the Fitzwilliam Museum Library. This is only cited where it provides information not given in *Museum Disneianum.*

Disney, J., jr., *Museum Disneianum* J. Disney, *Museum Disneianum, being a Description of a Collection of Ancient Marbles, Specimens of Ancient Bronze, and Various Ancient Fictile Vases, in the Possession of John Disney, Esq., F.R.S., F.S.A., at the Hyde, near Ingatestone*, 1846 f.

Disney, J., sr., *Cat. Hyde* J. Disney, *A Catalogue of Some Marbles, Bronzes, Pictures, and Gems, at the Hyde, near Ingatestone, Essex*, second edition, 1809.

EA P. Arndt, W. Amelung, G. Lippold and others, *Photographische Einzelaufnahmen antiker Sculpturen.*

Erg *Ergänzungsheft....*

FD École Française d'Athènes, *Fouilles de Delphes.*

GGA *Göttingische gelehrte Anzeigen.*

Handbook and Guide (1960) *Handbook to the Fitzwilliam Museum, Cambridge, with a Summary, Room-to-Room Guide*, fourth edition, 1960.

HdA *Handbuch der Archäologie.*

IG *Inscriptiones Graecae.*

ILN *Illustrated London News.*

Inst. *Institute of....*
Jb *Jahrbuch....*
JdI *Jahrbuch des deutschen archäologischen Instituts.*
JEA *Journal of Egyptian Archaeology.*
JHS *Journal of Hellenic Studies.*
JRS *Journal of Roman Studies.*
LAAA *Annals of Archaeology and Anthropology of the University of Liverpool.*
Lippold, *Kat. vaticanischen Museums* G. Lippold, *Die Skulpturen des vaticanischen Museums* III. 1–III. 2.
MA *Monumenti antichi.*
MAMA *Monumenta Asiae Minoris Antiqua.*
Marsden, *Cat. Disney Coll.* (J. H. Marsden), *Catalogue of a Collection of Ancient Marbles Presented to the University of Cambridge by John Disney, Esquire, F.R.S., F.S.A.*, cited here as issued as an appendix to Idem, *Two Introductory Lectures Delivered in the University of Cambridge*, 1852, 81 f.
MemAmAc Rome *Memoirs of the American Academy at Rome.*
Mendel, *Cat. Constantinople* G. Mendel, *Musées Impériaux Ottomans, catalogue des sculptures grecques, romaines et byzantines.*
Michaelis, *Anc. Marbles* A. Michaelis, *Ancient Marbles in Great Britain*, translated from the German by C. A. M. Fennell, 1882.
Mon. Piot *Monuments et Mémoires, Fondation Eugène Piot.*
Mus. *Museum of....*
NdSc *Notizie degli scavi di antichità.*
ÖJh *Jahreshefte des österreichischen archäologischen Instituts.*
PAE Πρακτικὰ τῆς Ἀρχαιολογικῆς Ἑταιρείας.
PhW *Philologische Wochenschrift.*
Picard, *Manuel* C. Picard, *Manuel d'archéologie grecque, la sculpture.*
PM Sir Arthur Evans, *The Palace of Minos at Knossos.*
RA *Revue archéologique.*
RE G. Wissowa, W. Kroll, K. Mittelhaus, K. Ziegler, W. John (editors), *Paulys Realencyclopädie der classischen Altertumswissenschaft.*
RM *Mitteilungen des deutschen archäologischen Instituts, Römische Abteilung.*
SB bay Ak. *Sitzungsberichte der bayerischen Akademie der Wissenschaften zu München.*
SCE *Swedish Cyprus Expedition.*
Suppl. *Supplement.*

Together with the following necessitated by additions made in the revision of the text:

Acc. *Accademia.*
ActArch *Acta Archaeologica.*
MdI *Mitteilungen des deutschen archäologischen Instituts.*
RhMus *Rheinisches Museum.*

I

NEOLITHIC AND BRONZE AGE STATUETTES

(A) NEOLITHIC

1 Obese female idol, standing naked

PLATE I

Presented by Professor R. M. Dawkins. From Avaritsa (ancient Meliteia), Thessaly. Inv.: GR.157*b*.1909.

P.H. 0·12 m., greatest depth 0·067 m. Medium-grained white marble with greyish mottling. Ankles chipped away behind; left fore-arm damaged; head missing. Back encrusted with cement; other surfaces somewhat corroded.

The bent arms are indicated somewhat schematically placed one above the other on the chest, perhaps as if folded. The breasts are not shown individually at all, but great emphasis is given to the abdomen and thighs and there are sagging pockets of fat at the belly, knees and ankles. The feet are rudimentary, but have a flattened surface underneath on which the figure stands. In the stump of the neck there is a small hole, presumably for the attachment of a head. This may, however, quite well represent an ancient repair rather than relate itself, as has been claimed, to the later Thessalian practice of fashioning the heads as separate units.

The treatment of the body shows resemblances to Early Neolithic A terracotta figurines from Sesklo[1] and the idol has been claimed as a local Thessalian product. Whether this is justified or not it is impossible as yet to say, since it remains the sole example of the style in stone from that region. However, the material might possibly be an island marble and the figure belongs squarely in the broader Aegean tradition of plump marble idols.[2] Amongst these, the affinities that it shows with the statuettes from Naxos and Gortyn, which have been placed as late as the beginning of the Bronze Age, would seem to dissuade too high a dating. It is to be noted that, in arriving at approximate absolute dates in this section of the publication, a moderately low chronology has been used, much as that advanced by Matz in *Handbuch der Archäologie* II, *Jüngere Steinzeit und Bronzezeit in Europa* 180.

Probably early–mid third millennium B.C.

A. J. B. Wace and M. S. Thompson, *Prehistoric Thessaly* 170, fig. 115; H. T. Bossert, *Altkreta* (3rd ed.) fig. 85; *Hesperia Suppl.* VIII (1939) 424; *AJA* LV (1951) 125.

(B) CYCLADIC

In the absence, as yet, of any adequate sequence based on dated find-groups, the following Cycladic idols are arranged according to such typological development as may perhaps be inferred from the figures themselves.[3] This is most conveniently to be assessed in the many plates of Chr. Zervos, *L'Art des Cyclades.*

[1] Chr. Tsountas, Αἱ προϊστορικαὶ ἀκροπόλεις Διμηνίου καὶ Σέσκλου 283 f., 290 f., pl. 32. 1–3; A. J. B. Wace and M. S. Thompson, *Prehistoric Thessaly* 68, fig. 35. For the later acrolithic idols with detachable heads referred to above, cf. Wace and Thompson, *op. cit.* 41, fig. 25.

[2] E.g. the standing idols from Asia Minor: *BSA* XIX (1912–13) 48 f., fig. 1; from Gortyn: *PM* I 50 f., fig. 13. 8; from Naxos: *Report of the Visitors to the Ashmolean Museum* 1946 13, pl. 1*d*; Chr. Zervos, *L'Art des Cyclades* fig. 36; from Aegina: *AA* 1910 48, fig. 1, G. Welter, *Aigina* 10, fig. 8; from Eleusis: Mylonas, Προϊστορικὴ Ἐλευσίς 139, fig. 115; from Sparta: *AM* XVI (1891) 52 f. nos. 1–2. Cf. also *Hesperia* XXV (1956) 175 f.; D. von Bothmer, *Exhibition from the Collection of Walter Cummings Baker* 10 no. 52, pl. 15. For the squatting and seated varieties see the material assembled in *AJA* LV (1951) 121 f. On interpretation see *PM* I 45 f.; *Essays Presented to Sir Arthur Evans* 55 f.; V. Müller, *Frühe Plastik in Griechenland und Vorderasien* 3 f.

[3] The vast majority are from graves, although a few have been found inside houses, e.g. *Excavations at Phylakopi in Melos* (*JHS Suppl. Paper* IV) 11, 194 f. Only a few of the relevant grave-groups have been published, e.g. *AE* 1898 152 f.; *AM* XI (1886) 20 f. (found with *AM* XVI 49), XVI (1891) 48; Papavasilios, Περὶ τῶν ἐν Εὐβοίᾳ ἀρχαίων τάφων 4 f.; *AA* 1935 655 f. (found with Bossert, *Altkreta* (3rd ed.) fig. 409). For the most recent general treatment see

It is thus taken that from the fat, squatting and seated neolithic figures there may stem, directly or indirectly, the highly stylized, long-necked, fiddle-shaped idols (Zervos, figs. 53 ff.), occasionally betraying more naturalistic origins (Zervos, fig. 49).[1] It is further assumed that, perhaps parallel with these, there may emerge from its neolithic counterpart (see above) the early, long-necked, standing variety of Cycladic idol. This type tends either to have the arms rendered as simple stumps (Zervos, figs. 38–42, 106) or else to have the hands meeting below the chest in a primitive fashion (Zervos, figs. 43, 47–8, 105, 112). What little steatopygy there may have been in evidence on the neolithic idols has already vanished. From this type, by various stages (as witness, perhaps, **2–8**), presumably there gradually emerged the developed Cycladic idol with folded arms, back-tilted head and slightly flexed legs (**9–11**; Zervos, figs. 104, 107–10, 113–15, 163–4, 176, 246, 293–5). To judge from the position of the feet, the commonest type is now conceived as reclining rather than standing. Eventually, however, the modelling of these figures seems to have become rather weakened and over-refined, broadening in the frontal plane but being much reduced in depth (**12** and possibly **13**; Zervos, figs. 158, 165, 244–5, 247–55).

This typological sequence may be real, but must be of limited value for dating because of the enormous local differences that must have existed. For chronology, a higher limit is perhaps suggested by the neolithic affinities of the earlier pieces. In fixing a lower limit, it is to be observed that 'developed' idols seem to occur in contexts of Furumark's extended Early Cycladic II phase as well as in others of Early Helladic date in Attica and of the Early Minoan period in Crete.[2] However, some of the thin, 'over-refined' variety described above are, on internal evidence, probably at least contemporary with the Cretan Middle Minoan I phase (e.g. Zervos, fig. 253, an idol wearing a Middle Minoan belt and sheath).

2 Female idol — PLATE I

Presented by the Friends of the Fitzwilliam Museum. Said to have been found in a tomb in Paros, apparently with **3–7** below. Inv.: GR.8*c*.1933.

H. 0·122 m. Moderately fine-grained white marble (Parian ?). Front surface cleaned; back encrusted.

Cut from a perfectly flat, smooth slab of marble, 0·006 m. thick. The edges are slightly rounded, especially about the neck, and the top of the head is tapered slightly back. The pubic triangle is indicated by incision and the figure is probably to be understood as naked.

Probably mid–late third millennium B.C.

Annual Report to the Friends of the Fitzwilliam Museum 1933 I no. 2, fig. 2.

3 Female (?) idol — PLATE I

Source as for **2** above. Inv.: GR.8*a*.1933.

H. 0·086 m. Fine-grained, translucent Parian marble, slightly encrusted.

As compared with **2**, worked more completely in the round. The plane of the 'face' is inclined slightly backwards. A raised surface projects in front from hips to knees. This seems to represent a device, perhaps vestigial from the plumper idols of an earlier period, serving to distinguish thigh and knee and, on occasion, giving the legs a slightly flexed appearance.[3] Compare **8** below.

Probably mid–late third millennium B.C.

Bibliography as for **2**.

4 Female (?) idol — PLATE I

Source as for **2** above. Inv.: GR.8*b*.1933.

H. 0·065 m. Fine-grained, translucent Parian marble, much encrusted.

Despite its rounded forms, apparently worked from a flattish slab of marble of 0·009 m. maximum thickness. The face is tilted slightly backwards and has its nose and other details faintly indicated.

Probably mid–late third millennium B.C.

Bibliography as for **2**.

5 Female idol — PLATE I

Source as for **2** above. Inv.: GR.8*d*.1933.

H. 0·066 m. Shell. Back slightly encrusted.

Zervos, *op. cit.* 43 f.; on the technique, S. Casson, *Technique of Early Greek Sculpture* 15 f.; on origins, development and significance, W. A. Müller, *Nacktheit und Entblössung* 57 f.; *PM* I 47 f.; V. Müller, *op. cit.* 9 f.; K. Majewski, *Figuralna Plastyka Cykladzka* passim; J. Wiesner, *Grab und Jenseits* 131 f.; on suspected forgeries, *Hesperia Suppl.* VIII 423.

[1] Cf. also *AE* 1898 pl. 11. The idols of this kind have been assigned by A. Furumark to his Early Cycladic I phase (*Mycenaean Pottery, Analysis and Classification* 217 f.).

[2] Furumark, *loc. cit.* For the Cretan material, see Sir Arthur Evans, *Cretan Pictographs and Prae-Phoenician Script* 124 f.; S. Xanthoudides, *Vaulted Tombs of the Messara* 21 f., 121, pls. 7, 15, 21; *ADelt* IV (1918) 162 f.; *AA* 1933 298 f.; Zervos, *L'Art en Crète* figs. 106–15; cf. also *PM* I 115 and J. D. S. Pendlebury, *Archaeology of Crete* 86 f., although this detailed chronology is now open to question. For the Attic finds, see *AJA* XXXVIII (1934) 275, fig. 21; G. E. Mylonas, *Aghios Kosmas* 138 f., fig. 163; on dating (to near end of Early Helladic III), *ibid.* 161 f.

[3] Cf. Zervos, *L'Art des Cyclades* figs. 38, 40, 41. In the Cyclades, at least, this device does not seem to represent a 'split skirt'; cf. *BSA* XXXVI (1935–6) 122 nos. 8 and 13.

Cut from a curved shell (maximum thickness of wall 0·002 m.). Edges slightly rounded. Pubic triangle incised.

Probably mid–late third millennium B.C.

Bibliography as for **2**.

6 Female idol PLATE I

Source as for **2** above. Inv.: GR.8*e*.1933.

H. 0·042 m. Shell.

Much as **5** above.

Probably mid–late third millennium B.C.

Bibliography as for **2**.

7 Female (?) idol PLATE I

Source as for **2** above. Inv.: GR.8*f*.1933.

H. 0·031 m. Shell.

Cut from a flattish piece of shell (maximum thickness 0·0025 m.). Edges rounded.

Probably mid–late third millennium B.C.

Bibliography as for **2**.

8 Female idol PLATE I

Presented by Professor R. C. Bosanquet. From Amorgos. Inv.: GR.33*b*.1901.

P.H. 0·131 m. Fine-grained, translucent marble (Parian?). Head missing; repair at left knee. Surface somewhat corroded.

The legs are straight and naturalistically treated in front, where a slightly enhanced projection between hips and knees seems reminiscent of the device found on **3** above. Less attention has been given to the back and the rump is quite flat. To judge from the incised pubic triangle, the figure is to be interpreted as naked, but no attempt has been made to indicate the breasts. The stump-like arms are complete. For the general type, compare Zervos, *op. cit.* fig. 42.

Probably mid–late third millennium B.C.

9 Head from an idol PLATE 2

Presented by the Greek Government. From Phylakopi, Melos. Inv.: GR.53.1902.

P.H. 0·051 m. Moderately coarse-grained white marble (Naxian?). Broken away at neck.

The head is tilted back obliquely and the sides of the face are slanting. The nose is indicated. The rounded top to the head may suggest that this still belongs to a comparatively unevolved stage amongst the idols of the 'developed' class. Compare Zervos, *op. cit.* figs. 50 *middle*, 51.

Probably later third millennium B.C.

10 Naked female idol PLATE 2

Presented by Professor R. C. Bosanquet. From Amorgos. Inv.: GR.33.1901.

H. 0·258 m. Medium-grained, translucent white marble (Parian?). Damaged at nose, chin and toes and repaired at neck. Somewhat encrusted.

A typical 'developed' idol with back-tilted, level-topped head, folded arms and slightly flexed legs. Nose and breasts are indicated plastically and the pubic triangle is incised.

Probably later third millennium B.C.

CAH Plates I 114 *c*.

11 Naked female idol PLATE 2

Purchased. From Melos. Inv.: GR.17.1924.

H. 0·24 m. Medium-grained, translucent white marble (Parian?). Face damaged; repaired at neck. Surface corroded and encrusted, especially in front.

Much as **10** above.

Probably later third millennium B.C.

12 Naked female idol PLATE 2

Presented by Professor R. C. Bosanquet. From Amorgos. Inv.: GR.33*a*.1901.

P.H. 0·18 m. Fine-grained white marble with slight incrustation. Head and feet missing; right shoulder damaged.

A typical idol of the 'over-refined' class as described above. The body is very broad-shouldered, but extremely shallow in depth, and the flexing of the legs now shows as a slight curve when seen in profile. The pubic triangle is incised. For the possible appearance of this idol when complete cf. Zervos, *op. cit.* figs. 165, 251, 254.

Probably late third or early second millennium B.C.

13 Female idol PLATE 2

Presented by the Friends of the Fitzwilliam Museum. From Ios. Inv.: GR.4.1934.

H. 0·075 m. Medium-grained white marble, somewhat encrusted. Repaired at neck; slightly damaged at back of head.

The legs are straight, the hands placed between and under the breasts. The head projects backwards at the top, still echoing the back-tilted Cycladic tradition. The nose is rendered plastically. The long eyes are outlined and have eyebrows running parallel with them incised in the form of a V on top of the triangular head. This treatment of the face shows remarkable affinities with a clay figurine from the

Greek mainland published by C. W. Blegen (*Zygouries* 185, pl. 21. 1) and stratified to the Early Helladic II period.

However, the pose of the Fitzwilliam idol, with its hands between the breasts, suggests that it belongs to a slightly later period. This motif seems to be of Cretan origin and to make its appearance on Cretan terracotta figurines early in the Middle Minoan period, although it also persisted until much later.[1] In the light of these observations, it is perhaps simplest to regard this idol as a late and highly unusual variant of the Cycladic figures of the 'over-refined' class.

Early second millennium B.C. (?)

Annual Report to the Friends of the Fitzwilliam Museum 1934 1 no. 1.

(C) MINOAN

See also **186**, p. 114 below.

14 Human idol PLATE 2

Purchased. From Chersonesos, Crete. Inv.: GR.23.1901.

H. 0·04 m. Very fine-grained white marble. Both arms broken away at ends, but may never have been very much longer than now. Figure apparently preserved to its full height. Possible damage at lower part of left side, but this has been smoothed over in antiquity.

On J. D. S. Pendlebury's analysis (*The Archaeology of Crete* 52 f., 71 f., 86 f.), Early Minoan idols passed successively through a sub-neolithic, a highly schematic, and a more naturalistic phase, the last stage also producing imitations of imported Cycladic idols. The urgent need, however, for a detailed revision of the vase-chronology of the period may also call for some modification in this arrangement of the figurines. The present idol bears comparison with the almost aniconic creations of Pendlebury's middle phase, but the material and the backward slope of the face are suggestive of Cycladic influence.[2]

Later third millennium B.C.

R. C. Bosanquet and R. M. Dawkins, *Unpublished Objects from the Palaikastro Excavations* (*BSA Suppl. Paper* 1) 149 fig. 132.

---

[1] The Fitzwilliam Museum idol also bears an accidental resemblance to a much later descendant of these, the early 'ϕ-type' of Mycenaean terracotta figurine of about the fourteenth century B.C.; cf. A. Furumark, *Chronology of Mycenaean Pottery* 86 f. However, there is nothing to suggest so late a continuance of the Cycladic marble idols of the 'over-refined' class. Indeed, by the Late Bronze Age Cycladic stone sculpture seems to have been of a quite different character, e.g. *PAE* 1950 279, figs. 13–14.

[2] For comparable Cretan idols of the schematic type see R. B. Seager, *Explorations in the Island of Mochlos* 80, fig. 47. 5; R. C. Bosanquet, *Unpublished Objects from the Palaikastro Excavations* 149, fig. 131; S. Xanthoudides, *Vaulted Tombs in the Messara* 24 f., 121, pls. 15, 21; *PM* II 32, fig. 13*c*; *Ann.* XIII–XIV (1930–1) 243 f., fig. 58; *BSA* XXXVI (1935–6) 117 f., fig. 25, pl. 18; Zervos, *L'Art en Crète* figs. 92–6. For local imitations of Cycladic idols cf. Sir Arthur Evans, *Cretan Pictographs and the Prae-Phoenician Script* 124 f., figs. 125, 127–8, 130; Zervos, *op. cit.* fig. 109, *extreme left and bottom right.*

II

SCULPTURE OF THE ARCHAIC PERIOD

(A) LIMESTONE STATUETTES IN A MIXED STYLE FROM NAUKRATIS, ETC.[1]

The statuettes considered under this head are of a kind also commonly found in western Asia Minor and the Aegean islands. Their style is strangely mixed, part Cypriot, part East-Greek and part Egyptianizing.[2] The earliest and strongest element seems to be the Cypriot, although the sculptures in the 'mixed style' tend to be somewhat different from those actually found in Cyprus. In addition to Cypriot imports, it seems likely that one is confronted with local East Greek imitations of them and, in particular, the work of emigrant Cypriot craftsmen.[3]

The dating used here is based on stratigraphical indications. The earliest Greek material at Naukratis seems assignable to about 615 B.C. and this should also be the earliest possible date for the statuettes in the 'mixed style' from that site.[4] On the other hand, limestone sculptures of this kind have been found in Rhodes, Samos and Chios and at Old Smyrna in contexts whose latest material was of the end of the seventh century B.C.[5] The lower limit for a rich votive deposit on the Acropolis at Kameiros in Rhodes seems to fall about 570 B.C., whilst other limestone sculptures in Samos have been found in a context of *c.* 550 B.C.[6] It is less clear exactly when work in the 'mixed style' came to an end in East Greece, but products wholly Greek in character seem to be commoner from about the middle years of the sixth century B.C. and it is at least probable that the main flood of imported Cypriot terracottas may have stopped by that date.

15 **Head of a youth or a woman, from a statuette** PLATE 3

Presented by the Egypt Exploration Fund and the British School at Athens. From Naukratis. Inv.: GR.1.1899.

P.H. 0·047 m. Compact white Egyptian (?) limestone with brown patina. Broken away at neck; tip of nose missing. Surface chipped and worn.

The hair is treated after the fashion of an Egyptian 'layer-wig'. It is parted in the middle. The treatment of the features is almost without parallel. Despite the full modelling of cheeks and lips, the elaborate 'layer-hair' would seem to suggest quite an early date, and this is perhaps borne out by the affinities that seem to exist between this piece and Egyptianizing faience from Rhodes of about the late seventh century B.C.[7]

Egyptianizing style, perhaps of the end of the seventh or beginning of the sixth century B.C.

---

[1] For other similar limestone sculptures from Naukratis cf. Sir W. M. F. Petrie and others, *Naukratis* I 13, 36, pls. 1–2; E. A. Gardner, *Naukratis* II 55 f., pls. 13–15, 17; *BSA* V (1898–9) pl. 14. 7; M. C. C. Edgar, *Cairo Mus. Cat. Greek Sculpture* 2 f., pl. 1; *JHS* XXV (1905) 130, fig. 9; F. N. Pryce, *BMC Sculpture* I. 1. 181 f., pls. 39–41; *SCE* IV. 2. 318 f., figs. 44–8. Certain statuettes from Naukratis in the Fitzwilliam Museum have been excluded from this catalogue as being Egyptian rather than Greek in style. They are two limestone relief plaques of the so-called 'childbirth' type, showing a naked female figure, E.191.1899 and E.192.1899 (*BSA* V (1898–9) pl. 14. 1, 3), a group of the goddess Thoueris, with a votary, E.194.1899, and a soapstone figure of Isis, E.4.1909. On the other hand, the kitharode, **21**, has been included since, although a local Egyptian product, it shows connections with the 'mixed style'. The other border-line piece, **15**, appears to be Greek.

[2] For the limestone statuettes of Cypriot style cf. the flood of Cypriot terracottas over the same area and at its height at precisely the same time (*AJA* LXI (1957) 304), although having its beginnings rather earlier, e.g. at Samos. The Egyptianizing statuettes seem often to show closer affinities with the faience figurines and plastic vases of Egyptian style found in East Greek contexts of the period and perhaps actually produced in Rhodes (see Baron W. von Bissing in *SB bay Ak* 1941, II. 7. 81 f.) than with work from Egypt itself.

[3] On imported Cypriot sculptures at Naukratis, cf. the tale, Athenaeus XV. 675–6, E. A. Gardner, *Naukratis* II 55 f. For a later Cypriot sculptor working at Naukratis, see the signature, *BSA* V (1898–9) 32.

[4] *JHS* LVII (1937) 227 f.; the alternative interpretation (*LAAA* XXI (1934) 67 f.; *ActArch* XXX (1959) 147 f.) seems untenable.

[5] Rhodes: K. F. Kinch, *Fouilles de Vroulia* 12 f.; lower limit of deposit *c.* 600 B.C. (Professor J. M. Cook). Samos: *AM* LXXIV (1959) 27 f. Chios and Old Smyrna: unpublished; the authors are indebted to Professor Ekrem Akurgal, Professor J. M. Cook, Mr M. S. F. Hood and Mr John Boardman for access to this material.

[6] Kameiros: Pryce, *op. cit.* 158 f. (the late date claimed for B 388 is surely unjustified); R. A. Higgins, *BMC Terracottas* I 22 f.; further material from this deposit confused with later finds from elsewhere in *Clara Rhodos* VI–VII 279 f., although it is not certain that there is anything intrusive amongst the limestone figures. Samos: *AM* LV (1930) 16 f., fig. 5, Beilage 4, found with a number of statuettes as yet unpublished; on the earlier Samian contexts containing imported Cypriot terracottas see *AM* LVIII (1933) 141 f., LXV (1940) 57 f., LXXIV (1959) 32 f.

[7] E.g. C. Blinkenberg, *Lindos, Fouilles et Recherches* I pls. 55 no. 1256, 56 no. 1299.

16 Head of a woman, from a statuette

PLATE 3

Presented by the Egypt Exploration Fund and the British School at Athens. From Naukratis. Inv.: GR.2.1899.

P.H. 0·055 m. Faintly foraminiferous white limestone. Broken away at neck; left side of head damaged and surface chipped at nose, chin and cheeks. Red pigment used to indicate the beads of three superimposed necklets; traces of red also on the lips, the ear-ring in the right ear and, in a band, along the lower edge of the hair over the brow.

The back of the figure was left flat. The heavy, Egyptianizing features of the face and the long, stylized ear place this head in a well-defined group. An only slightly less evolved head in the same style occurs on an unpublished male figure in a context of the late seventh century B.C. at Old Smyrna. Closely comparable also are some of the limestone flute-player statuettes of the 'mixed style' and some pieces of Egyptianizing faience of approximately late-seventh-century date from Rhodes.[1]

Egyptianizing style of the end of the seventh or beginning of the sixth century B.C.

17 Statuette of a god or hero grasping a lion

PLATE 3

Presented by the Cyprus Exploration Fund. From Salamis in Cyprus. Inv.: GR.3*b*.1891.

P.H. 0·177 m. Foraminiferous yellowish limestone with a rather hard, gritty surface. The legs of the human figure missing from just above the knees; all the forepart of the lion also broken away. Surface worn. Possible traces of red pigment on flesh.

It is not clear whether by this stage the Greeks regarded the borrowed oriental motif of the 'Master of Animals' as a representation of a god such as Apollo or whether they had appropriated the present form of it to an exploit of Herakles.[2] But, whatever his identification, the naked youth stands stiffly with his left leg slightly advanced, holding the right hind-leg of the lion with his right hand and its tail with his left.

The nude kouros-type is attested amongst East-Greek limestone statuettes as early as the last quarter of the seventh century B.C. on stratigraphical evidence, and this variety representing a naked youth with a lion is closely akin.[3] For the dating and localization of the Fitzwilliam statuette, it is to be observed that it shows close stylistic affinities with material from the votive deposit at Kameiros in Rhodes, where the lower limit seems to fall *c.* 570 B.C., although it may be earlier than the latest version of the type from that find-group.[4] It is noteworthy that the treatment of the body has been completely Hellenized, even though that of the head remains in the tradition of the 'mixed style'; and it seems almost impossible, on the evidence at present known, to regard this figure as other than an import into Cyprus from East Greece.

Predominantly East-Greek work of the first quarter of the sixth century B.C.

JHS XII (1891) 161.

18 Statuette of a woman holding a bowl

PLATE 4

Presented by the Egypt Exploration Fund. From Naukratis. Inv.: GR.2.1887.

P.H. 0·198 m. Hard, compact, cream-white Egyptian limestone (the two lower fragments discoloured grey). Assembled from three fragments. Bottom part missing. Chips missing from nose, frontlet, left wrist, right elbow, right thigh.

The back of the statuette is slightly rounded, but otherwise left plain. The woman is dressed in a long-sleeved chiton, girdled at the waist, but with a long over-fold hanging down in front over the girdle after the Cypriot fashion. The vertical edge to the hair-mass over the brow may, in fact, represent a diadem whose details were originally rendered in paint. In certain other similar pieces this projects at the top or is even decorated plastically in front.[5] Around her neck she

---

[1] Flute-player statuettes: Blinkenberg, *op. cit.* pl. 70 no. 1709; Pryce, *op. cit.* 162 no. B 338, fig. 200—this last perhaps later, but presumably before 570 B.C. (Kameiros votive deposit). Faience: e.g. *Clara Rhodos* VI–VII 312 no. 20, fig. 50.

[2] See Pierre Amandry in *Syria* XXIV (1944) 149 f. on the significance of the Delphi ivory. Professor C. M. Robertson has suggested to the authors that the 'Master of Animals' of the limestone statuettes is probably also to be identified as Apollo.

[3] Dated seventh-century kouroi from Samos (*AM* LXXIV (1959) 30, Beilage 66) and Emborio, Chios (unpublished). For the type cf. Blinkenberg, *op. cit.* 437 f. nos. 1772 f., pl. 73. A few early Greek examples (e.g. *ibid.* no. 1775) still wear Cypriot-type 'shorts', *mitra*, etc. In Cyprus itself this clad kouros seems to continue the norm until much later: A. P. di Cesnola, *Atlas* pls. 11, 25, 42, 48, 50, 54, 67; M. Ohnefalsch-Richter, *Kypros, the Bible and Homer* pl. 214. 15; F. N. Pryce, *BMC Sculpture* I. 2. 15 no. C 7, fig. 6.

[4] For the treatment of body and head cf. the slightly earlier kouros, F. N. Pryce, *BMC Sculpture* I. 1. 160 no. B 330, pl. 35, G. M. A. Richter, *Kouroi* 92 no. 22, pl. 27 (Sounion Group); more closely for the head cf. Pryce, *op. cit.* 163 no. B 340, fig. 201. Of the type of the 'Master of Animals', later seems Pryce, *op. cit.* 162 no. B 337, fig. 199, about contemporary no. B 336 (*op. cit.* 162, pl. 37); the lanky human proportions and the treatment of the lion's head of no. B 335 (*op. cit.* 161, pl. 36) perhaps place it earlier.

[5] Cf. Pryce, *op. cit.* 166 f. nos. B 361–2, pl. 37, fig. 206; *Clara Rhodos* VI–VII 282 no. 8, fig. 8 (the two of them certainly, the one possibly, from the Kameiros votive deposit).

wears a string of beads with a large amulet in the middle. The type, the drapery, the necklet and the kind of bowl in the figure's hand all seem purely Cypriot.[1] However, the treatment of the face seems to belong to the 'mixed style'. Indeed, as may be judged by comparing this statuette with *Clara Rhodos* VI–VII 286, fig. 8 *left*, these female heads seem to follow a development parallel with that of the heads of the kouroi. A similar piece is attested from Kameiros, although it is not certain whether it is from the dated votive deposit, others from Lindos and Naukratis.[2]

Predominantly Cypriot work of the first quarter of the sixth century B.C.

19 Fragment of a statuette of a god or hero grasping a lion PLATE 4

Presented by the Egypt Exploration Fund and the British School at Athens. From Naukratis. Inv.: GR.5.1899 (formerly Egyptian Dept., inv. E.189.1899).

P.H. 0·135 m. Finely foraminiferous cream-white limestone, somewhat darker on the surface. Broken away above at the level of the hands and buttocks of the human figure, below just above that of his ankles. Surface chipped at many points, including the hind legs, rump and muzzle of the lion. Traces of black outlines on the eyes of the lion and of short, wavy, black lines, apparently indicating hair, on his mane and pelt.

On the type and its interpretation see **17** above. The naked youth grasps the lion by its tail and its left hind-leg. The beast's head, turned back on its assailant, is rather inadequately rendered, particularly about the jaws which end in a low, almost pig-like snout. The youth stands with his feet together, holding the lion high against his thighs whilst its fore-paws stretch down his legs and presumably claw his feet. This pose suggests comparison with another group from Naukratis where the youth's head shows a marked resemblance to Rhodian terracottas of towards the middle of the sixth century B.C.[3] The more elongated proportions of the human figure in the Fitzwilliam Museum fragment may perhaps indicate a slightly earlier date for it.

Predominantly East-Greek work of the second quarter of the sixth century B.C.

20 Fragment of a statuette of a standing woman PLATE 3

Presented by the Egypt Exploration Fund and the British School at Athens. From Naukratis. Inv.: GR.4.1899.

P.H. 0·08 m. Faintly foraminiferous white limestone. Head broken away, also left fore-arm and all the lower part of the body. Traces of red on the chiton.

The back of the statuette is slightly rounded but devoid of detail apart from an incision apparently indicating the edge of the veil behind the right elbow. The woman wears a short-sleeved chiton and, over it, a himation fastened at the left shoulder. The chiton is girdled with a broad belt, appearing in the centre, and the treatment of the himation immediately above seems to be modelled on a common Cypriot device for rendering an over-fold of the chiton. A veil hangs down behind from the head, extending at least as far as the elbows; its treatment at the right elbow might perhaps suggest that it is simply the himation drawn up over the head, but at the left shoulder himation and veil seem to be rendered as separate garments. The poor preservation makes dating difficult. Pose and drapery treatment place it close to **22** (*q.v.*) with which it may be about contemporary. In its fragmentary condition it is also impossible completely to exclude the possibility that this statuette might be a Cypriot import.

Predominantly Cypriot work of approximately the middle years of the sixth century B.C.

21 Fragment of a statuette of a kitharode PLATE 3

Presented by the Egypt Exploration Fund. From Naukratis. Inv.: GR.3.1887.

P.H. 0·059 m. Compact white Egyptian limestone. The whole figure missing from the waist down; also the left fore-arm with much of the kithara, the right shoulder and right upper arm. Chips missing from nose and hair to either side of head. Traces of black on the hair and the right eye; faint traces of red and black on the kithara.

The musician holds his instrument against his left shoulder, grasping it with his left hand while he plucks the strings with his right. The instrument itself seems definitely to be flat at the bottom and square in its

[1] Cf. M. Ohnefalsch-Richter, *op. cit.* pl. 214. 2; F. N. Pryce, *BMC Sculpture* I. 2. 95 f. nos. C 234–6, figs. 155–6; *SCE* III pl. 187 no. 1.

[2] Kameiros: *Clara Rhodos* VI–VII 282 no. 7, fig. 7. Lindos: for head-type cf. Blinkenberg, *op. cit.* 417 no. 1653, pl. 67. Naukratis: for head-type cf. *Naukratis* II pl. 15. 5, Pryce, *BMC Sculpture* I. 1. 194 no. B 457, fig. 234; for body-type cf. *Naukratis* I pl. 2. 1, Pryce, *op. cit.* 191 no. B 452, fig. 230.

[3] *Naukratis* II pl. 14. 10, Pryce, *op. cit.* 189 f. no. B 448, pl. 40. For the Fitzwilliam statuette, cf. also Blinkenberg, *op. cit.* 437 f. no. 1772, pl. 73.

lower section and so to be a kithara rather than the lyre more usually held by statuettes in the 'mixed style'. These latter, if we may include part-human instrumentalists as well, begin before the end of the seventh century B.C. and extend well down into the sixth century.[1] With the later examples of these the Fitzwilliam kitharode shows definite affinities in pose and treatment. However, the coarse rendering of his face and hair is quite foreign to the 'mixed style', but can be paralleled amongst a class of crude limestone plaques at Naukratis of local Egyptian workmanship; these had apparently already begun to be produced in the sixth century B.C., although they seem also to have continued in vogue in classical times.[2] The Fitzwilliam fragment presumably dates before the end of the 'mixed style'.

Local Egyptian version of a Greco-Cypriot motif of the sixth century B.C.

(B) CYPRIOT LIMESTONE STATUETTES[3]

The system of chronology used here is based on Greek stratigraphical evidence and the relationships between Cypriot sculptures and their dated counterparts of the 'mixed style'. There seems to be no other reliable course to follow. The arbitrarily low system of dating employed by the Swedish Cyprus Expedition actually flouts the Greek evidence without having any sound foundation of its own; equally misleading are previous attempts to equate stylistic with international trends or to treat early archaic Cypriot art as a debased and derivative form of archaic Greek art.[4]

22 Statuette of a standing man PLATE 4

Presented by the Cyprus Exploration Fund. From Salamis in Cyprus. Inv.: GR.3*a*.1891.

P.H. 0·126 m. Finely foraminiferous cream-white limestone. Lower part missing from slightly above the knees. Repaired at base of neck. Surface slightly chipped. Bright red himation; traces of red on lips and on brow just under lower edge of hair.

He wears a short-sleeved chiton, apparently girdled at the waist, and, over it, a red himation fastened on his left shoulder and with the loose end hanging down behind. The pose is a common Cypriot one with the right hand to the breast and the left to the side. However, the rounded treatment of the face shows affinities with Greek material, though not so much with Ionic creations of the mid-sixth century as with apparently antecedent work in the 'mixed style'. Here, such heads seem to have evolved in the second quarter of the sixth century from the austere features of the early kouroi.[5] The himation is rendered in the early, flat fashion, as on some Cypriot statuettes in the British Museum, although these suggest the influence of an Ionian sculptural type and a Rhodian terracotta one of the middle to third quarter of the sixth century B.C., whereas the Cambridge statuette seems to belong to a slightly earlier phase.[6]

Probably Cypriot work of the second quarter of the sixth century B.C., but showing points of contact with the 'mixed style' of East Greece.

JHS XII (1891) 160.

23 Head of a youth, from a statuette PLATE 4

Presented by the Cyprus Exploration Fund. From Salamis in Cyprus. Inv.: GR.3*c*.1891.

P.H. 0·126 m. Finely foraminiferous white limestone. Broken away at the base of the neck. Surface worn and chipped, particularly at the nose.

The back of the head shows some shaping, but is comparatively flat. The youth wears a Cypriot cap with the side-flaps in the raised position and fastened at the top (cf. **24** below). His head is probably more completely Cypriot in style than the preceding statuette's. Even so, the general structure of his face

[1] Sirens: Blinkenberg, *op. cit.* 449 f., pl. 76. Wholly human performers: Blinkenberg, *op. cit.* 427 f., pl. 70; *Clara Rhodos* VI–VII 281 no. 4, fig. 4; *Naukratis* II pl. 14. 14; Pryce, *op. cit.* 195 no. B 459, fig. 235; *SCE* IV. 2. 232, fig. 52. For a Cypriot example cf. Cesnola, *Atlas* pl. 12 no. 14.

[2] E.g. the 'childbirth' plaques, *Naukratis* I pl. 19. 7–9; *BSA* V (1898–9) pl. 14. 1–5 (see n. 1, p. 5 above); and the 'Baubo' reliefs, e.g. *JHS* XXV (1905) 128, fig. 8*a*. On the dating see *Naukratis* 40 f., *BSA* V (1898–9) 72, *JHS* XXV (1905) 129.

[3] This collection is now much smaller than it was earlier, the majority of the Cypriot limestone sculptures having been transferred in 1947 to the Museum of Classical Archaeology in Cambridge.

[4] On the Swedish Cyprus Expedition chronology see *AA* 1936 561 f.; *SCE* II 642 f., IV. 2. 92 f., 207 f.; the uninspiring stratified contents of a very provincial sanctuary are used to date Cypriot sculpture as a whole in terms of a system of vase-chronology resting on insecure scarab dates. For earlier attempts at a system of dating see, on the one hand, Sir John L. Myres, *Handbook of the Cesnola Collection, Metropolitan Museum of Art* 132 f., V. Müller, *Frühe Plastik in Griechenland und Vorderasien* 162 f., *BSA* XLI (1940–5) 100 f., on the other, F. N. Pryce, *BMC Sculpture* I. 2. 2 f., *JHS* XLVI (1926) 163 f.

[5] Cf. the example possibly from the Kameiros votive deposit, *Clara Rhodos* VI–VII 282 no. 9, fig. 9. A more developed and apparently later example is attested at Naukratis: *Naukratis* II pl. 17. 2; Pryce, *BMC Sculpture* I. 1. 185 no. B 440, fig. 222.

[6] Cf. Pryce, *BMC Sculpture* I. 2. 27 nos. C 33–5, figs. 28–30.

closely resembles a small group of statuettes known from Samos as well as Cyprus.[1] These lack, however, the flat, raised eyes of a broad, very archaic appearance, although they, too, may be paralleled on not dissimilar heads from Ephesus, no less than Cyprus.[2] These circumstances suggest that the Fitzwilliam head belongs to a period when Cypriot imports and sculptures in the 'mixed style' were still current in East Greece.

Cypriot work of about the second quarter of the sixth century B.C.

JHS XII (1891) 160 f. (probably).

24 Upper part of a statuette of a man

PLATE 5

Presented by the Cyprus Exploration Fund. From Salamis in Cyprus. Inv.: GR.3.1891.

P.H. 0·09 m. Faintly foraminiferous white limestone. Everything missing below the level of the chest. Surface chipped, particularly at the face and the top of the cap. Red cap, himation and lips.

The statutette is worked in the round behind the head, but the back of the body is left flat. The figure represents a long-haired, bearded man wearing a red Cypriot cap with the side-flaps down and with the thongs with which they are fastened when in the raised position (as on **23** above) hanging loosely below. This motif is common on imported Cypriot terracottas in Greece, perhaps suggesting that it had enjoyed some vogue by the mid sixth century B.C.[3] He also wears a short-sleeved chiton and, over it, a red himation fastened on his left shoulder and brought round over the right, so that one may, with tolerable certainty, restore his right fore-arm as supported in the resultant fold of material, much as the later Greek 'Sophocles-type'. This treatment of the himation was already of great antiquity in Cyprus and seems to have continued in popularity down past the mid sixth century.[4] A close dating is difficult because of the damage to the face, but the eyes still seem fairly early.

Cypriot work of about the mid sixth century B.C.

JHS XII (1891) 160.

(C) A CRETAN GRAFFITO

25 Inscribed rock-cut drawing of a dolphin

PLATE 5

Presented by Vice-Admiral T. A. B. Spratt. From the northern environs of Erimoupolis (ancient Itanos), Crete. Inv.: GR.1.1854.

P.W. at level of inscription c. 0·285 m. Large natural lump of grey marble of overall preserved dimensions 0·7 × 0·35 × 0·18 m. Broken away at its upper and lower ends and also at its right edge, where the start of the inscription has been lost. Surface shows natural pitting. Repaired at two breaks that have opened on natural fault-lines in the stone.

The fish is shown in incised outline. There seems to be a measure of ichthyological unorthodoxy in the drawing, there being two dorsal fins instead of the one usual for contemporary dolphins on black-figure vases and two ventral fins in addition to the side fins. But it seems reasonably certain that a dolphin is intended. Later rock-cut versions of the same subject are known from further to the west in the Gulf of Mirabello in Crete and from Thera.[5] The retrograde inscription runs as follows:

[Τί]μο̄ν ἔγραφέ με.
Timon drew me.

It clearly serves to record, in portentous wise, the man responsible for the simple drawing. The suggested restoration of his name is Babington's. The force of the imperfect tense may be conative—i.e. almost '*tried to draw*'. On the use of the letter φ see M. Guarducci, *Inscriptiones Creticae* III 163. Dr L. H. Jeffery has tentatively assigned the inscription to *c.* 525 B.C., but would stress that Cretan letter-forms are not closely datable in this period.

Quite apart from the drawing, the stone itself resembles part of a fish in shape—a likeness that may have been stronger when it was complete and may have

[1] Samos: *AM* XXV (1900) 151 f. Cyprus: e.g. Pryce, *BMC Sculpture* I. 2. no. C 81, fig. 51.
[2] Ephesus: Pryce, *BMC Sculpture* I. 1. 35 no. B 2, fig. 30. Cyprus: Pryce, *BMC Sculpture* I. 2. 15 no. C 7, fig. 6, 30 f. nos. C 39, C 41, C 45, figs. 33–5, 33 no. C 52, fig. 40, etc.
[3] E.g. Blinkenberg, *op. cit.* 485 f. nos. 1994–9, 488 no. 2012, pls. 89–90.
[4] Cf. the early terracottas, *AM* LXV (1940) 62 f., 88 f., pl. 38 no. 344. On these earlier examples the garment worn is a fringed mantle, not unlike that on the Assyrian reliefs. For later limestone sculptures of the type, cf. Pryce, *op. cit.* 31 f. nos. C 41 (especially for the treatment of the himation at the left shoulder), C 48, figs. 34–7, 36 no. C 68, fig. 43. For limestone examples from Greece, cf. Blinkenberg, *op. cit.* 406 f. nos. 1584 f., pl. 65.
[5] *BCH* LIX (1935) 378 f., fig. 1, pl. 25; Baron Hiller von Gaertringen and P. Wilski, *Thera* III 98, fig. 79; *IG* XII. 3. 295 no. 1347.

provided the inspiration for the drawing. Nevertheless, as has been confirmed by Dr C. L. Forbes of the Sedgwick Museum, apart from the inscription and incised drawing it seems to have been shaped by no hand save that of nature. It thus takes its place as the earliest of a number of rock-inscriptions from the vicinity of Itanos, several of them accompanied by drawings in carved outline (Guarducci, *op. cit.* 158 f.). Previously Babington, Jahn, Michaelis and Roehl had regarded it as a fragment of large-scale sculpture in the round and even Vice-Admiral Spratt's views on the subject seem to have vacillated.

'Folk art' of about the second half of the sixth century B.C.

C. Babington in *Journal of Classical and Sacred Philology* II (1855) 108 f. no. 6; O. Jahn in *AZ* 1863 65; T. A. B. Spratt, *Travels and Researches in Crete* I 197, II 421 no. 20, pl. 1; A. Kirchhoff, *Studien zur Geschichte des Alphabetes* (4th ed.) 76; A. Michaelis, *Anc. Marbles* 248 no. 13; H. Roehl, *Inscriptiones Graecae Antiquissimae* no. 474; E. S. Roberts, *Introduction to Greek Epigraphy* I 47 no. 13; Chapman, *Handbook* (2nd ed.) 55; M. Guarducci, *Inscriptiones Creticae* III, *Tituli Cretae Orientalis* 158 no. 2, 162 f.; *JHS* LXII (1942) 15 no. IV. *a*. 3.; *Handbook and Guide* (1960) 9, 57; L. H. Jeffery, *The Local Scripts of Archaic Greece* 309, 310.

III

SCULPTURE OF CLASSICAL DATE

(A) ATTIC PUBLIC MONUMENTS

26 Fragment from the Erechtheion frieze
PLATE 6

Presented by the Reverend T. P. A. Fletcher. From the Acropolis, Athens; brought to England in 1841. Inv.: GR.113.1908.

P.H. 0·153 m., P.W. 0·154 m., P.D. 0·093 m. Medium grained Pentelic (?) marble. The whole of the upper part of the figure missing, as also the right leg and foot and much of the projecting mass on which these rested; chipped away are toes of left foot and parts of projecting folds of drapery. The present hole for attachment drilled in the underside is modern.

The fragment preserves much of the lower part of a draped human figure turned at a three-quarter angle to the right. It is in the form of a cut-out relief designed to be set against the contrasting dark background of the frieze, which is of Eleusinian stone. To this end its back has been cut flat with the claw-chisel and shows a measure of anathyrosis.

The drapery hangs low over the left foot and its folds bunch heavily as if of wool. Too little is preserved for any completely certain inferences to be drawn as to the nature of the garment, but it is probably a peplos. In that case the figure must be female, despite the somewhat heavy build of the left ankle and calf. The pose seems to have been misinterpreted by Fowler. The upward sweep of the drapery makes it reasonably clear that the missing right knee was bent and that the right foot rested on some object standing beside the figure. Of this only a small part of one vertical surface is preserved. Under the drapery between it and the left foot the underside has been hollowed out somewhat with the gouge. The kind of motif implied is already attested elsewhere on the Erechtheion frieze (e.g. Fowler 262 no. 78, pl. 44). The left foot is shod with a sandal.

This fragment was first recognized by Lethaby as belonging to the Erechtheion frieze. In view of its scale it has been assigned by Fowler to the frieze of the cella, which is only 0·617 m. in height as against the 0·683 m. of the north portico frieze.

409–6 B.C.

S. Casson, *Cat. Acropolis Museum* II 19 n. 2; Fowler in L. D. Caskey, M. Paton, H. N. Fowler, G. P. Stevens, *The Erechtheum* 265 f. no. 98, pl. 45; *AJA* LXIII (1959) 143 no. 25.

27 Relief from the top of a public inscription
PLATE 5

Transferred from the old University Library; presented to the University by Professor E. D. Clarke. Found on the site of ancient Sigeion in 1801. Inv.: GR.13.1865.

P.H. 0·285 m., W. 0·35 m., H. of relief 0·02 m. max. Pentelic marble with light brown patina. The entire lower part of the stele is missing; the framing of the relief is broken away at the corners and above the head of the central figure; faces of all three figures chipped, as also right arm of Athena and knees of warrior on right. Surface somewhat worn. Small modern (?) clamp-hole in top and three modern dowel-holes in underside. As with all the Clarke reliefs, it shows traces of mortar around the edges, presumably from its mounting in the old University Library.

The back surface of the relief is roughly dressed with the point. The position and nature of the break at the bottom of the fragment show that it is not a votive relief (which would have snapped at the tang immediately underneath), but the relief-heading of a much taller stele, doubtless inscribed with some public document such as a decree or treaty.

The relief itself is set in an architectural frame, flanked with antae and with an architrave above carrying a pitched roof of flat, Corinthian-type pantiles and raised cover-tiles faced with antefixes. On the left stands Athena, wearing a girdled peplos with a long over-fold, a diminutive aegis and a helmet. The plume of the helmet was probably once indicated in paint and extended up on to the architrave above her, the inscription over the goddess's head being interrupted at this point to allow it room:

Ἀθη νᾶ

Athena

Her shield rests against her left hip and her left arm is

raised to clasp a spear that must once have been shown in paint. She is being approached by two male figures. The foremost of these is clad in a himation and is probably bearded. He is followed by a young, beardless warrior wearing a helmet, breastplate, chiton, chlamys and, probably, greaves. His shield rests against the anta behind him. In view of their virtual isocephaly with the goddess these two cannot be mortal men, but should represent gods, heroes or personifications. The himation-clad figure might be Demos introducing the warrior, but, to judge from their identity of pose, both are more probably gods or heroes symbolizing cities in suit to Athens, shown in the guise of Athena. A little survives of the inscription over the head of the young warrior. It is not interrupted by the plume of his helmet, which is indicated plastically under the architrave, and, in view of the provenance of the relief, it is perhaps to be read:

[Πρω]τε̣[σ]ί̣λ̣αος
Protesilaos (?)

This relief had already been identified as Attic by Conze in 1864, but, misinterpreted by Michaelis as votive, it has since escaped attention and been omitted from the lists of Attic *Urkundenreliefs* of Binneboessel and Süsserott. If its provenance from Sigeion is not merely due to accident, it should have headed the local copy of some Athenian document to which Sigeion was a party. Its style indicates a date in the mid–late fourth century B.C. which may perhaps be fixed with greater precision by reference to the treatment of the figure of Athena. This, though of fifth-century derivation, finds its closest parallels in the third quarter of the fourth century B.C., especially in the 330's.[1]

C. third quarter of the fourth century B.C.

Clarke, *Marbles* 51 no. 29; Idem, *Travels* 4° II (=II. 1) 163, 8° III 205; *CIG* II 3635; *AA* 1864 172; Michaelis, *Anc. Marbles* 248 no. 15; Chapman, *Handbook* (2nd ed.) 41 f.; *JHS* LXII (1942) 15 no. 6. *c.*

(B) ATTIC GRAVE MONUMENTS

28 Grave-stele of a mother or child (?)

PLATE 6

Transferred from the old University Library; presented to the University by Professor E. D. Clarke. From Athens. Inv.: GR.18.1865.

P.H. 0·485 m., W. 0·364 m. max., H. of relief c. 0·013 m. max. Pentelic marble. The entire bottom part of the stele is missing, including the lower edge of the relief; the broken surface has subsequently been trimmed level, the lower part of the relief being mutilated in the process; crowning of stele partly broken away. Surface corroded by weather and chipped, e.g. at the face of the standing figure. Modern clamp-holes in top and bottom; cup-shaped hollow in point-dressed back of stele, perhaps from re-use as a door-socket.

The stele is crowned with a pediment which originally carried acroteria. There are no surviving traces of an inscription. The relief-panel is unframed and extends to the full width of the stone. On the right a woman is shown seated in a chair, dressed in a chiton and himation. A second female figure, likewise dressed in chiton and himation, is shown standing before her holding a child wrapped in swaddling clothes. It is difficult to assess whether this figure represents a nurse or a free-born member of the family, as her clothing might suggest. Also, in the absence of an inscription, it is impossible to tell with certainty which is, in fact, the deceased. The poor preservation of the relief is deeply to be regretted; a more adequate idea of its theme is perhaps to be gained from the stele of Eirene (A. Conze, *Die attischen Grabreliefs* no. 274, pl. 63). The treatment of the drapery motif of the seated mother, so far as this is still visible, seems of a kind current in the late fifth and the first quarter of the fourth centuries B.C.; that of the standing figure is also to be paralleled in work of the late fifth century and the beginning of the fourth century B.C., but the long, fluid quality of the folds appears rather to favour an early-fourth-century date.[2]

C. beginning of the fourth century B.C.

Clarke, *Marbles* 40 no. 18; Idem, *Travels* 4° III (=II. 2) 529 f., 8° VI 286; Michaelis. *Anc. Marbles* 250 no. 20; A. Conze, *Die attischen Grabreliefs* I 61 no. 277, pl. 64; Chapman, *Handbook* (2nd ed.) 45; *AJA* LXIII (1959) 142.

---

[1] Cf. J. N. Svoronos *Das athener Nationalmuseum* pl. 197 no. 2985, pl. 223 no. 2797; K. Schefold *Kertscher Vasen* 92. Cf. also Svoronos *op. cit.* pl. 221 no. 2802; *BCH* LVIII (1934) 164 f.

[2] For the lady cf. A. Conze *Die attischen Grabreliefs* I 29 no. 103, pl. 25; T. Dohrn *Attische Plastik vom Tode des Phidias bis zum Werken der großen Meister des IV Jahrhunderts* pls. 5*a*, 8*c*. For the nurse cf. Conze *loc. cit.*; H. Riemann *Kerameikos* II 16 f. no. 18, pl. 4, centre figure; cf. also 13 f. no. 17, pl. 3, left-hand figure.

29 Grave-lekythos of Hegemon PLATE 6

Transferred from the old University Library; presented to the University by J. Spencer Smith, Minister Plenipotentiary at the Ottoman Porte. Reputedly 'from the shore of the Propontis', but more probably from Attica. Inv.: GR.20.1865.

P.H. 0·94 m., max. diam. 0·395 m. Pentelic marble. Foot, handle and most of neck of lekythos broken away. Surface chipped and badly worn.

The shallow relief rests on a projecting base-line in imitation of *appliqué* metalwork. It stands out evenly from the surface of the lekythos and has, for the most part, been cut down from a shallow raised boss. On the right a dignified old man wrapped in a himation is shown shaking hands in farewell with a youth. The young man is wearing a chiton and a chlamys and has his petasos hanging at the back of his neck. He is leading his horse by the bridle and is attended by a small, himation-wrapped slave-boy with two hounds. As often, there is some uncertainty as to which figure represents the deceased. Commonly it is the horseman in scenes of this kind who is about to depart for another world, as, for example, on the loutrophoros in the Louvre (*Encyclopédie Photographique* III 206 f.) where the young Euthykles is saying goodbye to his parents. But here the young rider is attended. It is the old man who is shown alone, in the isolation of death. Also, the inscription naming the deceased is placed above his head:

['Η]γήμων
'Ẹπικηφίσι [ος]
Hegemon of the Epikephisian deme.

This lekythos ranges itself with a loosely related group of Attic grave-monuments assembled by Dohrn and assigned by him to the later part of the first quarter of the fourth century B.C.; further, he goes on to state that '*appliqué*' reliefs on a raised base-line such as this were not current before that date.[1] This seems hard to reconcile with the style of the Hegemon relief. The young horseman and hounds do not seem too far removed in time from their counterparts on a votive relief in the Museo Torlonia in Rome, usually assigned to the late fifth century B.C.; and the himation-motif of the older man has affinities with dated decree-headings of 400–399 B.C. and 398–397 B.C. and finds a very close parallel on a loutrophoros-stele from the Kerameikos which had already been incorporated in the Cononian wall by *c.* 393 B.C.[2] The theme of the horseman's farewell was, of course, to continue popular until later, as witness the externally dated lekythoi of Menyllos of the mid fourth century (*ActArch* V (1934) 60 f., fig. 14), but the style is no longer comparable.

C. beginning of fourth century B.C.

Clarke, *Travels* 4° III (=II. 2) 494 n. 1, 528 n. 1, 8° VI 238 n. 1, 283 n. 3; H. J. Rose, *Inscriptiones Graecae Vetustissimae* 418 no. 43; *CIG* II 2033; *AA* 1864 172; Michaelis, *Anc. Marbles* 250 no. 22; A. Conze, *Die attischen Grabreliefs* II 230 no. 1065, pl. 217; Chapman, *Handbook* (2nd ed.) 58; *IG* II–III² 6060; *JHS* LXII (1942) 14 no. I. 4; *AJA* LXIII (1959) 142; (NOTE: Fauvel's sketches in Bibliothèque Nationale, Paris, disprove alleged provenance, but give rise to false reading of inscription: *RhMus* XXI (1865) 386 no. 205; S. A. Koumanoudis, 'Αττικῆς 'Επιγραφαὶ 'Επιτύμβιοι 453; *IG* II 2017.)

30 Grave-stele of Theokles (?) PLATE 7

Presented by Professor Sir Charles Walston. Reputedly 'from Asia Minor', but more probably from Attica; originally acquired by W. Railton during his travels in Greek lands beginning in 1825. Inv.: GR.12.1885.

P.H. 0·57 m., H. of relief 0·05 m. max. Pentelic marble with golden-brown patina. The entire lower part of the stele is missing, as also both outer edges of the preserved upper portion, these last having broken away on natural fault-lines running vertically through the marble. Crowning of stele chipped, especially at the acroterion; on relief, hair over brow and tip of nose chipped away, hair at back of head repaired from original fragments. Surface slightly worn.

The back and top of the stele are roughly dressed with the point; its face shows abundant traces of the claw-chisel, especially on the background of the relief. The stele is crowned with a pediment bearing a central acroterion. Below the pediment is cut the inscription naming the deceased represented in the relief beneath:

[Θ]εοκλέης
Theokles

The restoration followed here is that proposed by Conze. It is by no means the only possibility, but

[1] Dohrn, *op. cit.* 143 f., 147–8; cf. especially the stele of Panaitios, Conze, *op. cit.* no. 1062, pl. 216, and the lekythos, Conze, *op. cit.* no. 1124, pl. 231, E. Kjellberg, *Studien zu den attischen Reliefs des V Jahrhunderts* pl. 12, figs. 40–1. On '*appliqué*' reliefs with a raised baseline on lekythoi, see Dohrn, *op. cit.* 185.

[2] Museo Torlonia relief: *AA* 1943 132, fig. 1; for bibliography, Dohrn, *op. cit.* 223 n. 107. Decree-headings: Svoronos, *op. cit.* pls. 203, 107 *right*. Kerameikos stele: Riemann, *op. cit.* 13 f. no. 17, pl. 3.

seems as likely as any. The shape of the pediment makes it possible to calculate the original width of the stele. This shows that, before the first 'E', there is space for four letters. But, as the space after the 'Σ' (four or five letters) is probably inadequate for patronymic or deme, a short name such as that restored, centrally placed over the tip of the dead man's cap, seems the most plausible interpretation. The same calculation of the width of the stele suggests that Theokles' raised right elbow extended right to its very edge, implying that the relief occupied the whole width of the stone and was without architectural framing at the sides. The dead man has a short, curly beard. He stands with downcast eyes and with his right hand raised to his pilos. This gesture recurs on a grave-lekythos (Conze, *Die attischen Grabreliefs* II no. 627, pl. 147). Its significance is not certain, but probably it is not analogous with the hand raised to the brow or tearing the hair in grief. The pilos was, *par excellence*, the headgear of travellers and soldiers on service abroad. Perhaps Theokles is to be seen as sadly donning his cap in readiness for the longest journey of all. It is not clear whether the gesture of clasping the pilos from behind (e.g. on hero-reliefs of Theseus such as *Encyclopédie Photographique* III 217) is related or not. There is a close attention to details such as the wrinkles over the knuckles of the raised hand; and the face conveys a delicate and beautiful sense of pathos.

The treatment of the head relates this fragment to the stele of Sosias and Kephisodoros in Berlin, which Dohrn has dated, probably rightly, in the earlier part of the first quarter of the fourth century B.C.; the pathos of expression is well echoed in a beautiful, if mannered, stele in Athens, possibly of slightly later date.[1]

First quarter of fourth century B.C.

A. Conze, *Die attischen Grabreliefs* II 195 f. no. 912, with text-fig.; Chapman, *Handbook* (2nd ed.) 55; *IG* II–III^2 11641; *JHS* LXII (1942) 14 no. I. 5; *AJA* LXIII (1959) 143 no. 4.

31 Grave-stele of a man PLATE 7

Presented by the Cyprus Exploration Fund. Found at Polis tis Chrysochou (the ancient Marion), Cyprus, in 1899. Inv.: GR.6.1890.

P.H. (excluding part concealed in mount) 0·885 m., P.W. 0·858 m., H. of relief 0·125 m. max. Pentelic marble. Entire left edge and whole of lower part of stele missing; the two remaining acroteria extensively broken away; surface of relief chipped and broken, particularly at brow, nose, lips and chin. The pupils of the eyes picked out in modern times. The front of the stele covered with faintly incised graffiti, some of them apparently the work of semi-literate modern hands, but the majority so closely superimposed as to be illegible.

The back and top of the stele have been left roughly dressed with the point; the side has been worked with the claw-chisel; the front of the relief is well finished and shows traces of the rasp on the drapery. The relief is set in an architectural frame in the form of a naïskos, with antae at the sides and, above, an architrave carrying a pediment with crowning and lateral acroteria. The relief figure extends beyond the inner edge of this frame above and to the side, as if standing in front of the building. It represents a long-haired, bearded old man, swathed in his himation, which he appears to be wearing over a kind of sleeved chiton. The resemblance of the drapery motif to that of the Lateran Sophocles is only superficial since, on the relief, the right arm hangs free outside the himation and might possibly have rested on a staff.

A profile version of this characteristic type of aged head may already have appeared on Attic grave-reliefs a little before the middle of the fourth century B.C.; but the frontal stance, the less idealized, more individual treatment of the face and the tragic cast of the eyes, no less than the heavy rendering of the folds of drapery, all show that the Cambridge relief should be contemporary with the elaborate Attic stelae of the third quarter of the fourth century B.C.[2]

In this case, unlike that of **29** and **30** above, the foreign provenance is beyond question, although both marble and style seem definitely Attic. Indeed, as pointed out by Sir John Beazley, there is a second Attic grave-stele from the same site in the Cyprus Museum (*AJA* LV (1951) 335; P. Dikaios, *Guide to the Cyprus Museum* (2nd ed.) 119). This relief, to judge from a photograph kindly sent the authors by Dr K. V. Karageorghis, seems of about the same date as the Cambridge example or possibly slightly earlier; it is not identifiably by the same hand. The Cambridge stele might conceivably be a simple import from Attica, but there are circumstances that also suggest the possibility that it might have been

[1] Stele of Sosias and Kephisodoros: C. Blümel, *Kat. Berlin* III 30 no. K 29, pl. 38; Dohrn, *op. cit.* 111 f., 128 f. Stele in Athens: Dohrn, *op. cit.* 141 f. no. 50, pl. 23 *c*.

[2] Head-type anticipated in profile on, e.g., the stele of Hippomachos and Kallias, H. Diepolder, *Die attischen Grabreliefs* pl. 23, Dohrn, *op. cit.* 168. For the later full-face handling as on the Cambridge stele, cf. the relief of Hippon, Diepolder, *op. cit.* 48, pl. 45. 1. For the frontal handling in depth, cf. also the dated relief of 347–346 B.C., Svoronos, *op. cit.* pl. 104 no. 1471, H. K. Süsserott, *Griechische Plastik des 4 Jahrhunderts* 58, pl. 4. 3.

executed in Cyprus by an itinerant Athenian sculptor. In the first place, it shows certain peculiarities of dress, of which the most remarkable is the non-Attic, oriental fashion of wearing a sleeved chiton under the himation. Secondly, there are a number of other classical grave-stelae from Marion in a style that is markedly Greek without its being specifically Attic (e.g. Dikaios, *op. cit.* 90 no. 5, pl. 22. 2; *AJA* LV (1951) 333 f., pl. 32*a*; *JHS and BSA Archaeological Reports* 1956 27 f., pl. 3*b*; *ibid.* 1957 46, pl. 4*c*); a few of these are carved in local limestone. But, unless it is the work of a very conservative craftsman, the Cambridge relief would seem to be earlier than the last quarter of the fourth century B.C., when the sumptuary laws of Demetrios of Phaleron ended the carving of such monuments in Athens itself and drove many of their artists abroad in search of employment.

C. third quarter of the fourth century B.C.

JHS XI (1890) 14, fig. 2; Chapman, *Handbook* (2nd ed.) 67; *AJA* LV (1951) 335; *Archaeology* VIII (1955) 13; *AJA* LXIII (1959) 143 no. 23.

32 Grave-loutrophoros PLATE 7

Bequeathed by the Rev. T. Worsley. Inv.: GR.1*b*.1885.

P.H. of ancient part 0·681 m., max. diam. 0·44 m. Pentelic marble. Foot missing and break trimmed level to receive the modern base on which it is mounted; entire upper part missing; this may have been fashioned from a separate piece of marble, fitted to the smooth, flat top and cylindrical, point-dressed socket, 0·279 m. in diam. and 0·219 m. deep, of the surviving part. In any case, trimmed top and socket seem clearly ancient. Surface chipped.

Conze mistakenly describes this vessel as a lekythos. In point of fact, the start of the springing of both handles of the loutrophoros is still visible on the upper part of the band of guilloche. This band is beautifully carved with a threefold cable-pattern developing to both sides from a point in the middle of the front of the vase where it is punctuated by two tiny palmettes, the one pointing upwards, the other downwards. The body of the vase is decorated with a tongue-pattern cut in relief and showing faint traces of the rasp.

This variety of loutrophoros, decorated with guilloche and a fluting of tongues, is found with vegetable ornament ranging in date from the middle years of the fourth century down to the time of the sumptuary laws of Demetrios of Phaleron; indeed, a somewhat schematic late type even survives those laws to appear in humble relief on kioniskoi.[1] The Cambridge vase may be early in this development, as seems to be suggested by the small, tight form of the palmettes on the guilloche, rather recalling those still in use on stamped black-glazed pottery towards the middle of the fourth century.[2]

Mid–later fourth century B.C.

A. Conze, *Die attischen Grabreliefs* III 362 no. 1703 *a* (with text-fig.); Chapman, *Handbook* (2nd ed.) 39; *AJA* LXIII (1959) 143 no. 27.

33 Lion's foot, from a statue PLATE 8

Transferred from the old University Library; presented to the University by Professor E. D. Clarke. From Athens, where acquired in 1801. Inv.: GR.12.1865.

P.H. (with plinth) 0·268 m., H. of plinth 0·085–0·09 m. Pentelic marble. Leg broken away above. Surface chipped and worn.

The fragment preserves the paw and lower part of the leg of a lion, somewhat larger than life-size. The foot rests on its own individual plinth, dressed with the point for insertion in a base. In the absence of any prominent indication of the 'raised claw' on the outer side of the leg, this is most probably to be interpreted as a back paw. The angle of the leg itself would well suit a striding Attic grave-lion of the usual type with back legs apart, belly arched and forepart low as if at bay and about to spring. The best-known examples are those from the grave-enclosure of Dionysios of Kollytos, but there are several others in existence and these have recently been collated in two important studies; see F. Willemsen, *Die Löwenkopf-Wasserspeier vom Dach des Zeustempels* (*Olympische Forschungen* IV) 129 f., together with the numerous plates there cited, and W. Llewellyn Brown, *The Etruscan Lion* 150. Certainty is not possible with so meagre a fragment, but the execution and the schematization of the claws seem to suit the date, from the mid fourth century on, appropriate to the type.

Probably mid–later fourth century B.C.

Clarke, *Marbles* 55 no. 37; Michaelis, *Anc. Marbles* 247 no. 12; Chapman, *Handbook* (2nd ed.) 38.

[1] For the type cf. Conze, *op. cit.* nos. 1436 (possibly earlier), 1717 f., pls. 367 f., also the stelae, nos. 1350 f., pls. 283 f. For the later part of the development see the stelae such as Blümel, *op. cit.* 51 f. nos. K 69–70, pl. 64; on their dating, cf. Möbius, *Die Ornamente der griechischen Grabstelen* 44, pl. 30*b*. For the survival of a similar variety on kioniskoi see, e.g., Conze, *op. cit.* no. 1772.

[2] *Hesperia* XXIV (1955) 172 f., pls. 66 f.

(C) ATTIC VOTIVE AND HERO RELIEFS

34 Fragment of a votive relief to Asklepios

PLATE 8

Bequeathed by C. S. Ricketts and C. H. Shannon. Provenance unknown. Inv.: GR.98.1937.

P.H. 0·482 m., H. of relief c. 0·06 m. max. Pentelic marble with a golden-brown patina and some incrustation. Assembled from three joining fragments; small part of the bottom edge of the stele preserved; otherwise broken away all round; back sawn away in modern times. The figure of Asklepios lacks feet, right elbow, left hand and head; break at the head trimmed level in modern times. Of the figure behind him nothing survives save the left forearm and hand, placed on his shoulder, and a small part of the veil.

The god is shown wrapped in his himation and leaning on his staff, around which a snake is coiled. The figure that once stood behind him with her hand on his right shoulder was probably that of Hygieia. The workmanship is of fine quality.

The treatment of the figure of Asklepios seems to be based on a fourth-century statue-type which recurs in the form of votive statuettes as well as on fourth-century reliefs dedicated at the Asklepieion in Athens and at the head of a possible Attic proxeny decree of about 332 B.C.[1] Closely related seems to be a second sculptural type which differs mainly in having an over-fold on the himation; it, too, is attested in sculptures in the round as well as on votive reliefs from the Asklepieion in Athens.[2] Although the motif clearly has much earlier antecedents, the head-types associated with these figures suggest a date towards the middle years of the fourth century B.C. Their appearance on votive reliefs should be contemporary or later.

C. middle–third quarter of the fourth century B.C.

35 Fragment from a votive relief (?)

PLATE 8

Presented by Dr J. Disney; originally acquired by T. Hollis in Venice. Inv.: GR.38.1850.

P.H. 0·406 m., H. of relief 0·045 m. max. Pentelic marble with rich, golden-red patina and faint traces of adhering mortar. Lightly cleaned at some points; minor recutting on head of figure. A little of the bottom surface and point-dressed back of the stele preserved; broken away at sides and above, as well as at the outer edge of the base. Of the single figure preserved, greater part of right arm and toes of right foot missing; surface chipped, e.g. on his cheek.

The fragment preserves the greater part of a male figure facing towards the left—in this case clearly an ordinary mortal. He is beardless, wears a himation wrapped tightly around his body and has sandals on his feet. His gaze is directed upwards slightly, suggesting that he is in the presence of a divinity who would naturally be rendered on a larger scale than mortal men. His right arm was raised, but whether in a gesture of adoration or simply to rest on the shoulder of a neighbouring votary it is no longer possible to tell. As the adorants seem to have been approaching from the right, the fragment is more likely to be from an ordinary votive relief than from a 'funerary-banquet' relief such as **36**.

The elongated proportions of the figure, the tightness of the garment about the body and the transverse folds at the knees all favour a date in the second half of the fourth century B.C., notwithstanding that, in its broad essentials, the drapery motif has much earlier antecedents.[3] It seems important, however, to observe that the fragment seems classical, not classicizing, in spirit and has little in common with stelae such as A. W. Lawrence, *Later Greek Sculpture* 35, pl. 60. Some of the individual traits of the face such as the deeps-et eye are original, but its present portrait quality is largely the work of misguided modern hands which saw in the fragment a relief of Caesar's assassin, Brutus.

C. second half of the fourth century B.C.

Memoirs of Thomas Hollis 820; J. Disney sr., *Cat. Hyde* 46 no. 94; J. Disney jr., *MS Cat.* 168; Marsden, *Cat. Disney Coll.* 84 no. 38; Michaelis, *Anc. Marbles* 261 no. 69; Chapman, *Handbook* (2nd ed.) 45.

36 Hero-relief

PLATE 8

Transferred from the old University Library. Brought from Athens by the Earl of Aberdeen. Inv.: GR.16.1865.

[1] Votive statuettes: e.g. E. Paribeni, *Cat. Sculture di Cirene* 83 no. 202, pl. 114. Votive reliefs: e.g. Svoronos, *op. cit.* pl. 35 no. 1345, U. Hausmann, *Kunst und Heiltum* pl. 12, Idem, *Griechische Weihreliefs* figs. 40, 48. Decree heading: Svoronos, *op. cit.* pl. 197 no. 2985, Süsserott, *op. cit.* pl. 5. 4, *IG* II² 406.

[2] Votive statuettes: *ÖJh* XXIII (1926) 8 f. (Schober's first variant); cf. also *AM* XVII (1892) 1 f., Kjellberg, *Asklepios* II 26. Votive reliefs: e.g. Svoronos, *op. cit.* pl. 38 *top right*; *EA* 1224.

[3] Earlier: Conze *op. cit.* no. 627, pl. 147; closer: Svoronos, *op. cit.* pls. 84, 191 no. 2949.

Total H. 0·22 m., H. without tang 0·177 m. max. Pentelic marble with a golden-brown patina. Left-hand corners broken away. Left edge chipped obliterating most of the head of the dedicant's eldest child; head of his smallest child also broken away. Surface worn and bruised, especially over the lower part of the framing of the relief. Modern dowel-holes in top and in underside of tang.

The stele has a tang underneath for insertion in a socket. The back surface of the stone has been left roughly dressed with the point; its sides show traces of claw-chisel work. The relief is set in an architectural frame, much as **27**. Before describing it in detail it will be best to touch on its significance. Stelae of this kind seem commonly to have been dedicated at sanctuaries in Athens, e.g. the Asklepieion, as a kind of memorial to the dead.[1] They show the symbolism of the chthonic cult of the true hero or demigod gradually usurped by the 'heroized' dead mortal. This example belongs to the period when reliefs of this kind became much more numerous and acquired a fixed iconography. Nevertheless, the type was still also able to be used, without significant modification, for votive reliefs to such deities as Zeus Teleios and the Eleusinian God and Goddess.[2] That the present example is a hero-relief, however, is revealed by the horse's head appearing at a high window above the figures of the dedicants. Originally probably little more than a personal 'status-symbol', this acquired a special funerary significance on monuments of this kind; see M. P. Nilsson, *Geschichte der griechischen Religion* I 358. Closely akin are the representations of the hero as a warrior mounted on horseback such as, e.g., **64**.

The hero or, more probably, 'heroized' dead mortal is shown as a bearded man lying on a draped couch, his left elbow supported on a pile of cushions. He has a polos on his head and wears a himation about the lower part of his body. With his right hand he holds on high a horn-shaped drinking-rhyton from which he is probably pouring a libation. His left hand, which commonly holds a cup in reliefs of this type, seems here to have been empty. Before him is a table apparently laden with ritual items of food appropriate to the funerary banquet (see **61**). His wife sits on the edge of the couch with her feet resting on a foot-stool. She wears both chiton and himation and in her left hand she appears to be holding the open casket usual to the type. Commonly the right hand of this figure is shown sprinkling incense from the casket either on a tall thymiaterion or else on a tiny censer standing on the table, but here this detail may have been omitted. Behind her a naked slave-boy is shown drawing wine from a lebes on a draped rod-tripod stand. The left part of the relief seems to be occupied by the figures of the dedicant, his wife and their three children. Two of the children stand in front of the anta of the architectural framing, as does also the edge of the couch on the other side of the relief. There seems to have been an inscription under the relief, of which only the last letter survives:

- - - - - - - - - - ν

The treatment of the head of the hero, as better seen on larger reliefs than the present, suggests that this fixed iconographic type for stelae of this kind can hardly have been established before the middle of the fourth century B.C. Further, the numerous examples of it extant would seem to indicate that it was followed for a considerable period.[3]

Second half of the fourth century B.C.

Clarke, *Marbles* 49 f. no. 27; Michaelis, *Anc. Marbles* 249 no. 18; Chapman, *Handbook* (2nd ed.) 42.

(D) UNCERTAIN

37 Relief fragment from a monumental base (?) PLATE 9

Bequeathed by C. S. Ricketts and C. H. Shannon. Provenance unknown. Inv.: GR.99.1937.

P.H. 0·663 m., P.W. 0·371 m., H. of relief 0·046 m. max. Probably Pentelic marble with the surface corroded by weather and showing traces of a red-brown patina. Preserved edges to left and underneath block; broken away above, to right, at lower left corner and in front at the bottom; back of block sawn away in modern times.

[1] On the significance of these *Totenmahlreliefs*, as they are called, see *AZ* XL (1882) 305; A. Furtwängler, *Sammlung Sabouroff* I 34; *AM* XXI (1896) 347; *JdI* XX (1905) 47 f., 123 f.; M. Bieber, *Die antiken Skulpturen und Bronzen in Cassel* 37 f.; B. Ashmole, *Ancient Marbles at Ince* 97; *Studies Presented to D. M. Robinson* I 594 f., 606 f.; U. Hausmann, *Griechische Weihreliefs* 25 f.

[2] Zeus Teleios: *EA* 3999; Eleusinian God and Goddess: Svoronos, *op. cit.* pl. 88, *Die Antike* XVIII (1943) 213 f., fig. 1.

[3] Very similar to the Fitzwilliam relief: Svoronos, *op. cit.* pl. 94 no. 1531 (the hero holds a cup in his left hand; a tall thymiaterion stands by the table); Blümel, *op. cit.* 69 f. no. K 100, pl. 81 (tiny three-legged censer on the table); W. Amelung, *Kat. vaticanischen Museums* I 711 no. 594, pl. 77. Also exported, e.g. British Museum 717 (from Halicarnassus); *Hesperia* XXIX (1960) pl. 60*a* (from Corinth).

Of the surviving figure, head missing, also much of right forearm and hand, part of the garland they are holding and the toes of both feet. Surface chipped and worn.

The relief shows a female figure of tall and slender proportions standing with her right leg slightly flexed and with the back of her left wrist resting on her hip. Her head was probably turned somewhat to her left. She wears a girdled chiton and, over it, a himation; the latter passes down across the front of her body, under her right arm, up over the back of her head, where it serves as a veil, and down again enveloping her left shoulder and arm. The drapery is skilfully and beautifully handled, the folds being often cut to a slightly exaggerated depth to achieve a bold play of light and shadow. The lower edge of the chiton is marked by a row of drillings. In her right hand the figure holds a laurel garland. It is shown at a somewhat oblique angle, merging into the relief-ground away from her and being in such high relief where it has broken away beside her right leg as to be almost free-standing.

It is not possible to tell with certainty what the purpose of the relief was. However, what survives of the preserved left edge seems to betray the anathyrosis appropriate to the junction between two blocks of a continuous frieze rather than the rustication that is a possible dressing for the end of a votive stele. Also it is clear that the figure with the garland stood in comparative isolation, strongly suggesting the kind of widely spaced composition favoured for the decoration of monumental bases. Indeed, several examples of these dating from the middle years of the fourth century B.C. show figures not unlike that of the Cambridge relief.[1] For dating, parallels may also be drawn with the sarcophagus of the mourning women from Sidon, which shows some kinship with Attic grave sculpture of the mid-fourth century, and, less precisely, with an Attic dated relief of 336 B.C. Closest of all, however, is an Attic votive relief in Athens.[2] It is of a slightly different scale from that of the Cambridge fragment, but repeats so many of its idiosyncrasies of style as to suggest that it might be from the same workshop. It was found at Thebes and so must at least be earlier in date than that city's destruction in 335 B.C.

Probably Attic work of the middle or early third quarter of the fourth century B.C.

[1] E.g. Mantinea Base: Svoronos, *op. cit.* pl. 30, Brunn-Bruckmann 468; Epidauros Base: Svoronos, *op. cit.* pl. 126, Hausmann, *op. cit.* fig. 18; Athens, National Museum 3078: Svoronos, *op. cit.* pls. 200–1; Athens, Acropolis Museum: O. Walter, *Beschreibung der Reliefs im kleinen Akropolismuseum in Athen* 184 f. no. 391 (perhaps to be compared with the dated relief of 336 B.C.?—see n. 2).

[2] Sarcophagus from Sidon: O. Hamdy Bey and T. Reinach, *Nécropole de Sidon*, especially pl. 7, *right-hand figure*. Relief dated to 336 B.C.: *Hesperia* XXII (1953) pl. 20*a*. Relief from Thebes, Athens National Museum 1140: Svoronos, *op. cit.* 440 f., pl. 72; *EA* 1248.

IV

ANCIENT COPIES FROM CLASSICAL ORIGINALS

38 Janiform herm PLATE 11

Presented by Dr J. Disney. Probably acquired in Italy. Inv.: GR.28.1850.

H. 0·295 m. Luna marble. Restored in marble; the left side of the neck and the whole of the upper right part of one of the two heads, including the looped-up hair, etc., of the head behind. The original surface, where it survives, corroded by weather; most of it, however, harshly cleaned in modern times, especially over the flesh. The shaft of the herm was fashioned from a separate piece of marble; relieving surface and a square dowel-hole (both somewhat recut) to receive it in underside. At sides, sockets and dowel-holes to receive separately attached projecting shoulder-slabs.

Both heads are of essentially the same type and seem to represent a youthful god, possibly Apollo. The hair is combed straight forward over the brow where it is arranged in three superimposed rows of tight spiral curls, held in place with a heavy head-band. At the sides, as here reinterpreted by the copyist, it is looped up over the head-band but has its curled ends hanging down over the ears against the cheeks. Behind this it descends to its full length on to the shoulders. An iron pin in the left shoulder-lock of the restored head is of uncertain function. If it represents the one-time point of attachment of an ancient minor repair, then the modern recutting has been severe indeed.

For the type see B. Schweitzer, *Antiken in ostpreußischem Privatbesitz* 172 f., *Genava* IX (1931) 91 f., *ActArch* VIII (1937) 142. It seems that a South Italian or Sicilian head-type of about the early second quarter of the fifth century B.C. has been adapted by the early Imperial copyists. Herms from Pompeii show that they were already copying these heads in the first century A.D. Modifications crept in, as here in the looped-up hair at the sides and something of the character of the face. Indeed, it is even possible that the modern error that saw these heads as feminine and, because of their frequent association with bearded heads of Dionysus, identified them as Ariadne may in fact echo a confusion existing in the minds of some of the copyists. Under the circumstances, this herm has strong claims to be considered as a Roman classicizing work; it is retained here because of the recent tendency to treat the type as ultimately stemming from a single source, despite the many variations.

A distinctly imprecise copy of the first–second centuries A.D., apparently based on a South Italian or Sicilian head of about the early second quarter of the fifth century B.C.

J. Disney sr., *Cat. Hyde* 14 no. 73; J. Disney jr., *Museum Disneianum* 45, pl. 23; *AZ* V (1847) 158; *GGA* 1849 444; Marsden, *Cat. Disney Coll.* 84 no. 24; Michaelis, *Anc. Marbles* 259 no. 59; Chapman, *Handbook* (2nd ed.) 44; A. B. Cook, *Zeus* II. I. 391 n. 2.

39 Statuette of Apollo (?) PLATE 10

Purchased. Formerly in the Disney Collection, having been given to Disney by a friend who had bought it from Flaxman in 1796. Restorations carried out in Rome in 1793 under Flaxman and Antonio d'Este. Inv. GR.2.1885.

P.H. of the ancient part c. 0·387 m. Pentelic marble (with restorations in Carrara marble). Restored in marble; head, including, in a separate piece, the hair-knot behind the shoulders, left hand, right arm from a little below the shoulder, both legs from below the knees and the entire base, tree-trunk support and quiver of arrows. The ancient part has been cleaned.

Flaxman and d'Este have restored the statuette as Apollo—an identification that may quite well be correct. For many details, including, in particular, the head, they have based themselves on a figure now in Budapest, but then at the Palazzo Odescalchi in Rome.[1] This, however, shows a different type and no safe inferences can be drawn from it. The god stands with his right leg slightly flexed. His left arm, lightly bent at the elbow, hangs close to his side. His torso is heavy and massive, especially in relation to the very short legs. Its surface detail is vigorous, although it has lost much of its precision in the modern cleaning.

[1] *EA* 1986–90; A. Hekler, *Die Antiken in Budapest, Abt.* I, *die Skulpturen* 174 f. no. 173.

The back is punctuated by a deep vertical hollow between the shoulder-blades and an even deeper oblique division between the shoulder muscles and the plump buttocks. The pubic hair has the characteristic early triangular outline. The hair-style is curious, with three waving locks falling close together on to the chest to each side of the head. The long knot of hair behind the shoulders may have had some ancient authority, since it seems as if the head may first of all have been restored to meet the existing indications and the replacement of the lower part of the hair at the back may only have been done as an afterthought. Yet it is noteworthy that the archaic hair-style, reminiscent of works such as the Apollo Philesios of Kanachos, combines strangely with a torso in the Severe Style. As it has not yet been possible to identify any other copy of this type, it is difficult to assess the soundness of the restorations. The head-type remains unknown. For the position of the right arm the evidence is confined to the surviving ancient part of the armpit. The feet may have been a little further apart and the calves may perhaps have been very slightly shorter.

Furtwängler has assigned the original from which this statuette is copied to an Attic artist of the circle of Kritios and Nesiotes, but the dumpy proportions and short legs would seem more appropriate to the Peloponnese or, possibly, northern Greece. The lingering archaism of the hair-style might also seem more plausible in such regions. A different but partly analogous conflict in styles is to be observed on the fifth-century-B.C. gems, A. Furtwängler, *Die antiken Gemmen* pl. 10. 18, J. D. Beazley, *The Lewes House Collection of Ancient Gems* 44 no. 49, pl. 3. The statuette has been tentatively included at this point as a free copy, possibly not without some modifications, from an original of the fifth century B.C., but its status is far from certain and it might equally be a new archaizing creation of Roman times of the kind noted under **103** below.

Careful work of about early Imperial date, seemingly based on a Greek type of c. 480–460 B.C., perhaps by a Peloponnesian artist, although it is no longer easy to evaluate to what extent this statuette is not simply a new Roman creation in the style of that period.

J. Disney jr., *Museum Disneianum* 47 f., pl. 24; *AZ* v (1847) 158; *GGA* 1849 447; Michaelis, *Anc. Marbles* 267, 333; A. Furtwängler, *Über Statuenkopien im Altertum* 49 f. with text-fig. (= *Abh. bay Ak.* xx. 3. 573 f.); A. Joubin, *La sculpture grecque entre les guerres médiques et l'époque de Périclès* 88 f., fig. 16; W. Amelung, *Kat. vaticanischen Museums* I 498; Chapman, *Handbook* (2nd ed.) 40; *AJA* LXIII (1959) 143 no. 14.

40 Head from a sphinx PLATE 10

Presented by Dr J. Disney. Probably acquired in Italy. Inv.: GR.18.1850.

P.H. c. 0·192 m., H. of face 0·149 m. (originally, before recutting, 0·152 m.). Pentelic marble with a golden-brown patina where the original surface survives. Only the head is preserved, trimmed and drilled underneath to fit a modern bust from which it has since been removed. Tip of nose broken away. Part of underside of chin restored in plaster and the whole of the chin recut in modern times to reduce the area of damage. Face, sides of neck, much of the left ear and a small part of the hair in its immediate vicinity harshly cleaned in modern times.

This head is clearly copied from the same original as **41**, under which both will be found discussed together. Before its harsh treatment at the hands of the modern restorer this was probably the finer copy of the two, as may be judged, for example, from the greater depth and variety of planes shown by the hair at the sides and over the brow. The face, too, may have shown a greater sensitivity, but here it is difficult to discount the consequences of the overworking.

A copy of early Imperial date from an original of the middle of the fifth century B.C. or very slightly earlier.

J. Disney sr., *Cat. Hyde* 7 no. 30; J. Disney jr., *Museum Disneianum* 21, pl. 11; *AZ* v (1847) 157; *GGA* 1849 445; Marsden, *Cat. Disney Coll.* 83 no. 10; Michaelis, *Anc. Marbles* 258 no. 49; Chapman, *Handbook* (2nd ed.) 52.

41 Head from a sphinx PLATE 10

Bequeathed by C. S. Ricketts and C. H. Shannon. Provenance unknown. Inv.: GR.96.1937.

P.H. c. 0·254 m., H. of face 0·152 m. Fine-grained greyish-white Italian marble with a golden-brown patina and root marks. Broken away at the base of the neck. Nose and part of the upper lip restored in marble. Very slightly chipped. Inlaid eyes missing.

The neck displays two faint 'Venus-rings' and shows a distinct curve in profile, with the chin tilted high in relation to the body. The head is copied from the same original as **40** and the following description applies to both. Both show the face of a young woman of graceful, if somewhat austere, countenance. Over the front part of the head her hair is combed forward, parted in the middle, divided over the brow and carried round across the tops of the ears to a knot of tight spiral curls at the back of the head. Over the back part of the head, on the other hand, the hair is simply combed backwards towards the knot, so that there is a kind of secondary, vertical parting a little behind the ears. The majority of the locks of hair have a subsidiary division lightly incised down their middle. Although the neck of **41** suggests that the head was looking straight ahead, both faces show a distinct asymmetry. In both cases the right cheek is deeper than the left (especially marked on **41**). There is also a vertical asymmetry with the left ear and its associated features distinctly lower than their counterparts on the right in relation to the vertical axis of the face.

The following copies are known from the same original:

Sphinxes: (1) Mantua, Palazzo Ducale. Free-standing statue of a sphinx. A. Levi, *Sculture greche e romane del Palazzo Ducale di Mantova* 18 f. no. 4, pl. 21.

(2) and (3) Rome, Palazzo Doria-Pamfili. Trapezophoron with two sphinxes and vegetable ornament of early Julio-Claudian date. *EA* 2317.

(4) Naples, Museo Nazionale 6862. Single table-support in the form of a sphinx; forepaws, of necessity, moved slightly further forward to spread weight. From the Casa del Fauno, Pompeii. *Museo Borbonico* IX pl. 43; S. Reinach, *Répertoire de la statuaire* II 704. 1.

(5) London, British Museum 1719. As (4). *A Description of the Ancient Marbles in the British Museum* X pl. 31; Reinach, *op. cit.* II 703. 7; A. H. Smith, *BMC Sculpture* III 85.

Herms: (6) and (7) Athens, Agora Museum S 553, S 554. Herms with heads in relief; front of head only shown. From the stage-front of the Odeion of Agrippa in the Athenian Agora. *Hesperia* V (1936) 10 f., fig. 10, XIX (1950) 66 f., pls. 46, 48.

Detached heads: (8) Rome, Vatican, vestibule to the Museum. On modern bust. G. Kaschnitz-Weinberg, *Sculture del Magazzino del Museo Vaticano* 31 no. 48, pl. 15.

(9) Liverpool, Walker Art Gallery. On modern bust. B. Ashmole, *Ancient Marbles at Ince Blundell Hall* 68 no. 175, pl. 2. (Confirmed by Professor Ashmole, who drew the authors' attention to this head.)

(10) and (11) Cambridge, Fitzwilliam Museum. **40** and **41** above.

All the above have identical heads of the same scale. The bodies of the sphinxes also seem perfectly consistent allowing for the minor modifications arising from their different roles. Possibly related, although on a smaller scale and with a head of rather different type, is the sphinx-support, *Collection Arthur Sambon (Sale Cat. G. Petit, 25th–28th May, 1914)* 15 no. 36, pl. facing 8. Quite unrelated, despite Poulsen's claims to the contrary, seems the throne-arm in the form of a sphinx in Copenhagen, F. Poulsen, *Kat. over antike Skulpturer, Ny Carlsberg Glyptotek* 346 f. no. 490, *Billedtavler* 37.

All eleven copies seem to show the same facial asymmetry. Yet the complete sphinxes reveal that the head was looking straight to the front. Indeed, these refinements only become meaningful if one may assume that the whole sphinx was turned at a three-quarter angle in relation to some larger composition and, probably, mounted at a high level as, e.g., on a column. Beyond this point, the further elucidation of the original statue must rest almost entirely on the evidence of the herms from the Odeion in the Athenian Agora and for the final word on the subject it will be necessary to wait for their definitive publication.[1] In the decoration of the stage-front youthful male herms seem to have alternated with those with the sphinxes' heads. Two of these are preserved. The one (*Hesperia* XIX (1950) pl. 49*a–c*) is too badly damaged for stylistic conclusions to be drawn from it; it wears a fillet and its hair-treatment could hardly date before the mid-fifth century B.C. The other, described as being of the same type, preserves a face closely akin in style to that of the sphinxes (*op. cit.* pl. 49*d*); the top of the head was added in a separate piece of marble, whether because of a fault in the stone or because of the presence of a spreading head-gear such as a petasos it is not clear. It seems reasonable to make certain basic assumptions: the allusive quality of the decoration was presumably able to be appreciated by the audience in the Odeion—i.e. the originals were known to them and probably in Athens; the heads are probably interrelated in some way, e.g. as being copied from the same group; and the subject probably had poetic or dramatic associations appropriate to the Odeion. In the period in which the originals should have been created and just afterwards, decorators of Attic vases such as the Achilles Painter, Polygnotos and his group and the Louvre Centauromachy Painter show one scene with such consistency as to suggest that they may be copying a major work of art.[2] On the left the Sphinx, in

[1] The authors are especially indebted to Professor E. B. Harrison for help in the identification of the Cambridge and Agora heads; also to Professor H. A. Thompson and the staff of the Agora excavations in Athens.

[2] E.g. Achilles Painter: L. D. Caskey and Sir John Beazley, *Attic Vase-Paintings, Boston* 45 f. no. 51, pl. 33; J. Sieveking, *Bronzen, Terrakotten, Vasen der Sammlung Loeb* 62, pl. 50; *JHS* XXXIV (1914) 192 no. 4, fig. 12*a*. Polygnotos and his group: *CVA* Oxford I pl. 16. 5 (Gt. Br. pl. 108); *CVA* Louvre VIII pl. 38. 3–4 (France pl. 518). Louvre Centauromachy Painter: K. A. Neugebauer, *Antiken in deutschem Privatbesitz* 41 no. 170, pl. 74.

the pose of nos. (1)–(5) above, crouches on top of a column. Before her, in chlamys and petasos, stands the youthful Oedipus holding two spears.

The original from which the sphinxes are copied would seem to have been created *c.* 460–450 B.C. We have seen that it was probably in Athens (possibly on the Areopagus or at Kolonos Hippios?). The treatment of the hair perhaps suggests that the artist had Peloponnesian connections. The popularity of the type with copyists of Roman date may have been limited to the late first century B.C. and the first century A.D.

A copy of early Imperial date from an original of the middle of the fifth century B.C. or very slightly earlier.

AJA LXIII (1959) 143 no. 10.

42 Head of a victorious young athlete by Polykleitos PLATES 12–13

Presented by the Viscountess D'Abernon. Found in Rome in 1864. Formerly Van Branteghem Collection, later in the possession of Sir Edgar Vincent, subsequently Viscount D'Abernon. Inv.: GR.3.1948.

P.H. c. 0·22 m., H. of face 0·154 m., W. of face (in front of ears) 0·117 m. Moderately fine-grained white marble (Pentelic?). Broken away at neck. Tip of nose restored in marble, small part of lower lip in plaster. Small area behind the right ear worked over in modern times. Surface otherwise intact, apart from very minor chips and abrasions. It shows a faint golden patina and numerous root marks. In the top of the head, somewhat forward from its highest point, there are remains of an iron bar, 0·005 m. in diameter. This presumably carried a meniskos, indicating that the copy was originally set up out of doors.

The boy-athlete has his head bent forward and to one side as, with his raised right hand, he adjusts the garland of victory upon it. At least, this seems the most likely interpretation, although it has been subject to dispute. There appear to be traces of a strut of approximately triangular section running forward from the lower edge of the hair above the right eye, presumably to make contact with the raised right hand. The area of hair between this strut and the right ear has not been worked in detail but only roughed out with the point, suggesting that this part may have been concealed by the close proximity of the fingers or, less probably, of what they held. For, even on a marble copy such as the present, the garland probably consisted of a hoop of wire to which were attached leaves of sheet-metal. It would seem to have been held in place by a groove running around the back and rear part of the left side of the head and by the fingers of the right hand. Probably it nowhere else made direct contact with the marble.

The statue-type to which this head belongs is also known from many other copies, including the comparatively intact 'Westmacott Boy' in the British Museum. For lists of these copies see *MA* XXVI (1920) 592 n. 3, *Art Bull.* XVIII (1936) 148 f., E. Paribeni, *Cat. Mus. Nazionale Romano, sculture greche del V secolo* 36 under no. 48. The original has been identified, with some plausibility, as Polykleitos' statue of Kyniskos. If this is correct, it was still probably not executed until the early third quarter of the fifth century B.C., some while after Kyniskos' Olympic victory in the boys' boxing contest which seems likely to have fallen in 460 B.C.

The modelling of the cheeks of the present copy shows a subtlety superior to that found on the majority of the others. The face is revealed as essentially asymmetrical, with the left cheek considerably deeper than the right. Also, there is a series of horizontal refinements, bridging the transition between head and neck angles. These can best be appreciated by relating the obliquely horizontal axis of the ears to the vertical axis of the face. These refinements seem to be present on the best copies.[1] The rather lean and characterless appearance of the heads of many of the others seems to arise from their partial or total neglect by copyists endeavouring to impose an arbitrary symmetry. There are traces of the drill at the inner corners of the eyes, in the nostrils and in the line separating the two lips.

A copy, apparently of about early Imperial date, from an original probably of about the early third quarter of the fifth century B.C.

AA 1892 99; A. Furtwängler, *Meisterwerke* 455 fig. 73; P. Paris, *Polyclète* 64 f. and text-fig.; *Burlington Fine Arts Club, Illustrated Cat. of Ancient Greek Art* (1904) 28 f. no. 45, pl. 33; *Art Bull.* XVIII (1936) 143, 149 no. 25, figs. 12–15; R. B. Bandinelli, *Policlito* 20, pl. 3 no. 25–6; C. Picard, *Manuel d'archéologie grecque, la sculpture* II. 1. 276 f.; *Archeologia Classica* I (1949) 128 f.; *Abh. Heidelberg* 1955. 1. 13 fig. 15 (wrongly cited as in the British Museum); *Handbook and Guide* (1960) 10; *AJA* LXIII (1959) 142 no. 1.

43 Head of an athlete (?) PLATE II

Provenance unknown. Inv.: GR.S.1.

P.H. 0·029 m. Pentelic (?) marble. Broken away at base of neck. Chipped and rubbed.

[1] E.g. D. Mustilli, *Il Museo Mussolini* 145 no. 10, pl. 90; E. Paribeni, *Cat. Museo Nazionale Romano, sculture greche del V secolo* 36 no. 47.

A tiny copy of a youthful male head of mid–late fifth-century-B.C. type. Presumably it is broken from a miniature copy of some major fifth-century statue such as Polykleitos' Doryphoros, but the execution is so bad as to make identification impossible.

A crude and tiny copy, presumably of later Hellenistic or Imperial date, based on some original of the mid–late fifth century B.C.

44 Youthful male bust PLATE II

Presented by Dr J. Disney. Probably acquired in Italy. Inv.: GR.31.1850.

H. 0·311 m. Luna (?) marble, showing a light brown patina where the original surface survives. Restored in marble; nose, most of upper lip and the pinned chlamys on the left shoulder; the last is a quite inappropriate addition in Proconnesian marble, made on the false assumption that this is a portrait bust. The face and the front part of the neck harshly cleaned in modern times; lower edges of the bust also largely repointed. Surface somewhat chipped. Traces of the copyist's primary drillings on the crown of the head.

Even before its harsh treatment at the hands of the modern restorer this was a rather imperfect copy. It shows a young man with a sword-belt over his right shoulder and a circlet in his hair, although, to judge from the hollow continuing its line around the back of the head, the circlet may here, as elsewhere, be a mistake on the part of the copyist for a 'beaked fillet'. This 'beaked fillet', although it long continued popular in Magna Graecia, is mainly attested in the fifth century B.C. in Greece proper.[1] The planes of the cheeks suggest that the nose and upper lip have been restored fairly correctly. They afford a typical profile of the second half of the fifth century B.C. (cf. **42**). The hair over the brow seems to show the influence of Polykleitos, although the original was probably the product of a much less skilled hand than his. A torso in Rome, perhaps copied from an original of the School of Polykleitos, has a similar sword-belt and angle of the head, although too little survives of the head itself to establish any identity; see H. Stuart Jones, *Cat. Museo dei Conservatori* 85 f. no. 18, pl. 30. It may well be that the drilled pupils are not merely an addition of the modern restorer; if so, the copy probably dates from the second century A.D. or later.

A copy, apparently of second-century-A.D. or later date, from an original of the later fifth century B.C.

J. Disney sr., *Cat. Hyde* 47 no. 229; J. Disney jr., *MS Cat.* 46; Marsden, *Cat. Disney Coll.* 84 no. 18; Michaelis, *Anc. Marbles* 260 no. 62; Chapman, *Handbook* (2nd ed.) 44.

45 Statuette of the Mother of the Gods PLATE II

Transferred from the old University Library. Presented to the University by Professor E. D. Clarke. From Athens. Inv.: GR.3.1865.

P.H. 0·188 m. Pentelic marble with a reddish-brown patina. Broken away are the head of the goddess, much of the back and the lower part of one side of her throne and the footstool in front of it with her feet resting upon it. Surface badly chipped, especially at the goddess's right arm and the diminutive lion in her lap.

The goddess sits on a massive throne. She wears a chiton, girdled above her waist, and over it a himation which passes over her left arm and shoulder, originally continuing around the back of her head, where it served as a veil, to come down again, probably under her right arm, and across her lap. Heavy ringlets of hair hang down on her shoulders. Her left hand does not seem to have held a tympanon, its usual attribute on these figures, but to have rested on her left knee by the back of the lion in her lap. Of this creature, all that remains clearly visible are the underside of his belly and the edge of his left haunch. The right hand of the goddess is missing. Most probably, on the analogy of the many complete examples, it held a phiale from which she was pouring a libation. The carving is clumsy and poor. The inclination of the goddess's body towards her left and the circumstance that her throne is higher on the left than on the right are merely due to accidental ineptitudes.

This is one of a large number of Attic votive statuettes all loosely based on a single sculptural type and apparently ranging in date between the later part of the fourth century B.C. and Imperial times.[2] The present undistinguished example shows extensive use of the flat chisel and is unlikely to be early in the series.

[1] E.g. C. Blümel, *Kat. Berlin* V 10 no. K 209, pl. 23; *EA* 3801 f.; cf. also *EA* 965 f.

[2] E.g. J. N. Svoronos, *Das athener Nationalmuseum* pls. 116–20, 198; O. Waldhauer, *Die antiken Skulpturen der Ermitage* III 20 nos. 250 f.; O. Walter, *Beschreibung der Reliefs im kleinen Akropolismuseum* 75 f. nos. 127 f.; F. P. Johnson, *Corinth* IX 48 nos. 57 f.; C. Blümel, *Kat. Berlin* III 74 f. nos. K 107 f., pls. 66, 85; E. Paribeni, *Cat. Sculture di Cirene* 90 f. nos. 231 f., pls. 120 f.; *AJA* XLI (1937) 184, fig. 9; etc. Some of the examples where this figure appears in a naïskos have been dated by associated reliefs or letter-forms to the later fourth century B.C., e.g. *Hesperia* VI (1937) 204, fig. 124, Blümel, *op. cit.* 74 no. K 107, pl. 66. The late Attic taurobolion altars still give much the same rendering of the Mother of the Gods; cf. Svoronos, *op. cit.* 474 f., pl. 80.

It is commonly assumed that these votive statuettes are small, free copies of the cult image by Pheidias in Athens, presumably dating to the third quarter of the fifth century B.C.[1] But these small votives may not copy the cult figure directly so much as a slightly later version of it, perhaps itself a votive statue (for the phenomenon cf. **47**). The over-fold of the chiton occurring on the few copies that Langlotz considers may go back to the Pheidian original has been replaced by high girdling of a kind in fashion in the second half of the fourth century B.C., but the type and pose and the general massing of the himation (all seen to better advantage on **46**) have been little changed.

A small, free copy of Hellenistic or Imperial date, perhaps based on a fourth-century version of a cult statue of the third quarter of the fifth century B.C.

Clarke, *Marbles* 55 no. 36; Michaelis, *Anc. Marbles* 246 no. 3; H. Graillot, *Le culte de Cybèle* 506; Chapman, *Handbook* (2nd ed.) 45; *AJA* LXIII (1959) 142.

46 Statuette of Cybele of the type of the Athenian Mother of the Gods

PLATE 11

Presented by Dr J. Disney. Probably acquired in Italy. Inv.: GR.6.1850.

H. 0·505 m. Luna (?) marble. The surface has been successively covered with dark moss-stains, painted white and finally imperfectly, though somewhat harshly, cleaned—apparently all before the statuette was brought to England in the eighteenth century. The modern restorations of the forearms, tympanon, object held in the right hand and part of the front of the base, including the left foot, had all been removed before the figure was painted. Also missing are the edge of the base to the goddess's right, the tip of her nose and parts of her veil in the vicinity of a repair across her neck; the join at this point, however, is quite certain.[2] *Chipped at top of throne-back.*

The type is essentially the same as that of **45** and the large class of Attic statuettes to which it belongs. The intrusive element of the lion on the goddess's lap is here missing and, although the drapery has acquired something of a Roman flavour, the statuette constitutes a reasonably orthodox copy. It shows the goddess seated upon a cushion on a throne with a tall, panelled back. On her head she wears a low polos whose vertical surface is incised in imitation of ashlar masonry, presumably on the false analogy of the mural crown. She is dressed in a chiton girdled high under the breasts and fastened along the upper arm. Over this she wears a himation which passes over her left arm and shoulder, around the top of her head, where it serves as a veil, down again under her right arm and over across her lap. She has shoes on her feet. These rest directly on the base, there being no footstool. Her face has been sadly mutilated in the modern cleaning of the surface. A small part still survives of the tympanon, resting on the seat of the throne where it was steadied by her left hand. Of her right hand and the phiale no traces remain beyond the dowel-holes for the modern restoration.

For a discussion of the type see **45**. The somewhat 'Romanized' treatment of this Italian version accords quite well, e.g., with the relief, W. Amelung, *Kat. vaticanischen Museums* I 880 no. 215, pl. 113.

An Italian version of Imperial date of the same general statue-type as **45**.

J. Disney sr., *Cat. Hyde* 3 no. 34; J. Disney jr., *MS Cat.* 108; Marsden, *Cat. Disney Coll.* 83 no. 3; Michaelis, *Anc. Marbles* 256 no. 37; Chapman, *Handbook* (2nd ed.) 49.

47 Statuette of Demeter

PLATE 12

Bequeathed by Professor W. R. Lethaby. Provenance unknown. Inv.: GR.11.1931.

P.H. 0·305 m. Pentelic marble with incrustation chiefly on the right side. Head broken away at base of neck. Arms missing (these were originally fashioned from separate pieces of marble and attached with dowels). Mantle hanging behind broken away at the edges where it originally extended out to both sides beyond the body of the goddess. Right foot broken away, as also edges of the plinth all round.

The goddess stands with her left leg slightly bent and with her weight on her right foot. She is clad in a peplos, seamed at the side in the Attic fashion and with kolpos and apoptygma. The over-fold is drawn high in front, partly by the weight of the mantle hanging behind, but, with the more abundant material under the armpits, it extends down much lower at the sides. She also wears a short mantle over her back. It is folded double at the top and pinned to

[1] Pausanias I. 3. 5; Arrian, *Periplus Ponti Euxini* 9. On the basis of a strangely vague statement in Pliny, *NH* XXXVI. 17, many scholars have tried, not very successfully, to resolve the problem by assigning the original to Agorakritos. See, in general, E. Langlotz, *Phidiasprobleme* 65 f. For older literature on the subject, see A. Furtwängler, *Statuenkopien im Altertum* 53 f. (=*Abh. bay Ak.* XX (1896) 3. 577 f.); F. Winter, *Altertümer von Pergamon* VII. 1. 69 f.; *JdI* XXVIII (1913) 1 f.; *AM* XXXVII (1913) 159 f.

[2] Formerly an area of plaster was wrongly inserted at the neck to give the head a forward tilt. Much of the paint, etc., has been recently removed with the aid of modern solvents.

her peplos at the shoulders. Behind, this constitutes a rather flat surface which, as other copies show, spreads outwards, flanking the figure of the goddess at the sides. These copies also reveal that her missing arms were both lowered. A little survives of the end of her hair, loosely bound behind her shoulders. The copyist has modified the proportions of the body somewhat, notably in narrowing the hips and pelvis. The seemingly excessive slenderness of the upper part of the body is more apparent than real, as the shoulders themselves were added separately with the arms.

This figure belongs to a class of votive statuettes which seem to copy freely, but with only minor variations, the same sculptural type: e.g. Venice, Museo Archaeologico 116.a; also, less precisely, nos. 15 and 33 in the same museum.[1] Closest of all to the Cambridge example in its treatment of the drapery and its over-slender hips is yet another statuette in Venice which has acquired a completely false fame as an alleged fragment from the Erechtheion frieze, *EA* 2647 *right*, *AA* 1943 132 f., fig. 1. It is actually a statuette in the round and a very good reversed copy of the same type. Despite Furtwängler's opinion to the contrary, all of the examples just cited seem to be of Attic workmanship. The goddess represented is identified as Demeter by her appearance on an Attic votive relief to Demeter and Kore from Rhamnus, now in the Glyptothek in Munich: A. Furtwängler, *Beschreibung der Glyptothek* (2nd ed.) 177 f. no. 198, Idem, *Illustrierter Kat.* pl. 24, Idem, *Ein Hundert Tafeln* pl. 27. The original from which these figures are copied would seem to date from about the beginning of the last quarter of the fifth century B.C., to judge from the very similar treatment of the folds of drapery shown by a figure on a dated relief of 421–420 B.C.—itself of a type repeated in votive statuettes.[2] In the apparent absence of copies of the Demeter figure that are larger than life-size, it may well be that the original was itself a votive statue rather than a cult image. It shows certain general resemblances to the Demeter of the type of Berlin K 172, which does seem to be derived from a cult image, although the pose, etc., are different. Further, a comparison between the Munich relief, cited above, and the great Eleusinian votive relief suggests that there may indeed be some kind of connection between the two types.[3] But if there is, one may still well be right in regarding the original of the Cambridge figure as an independent votive creation, loosely modelled on an Attic cult statue.

The date at which the Cambridge copy was executed is more difficult to determine. Some examples of the type, such as Venice 116.a, seem still of good classical date, but Louvre 198, a poor Italian version in Luna marble, shows that the original was still being copied in Imperial times. That the Cambridge statuette is not a contemporary version seems to be indicated by its harsh cutting, slender proportions and separately attached arms; for these last one may compare Louvre 3519, a statuette of similar but not identical type.

A copy of later Classical–early Imperial date from an Attic original of the early last quarter of the fifth century B.C.

AJA LXIII (1959) 143 no. 11.

48 Head of Hermes, after Alkamenes

PLATE 14

Presented by Dr J. Disney. Probably acquired in Italy. Inv.: GR.22.1850.

P.H. c. 0·326 m. Pentelic marble, badly pitted and eroded by weather over parts of the left side and back of the head. From a herm. Broken away at the base of the neck; missing are nose, inlaid eyes, tip of beard, lower part of the main hair-mass at the back and most of the locks hanging down on to the shoulders from behind the ears. Unsightly modern restorations of nose, eyes and shoulders have been removed. Chipped at ears, brows and edges of hair; plastic lids to the eyes also largely broken away. Faint traces of pitch bedding in eye-sockets seem ancient. Lips recut in modern times, presumably to conceal damage, and considerably reduced in size; moustache and beard in vicinity somewhat reworked at same time.

The god's powerful neck is broken away near the point where it met the top of the shaft of the herm. His undulating hair, combed so that it radiates from a point near the crown of the head, is held in place with a heavy band. The main mass of the hair at the back originally extended down to a pigtail-like knot be-

[1] Venice, Museo Archeologico 116 a.: A. Furtwängler in *Abh. bay Ak.* XXI (1898) 2. 25 f., pl. 6. 2; C. Anti, *Il Regio Museo Archeologico, Venezia* 34 no. 1, fig. on 33. Venice 15 and 33: Furtwängler, *op. cit.* 22 f., pls. 3, 4. 1; Anti, *op. cit.* 34 f. no. 2, 40 f. no. 4. Cf. also G. Mendel, *Cat. Constantinople* III no. 832; *Cat. Mus. Mariemont* no. G 10, pl. 23; *Clara Rhodos* V. 2. 157 f. – hybrids showing elements of Berlin K 172 or of a later (Kephisodotan?) style.

[2] Relief of 421–420 B.C.: E. Kjellberg, *Studien zu den attischen Reliefs des V Jahrhunderts* pl. 12, fig. 30, *figure at left*. Votive statuettes showing same type: e.g. T. Dohrn, *Attische Plastik* pl. 3; *Abh. bay Ak.* XXI (1898) 2. pl. 4. 2; Anti, *op. cit.* 35 f. no. 3.

[3] Demeter of the type of Berlin K 172, also called the Boboli-Berlin type: C. Blümel, *Kat. Berlin* IV 33 f. no. K 172, pls. 61–2; *EA* 279, 3418–22; G. Lippold, *Griechische Plastik* (*HdA* III. 1) 185 (original assigned to Alkamenes). Great Eleusinian votive relief: Svoronos, *op. cit.* pls. 24–5; Brunn-Bruckmann 7; Dohrn, *Attische Plastik* 40 f.; cf. also G. M. A. Richter, *Cat. Greek Sculptures, Metropolitan Museum* 27 f. nos. 34–5, pl. 32.

hind the shoulders. In addition, a long lock of hair hung down on to the chest from behind each ear. Over the brow the hair-style takes the form of three rows of tightly coiled spiral curls of archaic type. The drill has been used to separate and articulate these curls. They are not strictly symmetrical, being drawn back further over the left brow than over the right—an anomaly, widespread on the better copies, which seems difficult to account for. In contrast to the archaizing hair-style, the much-damaged features of the face were strictly classical. The individual curls of the originally square-tipped beard are shown in shallow but delicate relief.

This head is a moderately accurate copy of the type identified as representing Hermes and as being the work of Alkamenes by an inscribed herm from Pergamon; see F. Winter, *Altertümer von Pergamon* VII. I. 48 f. no. 27, pl. 9; E. Schmidt, *Archaistische Kunst* 43 f.; *AM* LV (1930) 207 f.; C. Blümel, *Kat. Berlin* IV 9 f. on no. K 134; L. Curtius, *Zeus und Hermes* 68 no. 1; V. H. Poulsen, *From the Collections of the Ny Carlsberg Glyptotek* III (1942) 77 f.; G. Lippold, *Die griechische Plastik* (*HdA* III. 1) 186; on the inscribed herm from Ephesus cf. *ÖJh* XXIX (1935) 23 f., G. M. A. Richter, *Metropolitan Museum, Cat. Greek Sculptures* 36. If Berlin K 134 is rightly regarded as the most accurate copy of the type extant, then the present example, like all the others, shows distinct shortcomings. The chief divergences are to be found in the treatment of the small curls above the ears, the surface detail of the hair at the back of the head and the grouping of the curls at the sides of the beard. But it relates itself directly to the Alkamenes herm rather than to the characterless type apparently already being reproduced in Attic workshops in the first century B.C. (cf. *JHS Archaeological Reports for 1958* 23 no. 7, fig. 43). The date of Alkamenes' original cannot be closely fixed, but must fall somewhere in the second half of the fifth century B.C.

A copy probably of late Hellenistic or early Imperial date from an original of the second half of the fifth century B.C.

J. Disney jr., *Museum Disneianum* 31, pl. 16; *AZ* V (1847) 158; *GGA* 1849 446 f.; Marsden, *Cat. Disney Coll.* 84 no. 14; Michaelis, *Anc. Marbles* 259 no. 53; Chapman, *Handbook* (2nd ed.) 51; *AJA* LXIII (1959) 142.

49 Statuette of Pan PLATE II

Transferred from the old University Library. Presented to the University by Professor E. D. Clarke. From a 'garden below the grotto of Pan at the foot of the Acropolis of Athens'. Inv.: GR.4.1865.

P.H. 0·86 m., including a base between 0·1 and 0·13 m. in height. Pentelic marble. Head broken away; an iron dowel and traces of wax, the one not improbably, the other certainly modern, bear witness to an attempt to effect a repair. Badly chipped at many points including left hand, right elbow and right shin. A large damaged area affecting the right side and back of the base and the tree-support has been redressed in modern times with the point. Much of the surface is badly corroded by weather.

The goat-legged god stands on a cylindrical base in front of a pillar-like support. This appears to be in the form of the trunk of a tree, but is very summarily rendered. He is wrapped in a mantle apparently fashioned from the complete skin of a goat or similar animal. This still has the hooves attached, one of which can clearly be seen trailing on the ground by the god's own left foot. This skin-cloak seems to be being worn with the pelt innermost—a common practice with shepherds to this day. The god has his right hand enveloped in the mantle. In his left he holds the syrinx. Of his head, all that survives are the lowermost strands of the beard on his chest.

On the type see W. H. Roscher, *Lexikon der Mythologie* III. I. 1417 f., R. Herbig, *Pan* 58, and, above all, F. Brommer in *RE Suppl.* VIII 978 f. The original seems to have been one that was extensively copied in Athens in Roman times both as a votive statuette and as a support-figure, some of the examples being exported. The copies show minor variations in detail between themselves. Closest to the Fitzwilliam statuette is a figure from Sparta in the National Museum in Athens: *AM* V (1880) pl. 12, *Marburger Jb. für Kunstwissenschaft* XV (1948) 40, fig. 52. The remainder tend either to advance the other foot or to have the folds of the goatskin cloak somewhat differently arranged. One may instance *AE* 1840 pl. 383 (from the Piraeus), text to Brunn-Bruckmann no. 725, 22 fig. 14 (from the west slope of the Acropolis, Athens), A. H. Smith, *BMC Sculpture* II no. 1439 (from Cyrene), H. Stuart Jones, *Cat.Museo Capitolino* 69 f. no. 18, pl. 13. The original is not easy to date. The blend of human and goat elements is more harmonious and convincing than in late fifth-century attempts to represent the god in this guise. On the other hand, there are no adumbrations of the Hellenistic period and the head-type still seems purely classical. This may usefully be compared with a detached head in the British Museum, *BMQ* VI (1931–2) 33 f., pl. 16.

A copy apparently of Imperial date from an original probably of the early–mid fourth century B.C.

W. Wilkins, *Antiquities of Magna Graecia* 71;

Clarke, *Marbles* 9 f. no. 11; Idem, *Travels* 4° III (=II. 2) 479 f., 8° VI 218 f.; W. M. Leake, *Topography of Athens* (2nd ed.) 170; *AA* 1864 172; *AM* V (1880) 354 n. 5; Michaelis, *Anc. Marbles* 246 no. 4; S. Reinach, *Répertoire de la statuaire* II 67. 1; W. H. Roscher, *Lexikon der griechischen und römischen Mythologie* III. 1. 1418; Chapman, *Handbook* (2nd ed.) 42; *RE Suppl.* VIII 979; *AJA* LXIII (1959) 142.

50 Janiform herm PLATE 14

Presented by Dr J. Disney. Probably acquired in Italy. Inv.: GR.19.1850.

P.H. of the ancient part 0·178 m. Luna (?) marble with a pale creamish-brown patina. Restored in marble: whole bust below the middle of the necks, tips of the noses of both heads. Chips missing from garlands, hair, ears and beard. Surface of the flesh parts cleaned in modern times. One of the ivy leaves of the silen's garland recut.

The janiform herm has linked the head of an old bearded silen with that of a youthful satyr. Both are characterized by long, pointed ears and both heads are garlanded, the elder with ivy, the younger with fir or pine. The latter garland was boldly undercut and has suffered severe damage as a consequence, but it clearly shows pine-cones nestling amongst the needles. The silen's beard and the hair over the young satyr's brow have both been given a vigorous, somewhat impressionistic treatment with the drill. The silen shows a receding hairline. The modern restorer may not be entirely to blame for the unfortunately asymmetrical position of his nose.

One cannot expect a decorative combination of this kind to be made up of meticulously exact copies. Nevertheless, both heads seem to be derived from fourth-century-B.C. originals. The youthful head seems to be based on the young satyr pouring wine of Praxiteles or some closely similar and otherwise unknown work of the second quarter of the fourth century. On the Praxitelean statue see W. Klein, *Praxiteles* 182 f.; F. Weege, *Der einschenkende Satyr aus Sammlung Mengarini (89th Berlin Winckelmannsprogramm)*; G. E. Rizzo, *Prassitele* 17 f., pls. 19 f.; C. Picard, *Manuel* III 415 f. If the Cambridge satyr has in fact been derived from it, then the fillet has been omitted, a pine-garland substituted for that of ivy, perhaps to form a contrast with the silen, and the angle of the head of necessity changed to meet the exacting requirements of the janiform partnership. Apart from this, the facial type corresponds closely.

The head of the silen has been little modified save in respect to its angle. It belongs to the variously restored type, W. Amelung, *Kat. vaticanischen Museums* I 42 f. no. 28, pl. 5, 671 f. no. 544, pl. 71, G. Lippold, *ibid.* III. 1. 8 f. no. 491, pl. 3. Also comparable is the related, though not identical, head in Venice, *EA* 2639 f. The Vatican silens seem to be copied from an original of about the end of the fourth century B.C. which has been loosely associated with the circle of Lysippos.

A copy of about the first–second centuries A.D. from originals of the second quarter and end of the fourth century B.C.

J. Disney sr., *Cat. Hyde* 14 no. 72; J. Disney jr., *Museum Disneianum* 23, pl. 12; *AZ* V (1847) 158; *GGA* 1849 444; Marsden, *Cat. Disney Coll.* 84 no. 25; Michaelis, *Anc. Marbles* 258 no. 50; Chapman, *Handbook* (2nd ed.) 44; A. B. Cook, *Zeus* II. 1. 388, fig. 297.

51 Torso of the Apollo Sauroktonos of Praxiteles PLATE 15

Bequeathed by C. S. Ricketts and C. H. Shannon. Provenance unknown. Inv.: GR.94.1937.

P.H. c. 0·85 m. *(0·77 m. visible above mounting). Pentelic marble, showing a brown patina over the front of the body, root marks at the sides. Head and limbs broken away; only the torso preserved with the stumps of the arms and the upper right thigh. The left shoulder had also been broken away and the repair at this point has involved the restoration, in hard, tinted cement, of areas above the left nipple and to the left of the neck and behind the left shoulder. The surface has been chipped and rubbed at many points, especially at the back. On the right shoulder there are faint traces of a modern square outline in paint enclosing an obliterated number—possibly 'J2'?*

This is an outstandingly fine copy of Praxiteles' famous statue showing the youthful Apollo standing with his left leg slightly flexed and leaning his raised left elbow against the trunk of a tree; he is represented as using his raised left hand to attract the attention of a lizard crawling up the tree whilst his right hand is being brought stealthily across his body to smite it. For lists of other copies see W. Klein, *Praxiteles* 108, W. Amelung, *Kat. vaticanischen Museums* II 450, M. Bieber in *Allgemeines Lexikon* XXVII 357; on the date of the original see *JdI* XLIII (1928) 18 f., H. K. Süsserot, *Griechische Plastik des vierten Jahrhunderts* 136; for assessments of the figure and motif cf. G. Rodenwaldt, *Theoi rheia zoontes* (*Abh. berliner Ak.* 1943) 5 f., K. A. Pfeiff, *Apollon* 121 f.

The present copy is in a sadly fragmentary state. Nevertheless, it is doubtful whether any other shows the torso of the god to quite such good advantage or, one may infer, so faithfully. This is to be seen to best purpose on the less severely damaged front and right side of the figure. Notable are the delicate transitions in plane at all points save the pubic region and the right armpit. Even such seemingly sharply defined points as the nipples and the collar-bone are in fact no more than gently undulating curves. The seeming precision is born of the play of shadow on a surface itself without precise divisions. But this softness is by no means devoid of muscular structure. Note, for example, the vertical groove down the front of the tensed right thigh. There is a subtle rhythm in the undulating planes of chest and belly and an exquisitely sensuous quality which does much to justify the high repute once enjoyed by the original. There seem to be no traces of a strut against the left side of the chest and it is unlikely that one is concealed in the damage above the left nipple.

A copy, probably of late Hellenistic or early Imperial date, from an original of the late second quarter of the fourth century B.C.

Vita d'Arte XXVII (1910) 2, text-fig. (in the background of a self-portrait of Charles Shannon painted in 1907); J. Chittenden and C. Seltman, *Greek Art* 36 no. 154, pl. 42; *Handbook and Guide* (1960) 10, 57; *AJA* LXIII (1959) 143 no. 20.

NOTE: For reasons of stability, at the time of writing this torso had still to be displayed at the wrong angle as viewed from the side. This has now been corrected by providing support at the left shoulder.

52 Torso of Eros, after Praxiteles (?)

PLATES 16–17

Presented by the Cyprus Exploration Fund. Found at Salamis in Cyprus in an area subsequently revealed as a second-century-A.D. gymnasion-complex. Inv.: GR.18.1891.

P.H. c. 0·362 m. Medium-grained Parian marble. Head, arms and wings broken away; legs missing from thighs. A strut or, more probably, the back of the left hand broken away from the lower part of the chest. Surface somewhat chipped and abraded.

The little god stands with his wings furled and with his weight carried on his right leg, the left being slightly flexed to the side. His left arm was probably bent forward at the elbow and his left hand may have rested against the left side of the body in the vicinity of the diaphragm. At least, the curious shape of the attachment at this point is hard to account for in a strut whereas it does seem to suit the imprint of the thumb and the backs of the knuckles of the first and adjoining fingers lightly pressed against the flesh. The right upper arm hung almost vertically against the body, but pressed slightly backwards against the shoulder-blade. The right forearm made no contact with the body and must have been bent away from it. Too little survives of the neck for certain inferences to be drawn as to the angle of the head. Perhaps it was bent very slightly forward and to the left. The surface finish of this statuette is exceedingly beautiful. Perhaps conservative techniques have been used in the carving to bring out the coveted texture of the Parian marble.

This statuette is of essentially the same type as the statue from Nicopolis ad Istrum now in Sofia Museum, *RA* ser. 4, X (1907) 273 f., pl. 15, *JdI* XXIV (1909) 60 f., pl. 6. This has been claimed to be the only extant copy of Praxiteles' Eros of Parion, whose appearance is known to us from coins; cf. *JHS* IV (1883) 270 f., *SB bay Ak.* 1913. 4. 21 f., pl. 2, figs. 1–4, L. Lacroix, *Les réproductions de statues sur les monnaies grecques* 315 f., pl. 28. Of recent years the Sofia Eros has been decried as a free Roman creation and had its relevance disputed because of its lifeless character and because of discrepancies existing between it and the coin type. Before the Cambridge statuette all of these objections fall to the ground. The existence of the two examples shows both to be copies. The Cambridge Eros is anything but lifeless and it appears to have lacked both of the divergent features shown by its counterpart in Sofia, viz. the massive support against the right flank and the inappropriate position of the left arm. Like the Eros Borghese in the Louvre it probably obtained its secondary support at the left elbow and this could well take the form of the hanging mass of drapery shown on the coins. The small scale and the surface finish of the Cambridge statuette suggest that it is a free version rather than a mechanically exact copy. Even so, it is rewarding to compare it with Praxiteles' Apollo Sauroktonos (**51** above) and the intimately related torsos of Eros Sauroktonos in Naples and New York: G. Rizzo, *Prassitele* 41 f., pls. 65 f., G. M. A. Richter, *Cat. Greek Sculptures, Metropolitan Mus.* 68 no. 107, pl. 86. An Eros Sauroktonos from Cyrene has an excessively soft-textured body and may represent an attempt by the copyist to approximate in spirit to the present type; cf. E. Paribeni, *Cat. Sculture di Cirene* III no. 310, pl. 148.

It is difficult to fix the date at which the Cambridge statuette was carved. It is incomparably finer than typical second-century-A.D. sculptures from the gymnasion such as **56** and **98**, but the area has yielded little that is earlier.

A free copy of Hellenistic or Imperial date from an original of the middle years of the fourth century B.C.

JHS XII (1891) 125 no. 1; *AJA* LXIII (1959) 143 no. 13. (It has since been verified that the new fragments discovered by Dr K. V. Karageorghis do not belong to this statuette.)

53 Head of Plato PLATE 15

Presented by Dr J. Disney, who had purchased it in London in 1823. Inv.: GR.23.1850.

P.H. 0·355 m. Luna marble. Underside of neck recut in modern times for attachment to a modern bust from which it has since been removed; part of underside of beard also recut, perhaps at same time. Tiny chips missing from tip of nose, ears, left cheek, etc., but, in general, the head is remarkably intact. Surface shows traces of root marks and is slightly encrusted at the back of the head.

This well-preserved, life-size head is one of sixteen copies described and illustrated by R. Boehringer in *Platon, Bildnisse und Nachweise* that, despite variations, seem ultimately to go back to the same Greek original of the fourth century B.C.—most probably the bronze statue of the philosopher by Silanion in Athens. To the examples listed by Boehringer others have since been added, e.g. *AM* LXIII–LXIV (1938–9) 163 f., *RM* LV (1940) 90 n. 9, *BCH* LXXVI (1952) 271, fig. 67 (photograph reversed according to Charbonneaux), *AJA* LXVI (1962) 269 f.

It is to be noted that the Cambridge head shows a transition in the horizontal planes of the eyes and mouth such as might be consistent with its having been originally inclined slightly to the right. This might seem to accord with a seated body-type for a statue of Plato that has been associated with these heads by some scholars.[1] This has, however, been widely considered as of rather later origin and the refinements in question appear to be absent from some of the best copies of the head-type. The hair over the back half of the Cambridge head is not, as described by Boehringer, worn away by weathering. The cutting is actually sharper here than elsewhere, but the relief is very much shallower. It seems clear that the copyist's model, whether a frontal herm such as Boehringer no. 3 or simply a plaster-cast of the front half of the head, stopped short just behind the ears. Behind this point he was obliged to extemporize and this shallow, lank hair at the back of the head, which recurs on none of the other copies, helps to suggest a date for the Cambridge example in about the first half of the first century A.D. The copyist's hand is probably also to be detected elsewhere. The fringe of hair over the brow has good authority, but its extreme schematization here and the way that it curves upwards slightly at the corners of the brow suggest the influence of a popular hair-style of Julio-Claudian times. The widely divergent treatment at this point on the Holkham Hall head, Boehringer no. 12, might possibly partly arise from an attempt to emphasize those other elements more congenial to second-century-A.D. fashion.[2] The eyes of the Cambridge head are rounder and less delicately shaped than on the closer copies and the lids do not overlap their outside corners. The upper lip is clumsy and the corners of the mouth are lost in an unfortunate fashion under the moustache. The face tends to present an undulating plane rather than sharply differentiated units and a similar deliberate imprecision, not due to wear and amounting to a kind of impressionistic handling, is in evidence on the beard and the hair over the front half of the head. In general, the Fitzwilliam head seems a very careful and well-finished Italian copy, but one in which the skill and realism appropriate to Roman portraiture may sometimes come between us and the fourth-century-B.C. original.

Plato, son of Ariston, lived from 427 to 347 B.C. The present portrait-type clearly shows the philosopher in his later years. If, as seems probable, its original was a contemporary likeness, then it would seem most plausibly assignable to about the middle years of the fourth century B.C. A closer dating to shortly before 363 B.C. has been based on a possible identification of the original's dedicator; see K. Schefold, *Die Bildnisse der antiken Dichter, Redner und Denker* 34 f., 74, 205. Nevertheless, the matter remains rather uncertain, in particular as it is not easy to apply a close stylistic dating to a portrait such as this. The artist, Silanion, would seem to have continued active until considerably later.

A copy of the first century A.D. *from an original of about the second quarter–middle of the fourth century* B.C.

---

[1] *Monumenti Inediti* III pl. 7; G. Lippold, *Griechische Porträtstatuen* 55 fig. 7; *From the Collections of the Ny Carlsberg Glyptothek* I (1931) 44, fig. 36; A. Hekler, *Bildnisse berühmter Griechen* 22 f., pl. 6; K. Schefold, *Die Bildnisse der antiken Dichter, Redner und Denker* 210; M. Bieber, *Sculpture of the Hellenistic Age* 44; G. S. Dhondas, Εἰκόνες καθημένων πνευματικῶν ἀνθρώπων 51 f., pl. 20. Cf. also *JdI* XXXII (1917) 167, fig. 7.

[2] F. Poulsen, *Greek and Roman Portraits in English Country Houses* 32 f. no. 5; E. Pfuhl, *Die Anfänge der griechischen Bildniskunst* 29, pl. 4; *From the Collections of the Ny Carlsberg Glyptothek* I (1931) 41 f., fig. 35; *JdI* XLV (1930) 49 f., XLVII (1932) 250 f., XLIX (1934) 180 f.; L. Laurenzi, *Ritratti grechi* 94 no. 21; C. Picard, *Manuel* III 816 f.; *AJA* LXVI (1962) 269 f.

J. Disney jr., *Museum Disneianum* 33 f., pl. 17; *AZ* v (1847) 158; Marsden, *Cat. Disney Coll.* 84 no. 15; Michaelis, *Anc. Marbles* 259 no. 54; *JdI* v (1890) 169 f.; Chapman, *Handbook* (2nd ed.) 44; J. J. Bernoulli, *Griechische Ikonographie* II 28 no. 10; *JdI* XLVII (1932) 247 n. 1; R. Boehringer, *Platon, Bildnisse und Nachweise* 20 f. no. 9, pls. 40–8; M. Bieber, *Sculpture of the Hellenistic Age* 43; *AJA* LXIII (1959) 142; G. M. A. Richter, *Greek Portraits* II (*Collection Latomus* XXXVI) 16, pl. 2. 7.

54 Bust of Ganymedes (?) PLATE 16

Presented by Dr J. Disney. Acquired at the Duke of Argyle's sale, 1771. Inv.: GR.13.1850.

H. 0·398 m. Luna (?) marble. Restored in marble: tip of nose and upper part of cap—this last perhaps also originally carved from a separate piece of marble. Much of the hanging flaps of the cap broken away; at the sides an attempt has been made to render this damage less conspicuous by filing the broken surfaces smooth, with the result that the right flap becomes curiously attenuated and the left one vanishes altogether for a space. Also filed smooth in modern times behind the shoulders where the surface seems originally to have been left rather rough. Minor recutting on the hair above the left eye. Vertical edges and underside of bust also apparently recut. The surface shows small patches of incrustation, mainly on the hair.

The bust bears a youthful male head, clad in a Phrygian cap worn with the flaps hanging down at the back and sides. The head is turned slightly to the left and also bent a very little forward and over to the left side. The lips are slightly parted and the eyes wear a dreamy and tender expression. The surface of flesh and cap is well polished and forms an effective contrast to the rougher texture of the deeply cut hair.

An exactly reversed copy of the same type occurs on a bust in the Vatican; see W. Amelung, *Kat. vaticanischen Museums* I 715 no. 599, pl. 77. There is also a marked similarity in technique and finish and it is possible that the Cambridge and Vatican heads may have been created as a matching pair. They were probably carved as busts, although the apparent retrimming of their under-surfaces makes it impossible entirely to exclude the alternative that the heads were intended for insertion in draped matching statues, e.g. as Mithraic dadophoroi.[1] However that may be, the heads themselves are probably copied from a Greek original of about the third quarter of the fourth century B.C.[2] The most striking comparison is that afforded by the heads of the so-called 'Eubouleus'-type, e.g. A. W. Lawrence, *Classical Sculpture* pl. 100. This type has commonly been regarded as copied from an original by Praxiteles, possibly that artist's Iakchos, but, in the most recent detailed discussion of it, Professor E. B. Harrison has come to the conclusion that the original is more likely to have been a contemporary portrait of Alexander the Great and that its sculptor was more probably Leochares; see *Hesperia* XXIX (1959) 382 f. With this suggested attribution to Leochares the style of the Cambridge and Vatican busts also does not seem in disaccord, but they are quite clearly different in type from Leochares' group of Ganymedes carried by the eagle which is known from poor Imperial copies. Their appropriate body-type is perhaps rather to be sought in a statue of Ganymedes in Naples, a work showing the influence of Praxiteles; cf. G. C. Fiego, *Museo Nazionale di Napoli, le raccolte archeologiche* (2nd ed.) 15, fig. 39. Its present head seems to be a restoration, but the traces of the hanging flaps of the Phrygian cap on the shoulders appear likely to have corresponded with those on the Fitzwilliam bust.

A copy of Imperial date from a Greek original of the third quarter of the fourth century B.C.

J. Disney sr., *Cat. Hyde* 4 no. 11; J. Disney jr., *Museum Disneianum* 11, pl. 6; *AZ* v (1847) 157; Marsden, *Cat. Disney Coll.* 83 no. 12; Michaelis, *Anc. Marbles* 257 no. 44; Chapman, *Handbook* (2nd ed.) 57.

55 Statuette of Sarapis PLATE 18

Purchased. Reputedly from Eleusis. Inv.: GR.87.1907.

P.H. c. 0·41 m. Moderately coarse-grained white island marble (Parian or Naxian ?). Broken away are the head of the god and most of his left arm, together with much of the part of the himation hanging down in front of it. Also missing are his throne and footstool; these were carved from a separate piece (or pieces) of marble and a large dowel-hole, about 3 cm. square, served to attach the body to the seat of the throne. Both feet are also missing; they, too, were carved separately, perhaps in the same block as the

[1] Cf. the dadophoroi from a Mithraeum five miles from the Porta Portese: F. Cumont, *Textes et monuments figurés relatifs aux mystères de Mithra* II pl. 2; A. H. Smith, *BMC Sculpture* III 89 no. 1722; W. Amelung, *Kat. vaticanischen Museums* I 538 f. no. 352, pl. 56; M. J. Vermaseren, *Corpus Inscriptionum et Monumentorum Religionis Mithriacae* I 202 f., nos. 506–7, figs. 147–8.

[2] The authors are also indebted to Dr E. Paribeni for drawing their attention to the head of Paris or Ganymedes, *Bull. Comm. Arch. Communale di Roma* 1883 pls. 17–19, no. 13; the type is different from that of the Cambridge bust, but the style is very similar.

footstool; an iron pin served to attach the advanced right foot to the body, but for the left foot there is nothing save a slightly hollowed cutting. In addition, most of the right arm is missing; this, too, was worked separately and attached with a dowel c. 0·0065 m. in diameter at the bottom of the sleeve. Chipped at the right knee and at various points on the drapery. Repaired at a break running through the right thigh and knee and down through the lower part of the himation between the feet. Roughly hollowed out with the point and gouge behind the legs. Brown incrustation on back of figure. Isolated rust stains on chest.

Of the god's head nothing survives save the ends of his hair on his shoulders. He is shown seated, clad in a sleeved chiton over which he wears a himation. This is draped across his lap and passes up under his right armpit and around his back to hang down again over his left arm. This part of his cloak trailing down in front of his upstretched arm was boldly undercut, being supported below the level of the chest by only a single strut to the body and one to the main mass of the himation behind. The space below the arm was otherwise hollowed out with the drill and the point.

Literary descriptions, representations on coins and the numerous other copies extant leave little doubt that this statuette reproduces on a small scale the famous Alexandrian cult-image of the god, Sarapis, the Egyptian Osiris-Apis, reputed to be the work of Bryaxis; see *RA* ser. 3 XLI (1902) 5 f., ser. 4 II (1903) 177 f.; W. H. Roscher, *Lexikon der griechischen und römischen Mythologie* IV 364 f., 373 f.; *JHS* XLII (1922) 31 f.; *Festschrift Paul Arndt* 115 f.; *Harvard Studies in Classical Philology* LI (1940) 61 f.; *Hesperia* XV (1946) 60 f.; *JHS* LXVIII (1948) 34 f.; *Atti Acc. dei Lincei* CCCXLV (1948) 450 f.; G. Lippold, *Griechische Plastik* (*HdA* III. 1) 257 f.; *JHS* LXXVI (1956) 131; *Bulletin du Musée National Hongrois des Beaux-Arts* XII (1958) 17 f.; *Genava* n.s. VIII (1960) 113 f.; *JdI* LXXV (1960) 88 f.; J. M. C. Toynbee, *Art in Roman Britain* 144 f.; *Mon Piot* LII (1962) 15 f. The original was one of the most famous statues of antiquity, but it must be admitted that there are few others about which so much uncertainty obtains as to both date and origin. It will suffice to cite the two most widely held views, both of them based on ancient testimonies. According to the first of these, the original was carved in the second half of the fourth century B.C. and was probably the work of the great Bryaxis; one version has it carried off to Alexandria from Sinope in the course of the third century B.C. The other interpretation makes the sculpture a third-century-B.C. creation produced in Egypt by a later artist of the same name. If the story of the transfer of the cult-image savours of the fanciful or legendary, it must at least be admitted that, so far as may be judged from the somewhat conflicting evidence of the copies, the statue seems to show distinct affinities with work of the second half of the fourth century B.C.—an impression which, contrary to that author's conclusions, seems if anything strengthened by Castiglione's valuable analysis of the head-type, as discussed under **57** below. Whether such stylistic elements indicate a late classical date or merely classicizing tendencies on the part of a later artist is more difficult to assess.

On the Cambridge statuette the treatment of some of the folds of drapery, e.g. over the chest, seems a trifle heavy; but in general and considering its vastly reduced scale this appears a sensitive and accurate copy, much superior to **56** below, and corresponding quite closely, e.g., with a somewhat later large-scale version in Alexandria Museum and a careful statuette in the Allard Pierson Museum in Amsterdam. Noteworthy, for example, is the quite good modelling of chest and abdomen as glimpsed through the thin material of the sleeved chiton. The surface has been brought to a good finish over initial rasp work.

A good copy, probably of about early Imperial date, from an original variously assigned to the second half of the fourth and the third centuries B.C. See also **56** *and* **57**.

AJA LXIII (1959) 143 no. 9.

56 Statue of Sarapis with Cerberus

PLATE 18

Presented by the Cyprus Exploration Fund. Found at Salamis in Cyprus in an area that subsequent exploration has shown to be occupied by a gymnasion-complex of the second century A.D. Inv.: GR.1.1891.

P.H. 0·98 m., H. of base 0·11 m. max. Flesh parts in medium-grained, translucent Parian marble; remainder in a fine-grained bluish-grey marble, reputedly of Cypriot origin. All the flesh parts were worked separately in Parian marble and attached to the grey-marble body. Little of them survives, viz. the bottom edge of the neck, shaped underneath to fit its socket, the end of a marble tenon, c. 0·045 × 0·034 m., at the point of attachment of the raised left arm, and the fore-part of the advanced right foot. The characteristic sandal-type and bent little toe confirm that this last fragment belongs to the present statue. An iron dowel also survives for the attachment of the white-marble part of the right arm; there is also a hole for a metal pin to steady the elbow at the edge of the right arm of the throne. The left foot is completely missing, but its position is shown by a roughened area on top of the footstool. Of the grey-stone elements, broken away are both knees of the god, together with the drapery over his advanced right leg, the muzzles of the three heads of Cerberus, and the front edge of the profiled base with the outer part of the footstool resting upon it (the right foot is now mounted partly on a modern block). Numerous chips missing from the throne and the drapery. Repaired across the base to the right of the god and through the forelegs of Cerberus.

The whole group rests on a base with a grooved profile whose top is inclined slightly forward towards the spectator. In plan, this is flat at the back, but otherwise of an oval shape save that there are clear indications that it bulged out in front in the middle to accommodate the outer edge of the footstool and the right foot resting upon it. The statue-type is the same as that of **55**.

The most striking feature of the present copy is the way it has been, so to speak, 'squashed up' and lost much of its monumental quality in the process. This is particularly noticeable in depth, both god and throne being twice as shallow as they should be and all their proportions being completely distorted as a consequence. Perhaps, in its second-century architectural setting in the gymnasion, this statue was paired with standing figures and the reduction in depth was a deliberate adjustment. If it was set in a niche the relief-like handling would be less disturbing. The throne of the god has also shrunk sideways from the original monumental construction to a squalid little chair in which his buttocks are hopelessly tightly wedged. Other confusions occur as a consequence. Thus the originally rich folds of the end of the himation hanging down from the left thigh as shown on **55** become mixed up with the left arm of the chair. They also, rather improbably, acquire tassels. A consideration of better copies such as **55** shows how completely imprecise is the rendering of the drapery detail on the present example. A mass of fussy little folds has emerged that can have had no authority from the original and which obliterates the distinction between chiton and himation. Against the right side of the throne crouches the three-headed Cerberus with a snake twined around his shoulders. The condition of the surface makes it impossible to tell whether his tail was also snake-headed; it may have been. His body, and especially his claws, are rather more leonine than canine. It is doubtful if his heads were distinguished as being of the different species described by Macrobius, *Saturn.* I. XX. 13–15. All seem to have had floppy dogs' ears and shaggy lions' manes. The larger central head had its jaws open. The back of the group was left flat and probably not intended to be seen, although some of the panelling of the throne is faintly indicated. A minor feature worthy of comment is the drapery with a tasselled fringe hanging down under the arms of the throne. The surfaces of both the grey and the white marble are well polished.

A somewhat imprecise copy of the second century A.D. *from the same original as* **55**.

JHS XII (1891) 125 f. no. 3, fig. 1; Chapman, *Handbook* (2nd ed.) 60; *AJA* LXIII (1959) 143 no. 21.

57 Head of Sarapis PLATE 18

Presented by Dr J. Disney. Acquired in Rome in 1752. Inv.: GR.15.1850.

P.H. of ancient part 0·22 m. H. of head (in front) 0·179 m. Medium-grained, translucent white marble (Parian ?), with brown incrustation on the hair. Only the head and neck are ancient. Restored in marble: bust, modius and part of hair to left of face. Minor restorations in plaster to neck and hair on the left side of the head. Surface of flesh apparently cleaned in modern times, possibly involving minor recutting at lips, eyes and top of brow. Bottom rim of modius is ancient, but has been recut save at the back.

The head was meant to be seen from the front only, the hair at the back being only shallowly cut with the flat chisel. This circumstance, combined with the comparatively small scale, the shallow depth and the shape of the neckline in front, favours the view that the head may have been originally set on a statue rather than a bust and possibly one such as **56** where a contrasting marble was used for the flesh areas. In front the extensive use of the drill has tended to set small channels between the individual locks of hair and beard. The pupils of the eyes, in their present condition, are smooth, but faint indications survive that they were originally indicated plastically and upturned. The modius has been restored on the analogy of heads such as that in the Villa Albani, *EA* 4313.

This head clearly stands in some relationship to Bryaxis' statue of Sarapis in Alexandria, the body-type of which has been considered under **55** and **56** above. However, just what that relationship is is by no means clear and the authors are indebted to Professor J. M. C. Toynbee for discussing the difficult problems that it raises. The matter has been recently debated from different points of view by Castiglione in *Bulletin du Musée National Hongrois des Beaux-Arts* XII (1958) 17 f. and by Kraus in *JdI* LXXV (1960) 88 f. Castiglione has argued, on the basis of Alexandrian coins, that Bryaxis' statue (a Hellenistic work in his view) was either replaced or partly modified in the time of Hadrian. In support of his view he has assembled the copies in marble and other material which he considers may go back to the original statue. To these one may probably add, as no. 15 *bis*, M. J. Vermaseren, *Corpus Inscriptionum et Monumentorum Religionis Mithriacae* I 274 no. 783, fig. 215. They differ mainly from the far more widespread variety, which Castiglione would designate as the post-Hadrianic type, in the detail of the hair. By no means all of his examples are identical and they would seem in fact to derive from at least three interrelated types. Of these, that most relevant to our inquiry, to judge alike from the evidence of the coins and the copies, has the hair parted in the middle with two locks (occasionally multiplying to four) falling very lightly on to the brow. The locks themselves are natural and springy and the hair lacks the curiously lank appearance that it usually assumes on the so-called Hadrianic and later type. Whilst Castiglione can hardly be said to have established his claim that Bryaxis' famous statue was arbitrarily replaced, his alternative suggestion that the huge timber-framed image may have undergone some modifications when it was re-erected inside the new second-century-A.D. Sarapieion remains a not unattractive hypothesis. In particular, damaged elements in the hair could well have been made good in stucco at this stage and some of their characteristics might possibly have been exaggerated in the process, as in the case of the hanging locks over the brow. Professor Toynbee, who was the first to postulate an ancient modification of the great Alexandrian statue, has suggested that this may have arisen as a consequence of damage caused by a fire in the Sarapieion in A.D. 183. This involves the assumption that the main changes had already been anticipated in the general trend of popular art.

The importance of Castiglione's contribution in assembling his 'earlier group' is very considerable. There remain, however, many questions that do not seem fully answered by his simple twofold division and that suggest the need for a detailed analysis of all the ancient Sarapis heads that seem in any way related to the Bryaxis-type. Kraus has already suggested that a few of the examples of Castiglione's 'later group' seem to have been carved earlier than the time of Hadrian. Although no such problem exists in the case of the Cambridge head which appears to have been produced at a somewhat later date than that Emperor's reign and belongs appropriately to Castiglione's 'later group', yet it stands in a curiously intermediate position. In spirit it seems to resemble a second-century-A.D. example of Castiglione's 'earlier type' such as his no. 16 (*op. cit.* fig. 19) more closely than a typical developed example of the 'later variety' such as *op. cit.* fig. 6. Indeed it seems possible that there may be present elements of a more gradual process of change in addition to the abrupt modification of type that has been postulated by Castiglione. Later again, the forelocks of this second variety grow longer and lanker than they are here and multiply excessively in number, possibly because the copyists tended to render as free-hanging the engaged locks at the sides of the brow. It seems reasonable to recall that much of the identity and, if one may be permitted the term, personality of the Hellenized Sarapis seems to have been bound up with his great cult-image in Alexandria. As his cult gradually spread throughout the ancient world, the countless new images that sprang up often tended to mirror the Bryaxis statue, in particular in the treatment of the head. But they would seem to have stood to it not so much in the relation of copies to an original as of variant portraits to the living model. As a result, it seems little wonder that the Sarapis heads bear such marked evidence also of the different periods that created them. Few, if any, are exact copies of the Alexandrian statue, but by comparing them all a picture of the original can be built up. From this it may be inferred that, apart from much of the detail of the hair, the Cambridge head provides a tolerably good version of the appearance of that of the Alexandrian statue. It may or may not be coincidence that the strange, brooding character of the face finds something of an echo in the Halikarnassian statue, perhaps of Maussolos, in the British Museum—a sculpture which many have regarded as a surviving earlier original work by the great Bryaxis.

A copy of the second century A.D. based either on the head of the statue discussed under **55** *above or on that of one of the numerous secondary cult-images that it inspired.*

J. Disney sr., *Cat. Hyde* 7 no. 29; J. Disney jr., *Museum Disneianum* 15, pl. 8; *AZ* v (1847) 157; *GGA* 1849 445; Marsden, *Cat. Disney Coll.* 83 no. 9; Michaelis, *Anc. Marbles* 258 no. 46; *RA* ser. IV, II (1903) 194; Chapman, *Handbook* (2nd ed.) 52; *AA* 1952 117 f., figs. 8 and 9; *AJA* LXIII (1959) 142.

58 Torso of Asklepios PLATE 16

Transferred from the old University Library. Presented to the University in 1808 by the Reverend R. Walpole. From the Hellenistic and Roman site of Knidos. Inv.: GR.6.1865.

P.H. c. 0·574 m. Moderately coarse-grained Parian marble with a golden patina and a light-brown incrustation. Broken away below at the level of the thighs. Right arm broken off at the shoulder and the snake-entwined staff on which this rested also missing; the remains of an iron pin at the right hip may represent the point of attachment of the top of the staff against the god's body. The broken surface at the base of the neck, just above the collar-bone, has been trimmed roughly level with the point in modern times; however, the original head was apparently carved from a separate piece of marble and attached by a dowel at an only slightly higher level. An ancient dowel-hole for its reception, 0·026 m. in diameter, is still preserved. Chipped at several points, including left shoulder, left hand and right hip.

The god is shown standing, wrapped in a himation. As is confirmed by more intact copies, his weight was carried on the right leg, the left being slightly flexed. His right hand originally rested on his staff against his right hip. The staff itself had a snake coiled around it. His left hand loosely clasps the edge of his himation beside his left hip. The thumb and first two fingers are outstretched; the other two fingers are closed around the woollen cloth. The surface has been finished with the aid of the rasp and polishing, but this treatment has been confined to the front of the small statue, the back being left roughed out with the flat chisel, and, more rarely, the gouge.

The Cambridge Asklepios is the only example, it seems, of this type from the Aegean area. Its provenance may therefore be significant. It is to be noted that a somewhat similar statue of Asklepios does seem to be represented on Knidian coins; cf. C. Picard, *Manuel d'archéologie grecque, la sculpture* III. 1. 563, fig. 235. 3–4. The closest parallels, however, are from a little further afield, on the coins of Alabanda in Caria, e.g. *BMC Coins, Caria and the Islands* 4 no. 21, pl. 2. 3.

The other known copies of the type have already been assembled by Waldhauer and Mustilli, but, if one may rightly judge from the published illustrations, they seem to need rearrangement. Identical with the Cambridge torso are:

(1) Oslo: *EA* 3304.

(2) Leningrad: O. Waldhauer, *Die antiken Skulpturen der Ermitage* I 12 no. 3, pl. 3.

(3) Cairo: C. C. Edgar, *Cat. Greek Sculpture* 7 no. 27440, pl. 3.

(4) Rome, Museo Capitolino: D. Mustilli, *Il Museo Mussolini* 25 no. 20, pl. 20; H. Stuart Jones, *Sculptures of the Palazzo dei Conservatori* 231 no. 7, pl. 90; etc.

(5) Toulouse: S. Reinach, *Répertoire de la statuaire* I 288; E. Ésperandieu, *Basreliefs de la Gaule* II 44 no. 912.

The following seem to belong to a related variant type with a different treatment of the left hand and of the drapery over the left arm:

(1) Rome, Museo Nazionale: *NdSc* 1935 81.

(2) Tunis: Reinach, *op. cit.* III 228. 1.

Also comparable is the torso of the statuette, H. B. Walters, *BMC Bronzes, Greek, Roman and Etruscan* 151 no. 837, pl. 26. Both Waldhauer and Mustilli regard the original from which these figures are copied as a classicizing creation of later Hellenistic times and compare it with the so-called Zeus of Pergamon dating from the middle years of the second century B.C. Some features seem to speak in their favour, such as the embroidered hem of the himation (not preserved on the Cambridge example) and the soft modelling of the chest and shoulders. As a result of the latter, Michaelis actually misinterpreted the Cambridge torso as that of a youth. None the less, it seems extremely hazardous to attempt to distinguish, on the basis of copies only, between original works of the fourth century B.C. and Hellenistic versions of them. Also, terracottas in the British Museum show that a sculptural type akin to the Cambridge torso was already popular in Caria in the mid-fourth century B.C.; see R. A. Higgins, *BMC Terracottas* I pl. 69, especially no. 522.

A copy of Imperial date either from an original of the middle–third quarter of the fourth century B.C. or from a late Hellenistic work in the style of that period.

Clarke, *Marbles* 53 no. 32; Michaelis, *Anc. Marbles* 247 no. 6; Chapman, *Handbook* (2nd ed.) 42.

V

SCULPTURE OF HELLENISTIC AND REPUBLICAN ROMAN DATE

(A) VOTIVE AND HERO RELIEFS

59 Votive relief to Pan — PLATE 19

Presented by Dr J. Disney. Probably acquired in Italy. Inv.: GR.36.1850.

P.H. 0·423 m., H. of relief 0·028 m. max. Pentelic marble, lightly cleaned but still showing traces of a golden-brown patina. In modern times the bottom surface has been cut level, removing all traces of a tang, and the point-dressed back of the stele has been partly ground smooth. Two modern dowel-holes in underside. Surface somewhat chipped and worn, notably at the face of the herm, the nose of Pan and his right hand, together with the vessel that he was holding.

The god, Pan, is shown standing at the entrance to one of his sacred caves, the texture of the surrounding natural rock being suggested by a rough and irregular dressing with the point. The god is ithyphallic and has goat's legs and horns. He stands frontally with a cloak or animal skin over his left arm and with a throwing-stick (λαγωβόλον or *pedum*) in his left hand. He is pouring a libation to a small, bearded herm at the cave entrance. The libation vessel is badly damaged, but was probably some form of two-handled cup. The herm appears to have its hair bound with a fillet. The hair itself seems to have been worn much like that of **93**.

Among the numerous votive reliefs dedicated to Pan the present example is unusual in that it shows the god by himself. The scene, with Pan pouring a libation to a herm, does not seem to recur, but appears not inappropriate in view of the bonds linking the cult of Pan with that of Hermes.[1] The treatment of the figure of Pan himself shows some kinship with statuettes such as those in Venice and Karlsruhe, *EA* 2648, 4369. His face still retains a classical character reminiscent of the head in the British Museum (*BMQ* VI (1931–2) 33 f., pl. 16) already considered in connection with the type of **49**. But the execution of the stele probably dates already from the beginning of the Hellenistic period, to judge, for example, from the head of the herm. As commonly with reliefs to Pan or the Nymphs, the architectural framing appropriate to other votive stelae has been replaced by the rounded shape of the cave. Here this is much more regular than is usual, approximating in form to the true arch, an architectural device that apparently first came into normal use in Greece in the late fourth century B.C.[2]

Probably Attic work of about the late fourth century B.C.

J. Disney sr., *Cat. Hyde* 5 no. 23; J. Disney jr., *Museum Disneianum* 73, pl. 35; *AZ* V (1847) 158 f.; *GGA* 1849 452 f.; *AA* 1849 57, 1864 170; Marsden, *Cat. Disney Coll.* 86 no. 66; Michaelis, *Anc. Marbles* 260 no. 67; Chapman, *Handbook* (2nd ed.) 56; W. H. Roscher, *Lexikon der griechischen und römischen Mythologie* III. I. 1463.

60 Votive relief — PLATE 19

Presented by Dr J. Disney. Probably acquired in Italy. Inv.: GR.37.1850.

H. 0·472 m., W. 0·643 m. Coarse-grained white island marble (Naxian?). Upper right corner of the stele broken away; other corners chipped, as also lower edge, left anta, head of god and right arm of goddess. Surface badly eroded by weather. Tang on underside sawn away in modern times. Modern dowel-holes in top and bottom.

The relief is set in an architectural framing much like that of **27**. The left-hand half of the field so enclosed is occupied by the figures of a god and a goddess. The god wears a himation and has his left arm raised to clasp a sceptre or staff, which must originally have been largely indicated in paint. Of the

---

[1] For votive reliefs to Pan and the nymphs see J. N. Svoronos, *Das athener Nationalmuseum* pls. 73–4, 96–100, 137; C. Blümel, *Kat. Berlin* pls. 71, 75; etc. On the dating of the Pan reliefs see *RE* Suppl. VIII 980 f. For scenes where Pan himself is making offerings cf. W. H. Roscher, *Lexikon der griechischen und römischen Mythologie* III. I. 1463, R. Herbig, *Pan* 48; on the bonds between Pan and Hermes see Herbig, *op. cit.* 17.

[2] See *Corinth* III. 2. 107 f., 121 f.; *BSA* LIII–LIV (1958–9) 120.

thunderbolt described by Michaelis as being in his lowered right hand there are no certain traces. The goddess behind him appears to be clad in a peplos with a long over-fold and has a light cloak looped over her arms. She seems to be wearing a stephane in her hair. She may also have held a staff or sceptre in her left hand, but this is less certain. The right-hand half of the relief-field is left blank and there is nothing to suggest the erasure of further figures in relief. Perhaps a votive inscription or figures of the dedicants were here once shown in paint; but it is noteworthy that, as the relief now stands, the eccentric positioning of the deities gives them a sense of presence and expectancy that is quite pleasing and satisfying. The back of the stele has been left roughly dressed with the point.

Michaelis's identification of the deities as Zeus and Hera is quite probably correct, although the possibility that, e.g., Asklepios and Hygieia are represented is perhaps not entirely to be excluded. Certainly the god approximates to a statuette of Zeus in the Vatican; the goddess, herself, may actually be represented on an all-too-ill-preserved Attic decree-heading. The fashion that she follows in wearing her cloak looped over her arms starts to appear on Attic reliefs of the last quarter of the fourth century B.C., including a dated example of 318–317 B.C.; the rather mannerized treatment of the drapery, as visible in the lower edge of the over-fold of the peplos, seems also to indicate a date fully as late as this.[1]

Non-Attic work of the last quarter of the fourth or beginning of the third centuries B.C.

J. Disney jr., *Museum Disneianum* 211 f., pl. 88. 2; Marsden, *Cat. Disney Coll.* 87 no. 70; *AA* 1864 171; Michaelis, *Anc. Marbles* 261 no. 68; Chapman, *Handbook* (2nd ed.) 46; *AJA* LXIII (1959) 142 (Michaelis no. 68 misquoted as no. 63).

61 Fragment from a hero relief PLATE 19

Transferred from the old University Library. Provenance unknown. Inv.: GR.17.1865.

P.H. 0·293 m., H. of relief 0·038 m. max. Pentelic marble with a patchy brown patina. Assembled from two joining fragments. Small part of the bottom of the stele preserved; broken away at the sides and above. Part of the broken left edge trimmed level in modern times and keyed to take plaster. Traces of the attachment of a modern metal support on the left side; modern dowel-hole in top.

The relief preserves a small part of a scene showing a 'heroized' dead mortal and his wife at a funerary banquet. For the type and its significance see **36**. In this case it has moved yet closer to the ordinary iconography of Hellenistic times in that the rectangular table has been replaced by a round one with its three feet in the form of animal's legs. The dead man is shown reclining on a draped banqueting-couch and wearing a himation about the lower part of his body. His raised right arm doubtless originally held the vessel from which he was pouring a libation or filling his cup. His wife sits beside him wearing a chiton and, over it, a himation, the edge of which she lightly clasps with her left hand. Her feet rest on a low footstool. The tall object standing on the edge of the table is probably to be interpreted as a low thymiaterion on which she is placing incense with her outstretched right hand. The table also carries items of ritual food, including the tall, pointed cakes that are perhaps to be identified with the πυραμίδες of ancient authors.[2]

This type is probably to be dated to about the last quarter of the fourth century B.C. It also occurs on a small number of Attic grave-stelae. These should either antedate the sumptuary laws of Demetrios of Phaleron or coincide with the first years of their enforcement, in the latter case treating the permitted hero reliefs as a loophole in the general ban on grave-stelae, etc. That they are not significantly earlier is shown by their late style, the letter-forms of their inscriptions and the occurrence of a not dissimilar hero relief at Priene.[3]

Attic work of about the last quarter of the fourth century B.C.

Michaelis, *Anc. Marbles* 249 f. no. 19; Chapman, *Handbook* (2nd ed.) 53.

62 Fragment from a votive or hero relief PLATE 19

Transferred from the old University Library. Presented to the University by Professor E. D. Clarke. From Athens. Inv.: GR.15.1865.

H. 0·575 m., H. of the three relief fields c. 0·02 m., 0·055 m., 0·07 m. max. Pentelic marble. Only the left-hand end of the stele is preserved, the rest having been broken away. Surface badly chipped, worn and pitted by weather; heads of the figures damaged. Point-dressed back of stele worn smooth by re-use, e.g. as a paving slab. Modern clamp-holes in top and bottom.

---

[1] Statuette of Zeus: W. Amelung, *Kat. vaticanischen Museums* II 226 no. 84A, pl. 8. Decree-heading with goddess of similar type: Svoronos, *op. cit.* pl. 197 no. 2986. Dated relief of 318–317 B.C.: Svoronos, *op. cit.* pl. 108.

[2] Cf. A. Furtwängler, *Sammlung Sabouroff* I text to pl. 30; *AM* XXI (1896) 350; cf. also *Corinth* XII nos. 2909 f.

[3] Attic grave-stelae with hero-relief scenes: A. Conze, *Die attischen Grabreliefs* II 258 f. nos. 1166 f. Priene hero relief: T. Wiegand and H. Schrader, *Priene* 375 fig. 473; G. Mendel, *Cat. Constantinople* II 157 f. no. 465.

The relief is set in the usual architectural framing (see under **27**) with some of the figures standing in front of the anta at the left edge. Three rows of dedicants or votaries are shown approaching the now lost figure of the deity or the 'heroized' man. In the back row the heads of four adults can be made out, but they are so badly damaged as to be no longer identifiable. The last of these figures, close against the anta, has one hand on the shoulder of a man in the next row, and it is possible that all four figures may represent the wives of the men shown in front of them. Four figures are preserved in this middle row, all apparently representing men clad in himatia. One of them has his hand on his neighbour's shoulder. In front again stand the children, of whom six are preserved, two girls wearing chiton and himation and probably four boys clad in the himation only. They show a refreshing variety of poses. One of the boys is carrying a garland.

For the triple row of dedicants one may compare J. N. Svoronos, *Das athener Nationalmuseum* pl. 70 no. 1429. The drapery motifs displayed by the children seem to be of quite early Hellenistic type.

Attic work of about the late fourth century B.C.

Clarke, *Marbles* 9 no. 10; Idem, *Travels* 4° III (=II. 2) 530, 8° VI 286; Michaelis, *Anc. Marbles* 249 no. 17; Chapman, *Handbook* (2nd ed.) 46.

63 Hero relief to Metrodoros PLATE 20

Transferred from the old University Library. Presented to the University in 1816 by Dr J. Fiott Lee. Inv.: GR.28.1865.

H. 0·501 m., D. 0·21 m., H. of relief c. 0·02 m. Medium-grained greyish-white Asia Minor marble (Proconnesian?). Patches of light-brown incrustation on surface. Chipped away at the lower left corner (at the side the damaged surface has been trimmed with the point and concealed with pigment) and at the edges of the antae and roof framing the relief; face of the deceased also severely damaged. Two tiny dowel-holes in top outer corners.

The top, back and underside of the stele have been dressed with the point; its sides and face show traces of the claw-chisel. The relief is set in an architectural framing, flanked by antae carrying an architrave which supports a flat roof. The framing of classical stelae had already shown the upward taper appropriate to its architectural components. However, here there is a difference in that the whole stele is tapered, being 4 cm. narrower at the top than at the bottom. A deliberate optical correction seems to have been attempted to compensate for the distortion arising from seeing a small, low monument of this kind from an unfortunately high angle (see also **64**).

The 'heroized' dead mortal is shown reclining on a draped couch, with his left elbow supported on cushions. He is wearing a sleeved chiton and a himation and appears to have a garland in his hair. A snake, coiled around the tree behind him, is drinking from the bowl in his left hand. This creature is a common symbol in the cult of the dead, perhaps representing the spirit of the deceased rising from the earth to partake of the funerary banquet. The dead man's wife sits on the end of the couch with her feet resting on a stool. She is clad in a high-girdled chiton with a himation worn over it. This may have been carried up behind to form a veil over the back of her head. She is holding out a small round pyxis to her husband. Before them stands a round table with its three legs terminating in hooved feet. Amongst the items of food that it bears there can perhaps be made out a pomegranate and a 'pyramidal' cake (see **61**). In the foreground two subsidiary figures are shown on a smaller scale. On the left appears a serving-girl in a high-girt chiton, apparently carrying a lidded cista. On the right a slave-boy in a girdled chiton is shown filling an oinochoe with wine from a krater. Underneath, and set somewhat to the right so as to be beneath the figure on the couch, is the inscription naming him:

Μητροδώρου τοῦ
Ἀπολλοδώρου

Of Metrodoros, son of Apollodoros.

The letter-forms find their closest parallels before the end of the reign of Attalos I of Pergamon, although a slightly later date is not entirely to be excluded. The style is that of western Asia Minor.[1]

Probably western Asia Minor work of the later third or earlier second centuries B.C.

H. J. Rose, *Inscriptiones Graecae Vetustissimae* 418 no. 42; *CIG* IV 6966; Michaelis, *Anc. Marbles* 250 no. 23; Chapman, *Handbook* (2nd ed.) 46; *JHS* LXII (1942) 16 no. VII. *b*. 4.

64 Hero relief PLATE 20

Lent by the Master and Fellows of Trinity College.

H. 0·504 m. Greyish-white medium-grained Proconnesian marble. Repaired across the middle. Tang broken

[1] For the general type with the snake in the tree cf. F. Winter, *Altertümer von Pergamon* VII. 2. 258 f. no. 323. For the drapery of the wife cf. Mendel, *op. cit.* III 192 f. no. 979.

away underneath. Faces of the two men on the couch and the taller slave-boy broken away. Minor damage elsewhere.

The stele has been roughly dressed with the point at the back and edges. The relief is enclosed in a plain frame without architectural pretensions but, as with **63**, this is markedly tapered towards the top where it is about 5 cm. narrower than at the bottom of the relief. Two men are shown reclining on a draped couch with their left elbows supported on cushions. The one to the left is dressed in a himation which leaves the upper part of his body bare revealing a rather plump and flabby chest. In his left hand he holds a drinking-cup of 'Megarian-bowl' type. His companion wears a sleeved chiton as well as a himation. With his right hand he is raising on high a rhyton terminating in the forepart of a goat whilst, in his left hand, he appears to be holding a Hellenistic kantharos. Before them stands a round table with lion's-claw feet. It carries the usual ritual foods including fruit and a 'pyramidal' cake (see **61**). To the right of the couch stand two slave-boys in girdled chitons. The figure of the smaller slave extends beyond the framing of the relief. He is shown drawing wine from a krater. Behind the slave-boys appear three shelves carrying drinking-bowls and phialai. Drapes are hung behind the 'heroized' figures on the couch. Above the drapes can be seen the upper parts of three symbolic horsemen wearing helmets of Hellenistic type and carrying round shields. The horses' heads have been somewhat scaled down to fit the space. Clearly these figures are related to the typical representation of the hero as a soldier on horseback (cf. **36**), although the purpose of the threefold rendering is more difficult to assess.[1] Is it just a simple matter of plurality and symmetry?

The stele is presumably dedicated jointly to two friends or kinsmen, other such double dedications being also known from Asia Minor.[2] To judge from such details as the bold cutting of the drape hanging in front of the couch, the execution of this stele is much later than that of **63**. The turned legs of the couch itself seem already to approximate to the Roman type. However, the other subsidiary details, such as drinking-vessels, helmets, etc., still seem essentially Hellenistic. Once again the style is probably that of western Asia Minor.

Probably western Asia Minor work of about the first century B.C.

AA 1864 172; Michaelis, *Anc. Marbles* 269 no. 109; *JdI* xx (1905) 124 no. 4; *AJA* LXIII (1959) 142.

(B) VOTIVE STATUES OF CHILDREN FROM CYPRUS

65 Right hand of a child holding a dove, from a statue — PLATE 20

Presented by the Cyprus Exploration Fund. From Paphos. Inv.: GR.10.1888.

P.H. as mounted 0·148 m. Pentelic marble. Broken away at about the middle of the forearm; head of dove and lower part of the hanging drapery also missing. Damaged at the tail of the dove and the fingers of the hand, in particular the little finger. Surface chipped. Faint traces of red pigment on the himation, but this seems likely to be from an extraneous source.

This fragment clearly comes from the statue of a child of about life-size or slightly smaller. The youngster, who might equally have been a boy or a girl, was apparently wrapped in a himation, the end of which was brought forward from behind and looped over his right forearm. In his right hand he holds a dove—an appropriate offering for the Paphian goddess, although it is to be remarked that the same bird is also held by many of the Attic child-statues. The dove's feet are shown raised against its breast.

Child-statues of this kind were often dedicated in Hellenistic Cyprus. The present example, however, may well come from an imported Attic figure of the kind carved in the later fourth and third centuries B.C. and well exemplified by the statues of little girls dedicated to Brauronian Artemis.[3]

Probably Attic work of about the later fourth or third centuries B.C.

JHS IX (1888) 168.

66 Head of a young girl, probably from a statuette — PLATE 20

Presented by the Cyprus Exploration Fund. From Paphos. Inv.: GR.11.1888.

[1] Cf. the appearance of three warrior figures in a similar position: *JdI* xx (1905) 134 f. no. 4, fig. 25.

[2] E.g. Mendel, *op. cit.* III 188 no. 975; this example also shows similar shelves in the background. For the rhyton-type cf. *JdI* xx (1905) 52 no. 6, fig. 4.

[3] For Cypriot examples see *SCE* IV. 3. 85 f., pls. 3, 6, 7. 2–3. For the Attic type see under **66**; cf. also A. W. Lawrence, *Later Greek Sculpture* pl. 21.

P.H. c. 0·141 m. Moderately compact creamish-white Cypriot limestone, golden-brown at the surface. Broken away at the top of the neck. Badly chipped, especially at the nose, brow and chin. Surface bruised and worn. Traces of red pigment on the hair.

This charming head of a little girl is probably broken from a votive statuette of the kind just considered. It is distinctly smaller than life-size and shows a suggestion of portraiture in the rather angular treatment of the planes about the eyes. The hair is arranged as a series of coils brought backwards and upwards to the point where they merge into a long plait carried twice round the crown of the head.

This head clearly shows the influence of Attic child-statues of the late fourth century B.C. (cf. for example, *EA* 66, 1992). However, its execution is probably considerably later, to judge from the way in which the tear-ducts are shown in the corners of the eyes. The hair-style, too, does not show the long plait around the greatest circumference of the head as on the Attic little girls; nor does it display the small 'bun' low at the back of the head of the typical early Hellenistic *Melonenfrisur*. This variant with the coiled plait almost at the top of the head seems also to appear in the first century B.C.; close, too, is a very common hair-style of early Antonine times (see **132**).

Cypriot work of late Hellenistic or Imperial date.

67 Fragmentary head of a baby, probably from a statue

PLATE 21

No record of acquisition (probably presented by the Cyprus Exploration Fund in the later part of the nineteenth century). Inv.: GR.S.2.

P.H. c. 0·12 m., greatest dimension 0·171 m. Medium-grained Parian marble. Only the upper front part of the head is preserved. Chipped at nose and brows. Inlaid eyes missing.

The fragment seems to be from a life-size head representing a child a year old or less. The plump, immature features are shown with considerable skill. The scalp is as yet innocent of hair. This is a circumstance almost unheard-of among Hellenistic and Roman sculptures of babies, a rare exception being, perhaps, G. M. A. Richter, *Roman Portraits, Metropolitan Museum* fig. 33. It is, on the other hand, almost the hallmark of a fifth-century-B.C. type of naked, crawling toddler of which the best-known copies are to be found among Rhodian terracottas. This type is important in Cyprus, where a whole class of votive sculptures seem to have been modelled on it, having their hey-day in Hellenistic times.[1] Possibly, in the present case, the artist has gone back to this model in some respects while retaining the softer features of a later era. The head is probably no earlier than late Hellenistic.

Probably of late Hellenistic or early Imperial date.

(C) MISCELLANEOUS SCULPTURE IN THE ROUND OF MID-HELLENISTIC DATE

68 Fragment from a votive statuette

PLATE 21

Presented by the Cyprus Exploration Fund. From Paphos. Inv.: GR.12.1888.

P.H. 0·085 m. Moderately compact white Cypriot limestone with a creamish surface. Only the base and lower part of the statuette preserved; everything missing above the level of the knees. Surface chipped, especially at the edges of the base. Back of the base trimmed off irregularly.

Statuette and base are carved from the one piece of limestone. The base is rectangular with a projecting moulding at the top. The figure is that of a woman or a goddess—possibly that of Aphrodite herself, although, if so, she is represented fully clad. She stands with her left leg flexed and her weight carried on her right foot. She wears sandals and a very full chiton which trails on the ground. The bottom corner of a himation worn over the chiton is visible against her left side, probably where it hung down under her left arm. The appearance of the complete figure may readily be visualized by reference to Hellenistic reliefs such as *EA* 1745. The front of the base carries the dedication:

'Αρτεμίδωρος 'Αφροδίτηι

Artemidoros (dedicated it) to Aphrodite.

The letter-forms show a general resemblance to those met with in Egypt on Ptolemaic inscriptions of the late third and earlier second centuries B.C. and recent work on the Hellenistic inscriptions of Cyprus seems

[1] On the Cypriot type see *Opuscula Atheniensia* II (1955) 75 f. For its Greek terracotta antecedents cf. e.g. *Corinth* XV. I. pls. 40–1, nos. 61–3, R. A. Higgins, *BMC Terracottas* I pl. 45 nos. 257–60, pl. 56 no. 372.

to confirm that they are probably to be assigned to this period; see *AJA* LXV (1961) 93 f., *BSA* LVI (1961) 2 f. Indeed, on the basis of the rather inadequate publication of the Cambridge inscription in *JHS* IX (1888) 254, Professor T. B. Mitford has already advanced a tentative dating for it at the beginning of the second century B.C. In corroboration, it is to be noted that the style of the statuette finds parallels among mid-Hellenistic reliefs and the more advanced Tanagra figurines.

Cypriot work of about the end of the third or early second centuries B.C.

JHS IX (1888) 223 no. 13, 254 no. 122; *BSA* LVI (1961) 19 no. 50.

69 Head of a girl PLATE 21

Bequeathed by C. S. Ricketts and C. H. Shannon. Provenance unknown. Inv.: GR.95.1937.

H. c. 0·276 m., H. of face 0·139 m. Even-textured, fine-grained white marble (Proconnesian statuary?). Designed for insertion in a statue, but the point-dressed surface below the neck has been recut with the gouge in modern times at the right side and the back. Modern restorations of hanging locks to either side of the neck have been removed; the surface has been recut and iron pins inserted to receive them. Also recut are the front of the neck and probably much of the hair detail at the back of the head. Minor trimming and cleaning elsewhere on the hair and at the edges of the taenia. Badly chipped at the nose and lips; minor chips missing from the cheeks, brow, neck and hair. Very small restorations in plaster on the left cheek.

The attempt to restore long locks at the sides of the neck was presumably based on heads of fourth-century type such as *EA* 2457 f. It must have looked sadly inappropriate on the present, comparatively short-haired, young woman. Her hair is actually bound with a taenia or fillet and probably originally hung straight down behind to the nape of the neck. It is lightly parted over the middle of the brow where it is worn quite short. At the sides it is tucked up under the head-band from which its ends hang down behind the ears as short, loosely coiled curls. These have been largely obliterated in the recutting, although they survive rather better at the left side where the restorer seems to have been content with trimming an ancient break. There is a marked conflict between the axes of body, neck and head in keeping with the Hellenistic love of torsion for its own sake. The body-type can only be guessed at although it is noteworthy that the angles of what survives would suit a common variety of seated draped female figure with the hand under the chin—a type actually used as a vehicle for portraits. This could account for the recutting of the front of the neck, but there are no traces of attachment under the chin. The transition between head and neck angles is bridged by refinements such as those remarked on **42**. The face suggests rather an idealized portrait of a mortal girl than the purely ideal type appropriate to a goddess. Notable are the masterful brow and petulant chin as seen in profile.

The girl's eyes have the intense look of the Pathetic Style of the second century B.C. and the head is quite probably as late as the middle years of that century. Her hair-style, in so far as it can now be interpreted, is rather unusual. It seems to show some kinship with the Egyptian Isis-coiffure worn by Ptolemaic royal ladies portrayed in the guise of the goddess, Isis.[1] The hair over the brow, which has not been tampered with, seems reasonably close to this, but the distinctive hanging curls at the sides were probably so completely Hellenized that it is difficult to be sure that there was any direct link with the Egyptian type. Indeed, apart from the question of the hair-style, this head seems closer to Asia Minor than to Alexandrian work.[2] The carving has been skilful but rather rapid.

C. mid–late second century B.C.

C. Winter, *Treasures of the Fitzwilliam Museum* no. 13 (with pl. facing); *AJA* LXIII (1959) 143 no. 26; *Cat. Treasures of Cambridge (Exhibition at Goldsmiths' Hall, London, 17th March–18th April, 1959)* no. 458.

[1] Cf. A. Adriani, *Testimonianze e Momenti di Scultura Alessandrina* (*Documenti e Ricerche d'Arte Alessandrina* II) pls. 5–6, 8–11.

[2] Cf. Winter, *op. cit.* VII. 1. 132 f. no. 115, pl. 10, Beiblatt 16; K. Schefold, *Meisterwerke griechischer Kunst* 270 f. no. 365. Compare also E. Paribeni, *Cat. Sculture di Cirene* 48 no. 80, pl. 63, G. Traversi, *Statue iconiche feminile cirenaiche* pls. 24. 2, 25. 3, 26. 3.

(D) UNCERTAIN

70 Fragment: youthful head and left hand

PLATE 23

Bequeathed by C. S. Ricketts and C. H. Shannon. Provenance unknown. Inv.: GR.97.1937.

P.H. at angle mounted 0·156 m., H. of face 0·077 m. Pentelic marble. The head broken away at the base of the neck, the hand at the wrist. Chipped at the nose, brow, chin, forefinger and thumb. Recut below the wrist. Heavily encrusted on the right side of the head, which also shows possible traces of stucco.

The back of the fragment has been only very roughly dressed with the point, suggesting that the piece is either from a sculpture in the round whose back was concealed by some kind of architectural framing or else from an extremely high relief, both head and hand being completely disengaged from the relief-ground. The fragment preserves a youthful head wearing an expression of pain or grief and a left hand clutching it by the hair. Little attention is given to detail, but the effect is powerful and vigorous. The eyes are deep-set at the inner corners and the skin-texture is finished with the rasp.

Different interpretations suggest themselves according as head and hand be regarded as belonging to the same figure or to two separate persons. In the former case the fragment might be from a figure such as that of a mourning siren, tearing its hair in grief.[1] It is, however, to be noted that the style appears considerably more advanced than that of the latest extant Attic grave-sirens, which would seem to have come to an end with the sumptuary laws of Demetrios of Phaleron, although not necessarily later than that of their successors at Alexandria and elsewhere. The angle of the hand and wrist is also slightly unnatural, although this anomaly may be entirely due to the inadequacies of the modern mounting.

If, on the contrary, head and hand be regarded as belonging to two distinct figures, then the fragment probably derives from a battle group, the assailant seizing his victim by the hair as he prepares to thrust home with the weapon in his other hand. The sex of the young head is not clearly indicated. It might, on this interpretation, represent an Amazon or possibly, in view of the heavy jaw and shaggy hair, a young Gaul or giant. Interesting parallels may be drawn with a mid-second-century-B.C. fragment of a battle scene from Priene, although the Cambridge sculpture does not appear to be of Asia Minor workmanship.[2]

C. third–second centuries B.C.

(E) ROUND ALTARS FROM DELOS

71 Round altar

PLATE 22

Transferred from the old University Library. Presented to the University by the Rev. B. Harvey. From Delos. Inv.: GR.26.1865.

H. 0·612 m., upper diam. 0·6 m. Medium-grained Parian marble. Edges chipped. Cracked on one side. Surface very badly eroded by weather. The top has a point-dressed relieving surface and the cutting for a central dowel for the attachment of an upper member.

In its present condition, this altar lacks both the spreading base-moulding and the projecting upper lip usual to the type (cf. **72**). The first was probably carved separately in the same block as the plinth. The upper member, too, which seems to correspond with the functional thymiaterion-bowl of the Delian terracotta altars, may have been fashioned from a separate piece of marble. The altar is decorated with four bull's heads in relief, symbolizing the trophies of the sacrifice actually nailed up on temple buildings. As on a feast-day, the bulls' heads are decked with garlands, bound about with fillets over their horns. The ends of the fillets hang down to either side of the heads and the garlands seem to be made up of leaves, flowers, grain and fruit, much as on **72**, although here the poor surface condition prevents a closer identification of the different items. A bunch of grapes hangs down from the middle of each garland. Above each is set a rosette. In the absence of the heavier mouldings referred to above, the present member has

[1] Cf. the earlier siren, J. Charbonneaux, *La sculpture grecque au Musée du Louvre* pl. 35.

[2] Istanbul 1047: T. Wiegand and H. Schrader, *Priene* 112 f., fig. 88, Mendel, *op. cit.* II 95 f. no. 340; on dating cf. *ÖJh* XXX (1937) 28 f.

a simple, rounded, projecting profile at the top and bottom.

This example clearly belongs to a distinctly later stage of development than the Pergamene round altar of Eumenes of the second quarter of the second century B.C. and is less naturalistic in the handling of the plant forms; cf. F. Winter, *Altertümer von Pergamon* VII. 2. 337 f. no. 418, pl. 41. It is, in fact, of a kind richly attested in Delos where the vast majority of dated examples of comparable style seem to belong to the last quarter of the second century B.C.[1] The variant motif where bulls' skulls or boukrania have replaced the fully fleshed heads under the garlands had also been adapted to Delian round altars by the late second century B.C.; cf. *Délos* XVIII 382 f., pl. 109, *Inscriptions de Délos* 2152 (112–111 B.C.). Presumably it continued into the first century B.C., paving the way for its extensive employment on Roman monuments of early Imperial date, such as, e.g., **145**. The French excavations in Delos have revealed that these round altars were abundantly used as dedications in the sanctuaries of the gods, but that they also occurred in private houses where they served both domestic cults and those of deceased members of the family. They were also commonly used as grave-monuments on the nearby island of Rheneia. As well as being a functional altar, the type lent itself to adaptation as a statue base; cf. **91**.

Late second or beginning of first centuries B.C.

Clarke, *Marbles* 47 f. no. 25; Michaelis, *Anc. Marbles* 252 no. 29; Chapman, *Handbook* (2nd ed.) 59.

72 Round altar with a male figure in relief

PLATE 22

Bequeathed by the Rev. T. Worsley. From Delos. Inv.: GR.1*a*.1885.

H. 0·77 m., upper diam. 0·648 m. Moderately coarse-grained white marble (Parian or Naxian ?). Large parts broken away from the top, which is also cracked and worn smooth by the weather; smaller chips missing from the moulding at the bottom and the relief decoration of the drum, notably from the face, right knee and foot of the human figure. The top has a shallow rectangular hollow in the middle, c. 0·14 × 0·075 m. Drapery of the human figure partly cleaned in modern times. Surface corroded at the sides, but still shows traces of a primary shaping with the point under the claw- and flat-chisel work.

This altar shows the heavily projecting upper and lower profiles discussed under **71**. Three bulls' heads are represented on its sides, but in front the place of a fourth is taken by the figure in relief of a beardless young man clad in a himation. He stands on a low, profiled base and is rendered in a heavily classicizing manner. Bound with fillets over the bulls' heads and the shoulders of the human figure are rich garlands which hang down between them. These are woven of flowers, ears of corn, ivy leaves and berries, pine needles and cones, grapes, apples and probably other fruit besides.

Apart from the human figure in relief, the type is much the same as that of **71** and this altar should be of about the same date. The young man in relief constitutes a typical himation-wrapped figure of late Hellenistic times such as *JdI* XX (1905) 129 no. 19, fig. 22, G. Mendel, *Cat. Constantinople* III 118 f. no. 903, *EA* 3085. The type gradually becomes more fixed and schematized as one enters the early Imperial period (cf. **132**). Possibly the altar's dedicator is represented, but much more probably the monument is funerary in character and this is the dead man that it honours. For round altars in funerary cults, whether in the house or over the grave, see *BCH* XXXIII (1909) 515 f., *Clara Rhodos* V. 2. 9 f. no. 27, pl. 1, figs. 1–4. A Delian altar with a very similar figure in relief is in the Ashmolean Museum in Oxford; cf. Michaelis, *Anc. Marbles* 564 no. 96.

Late second or beginning of first centuries B.C.

Chapman, *Handbook* (2nd ed.) 55.

(F) ETRUSCAN CINERARIA

73 Lid from a Volterran cinerarium

PLATE 22

Presented by Dr J. Disney. Acquired at Volterra in 1829. Inv.: GR.49*a*.1850.

H. 0·399 m., L. 0·545 m. Foraminiferous yellow Volterran tufa. Surface slightly chipped, e.g. at the phiale.

This was originally acquired as the lid of the cinerarium **74**, which it is too narrow to fit. It is

[1] See W. Déonna, *Délos* XVIII, *le mobilier délien* 380 f., pls. 106 f. Dated examples: *Inscriptions de Délos* 2153, 107–106 B.C. according to Roussel or 104–103 B.C. according to Dinsmoor (= *Délos* XVIII pl. 106, fig. 938), 2449, *c.* end of second century B.C. (= *Délos* II 59 no. 2, fig. 82, *Délos* XVIII pl. 107, fig. 946); cf. also *Inscriptions de Délos* 1719 (*c.* end of second century B.C.), 2102 (122–121 B.C.), 2233 (107–106 B.C.), 2258 (before 118–117 B.C.).

carved to represent a beardless man dressed in a chiton and a himation. He is shown lying on his left side, as if at a banquet, with his legs bent back at the knees. He holds a phiale in his right hand and his left arm is supported on a cushion. The head has an individual character, but seems more of a generalized likeness than a realistic portrait. A marked emphasis on the head and, to a lesser extent, the hands has resulted in a certain disproportion in the parts. The head itself is garlanded and tilted back somewhat to meet the gaze of the beholder. It is rather shallow and domed. Short, cropped hair appears around the brow and the lips are treated in a harsh, angular fashion. The underside of the lid has been partly hollowed out with the point.

This lid is a typical product of Volterra. A not dissimilar example of not very markedly earlier style has recently been published by Fiumi as part of a grave-group of the second half of the third century B.C.; see *Studi Etruschi* XXV (1957) 378 f., fig. 11. If this evidence be accepted it would call for some revision of Pryce's hypothesis in *BMC Sculpture* I. 2. 215 that the Volterran urns are merely a late development from the Chiusan. Some of Fiumi's other contexts have, however, been recently called in question in *RM* LXVII (1960) 48 f. and his contention that at Volterra alabaster had almost completely replaced tufa as the material used for cineraria by *c.* 230 B.C. does not seem to be borne out by some of the other material that he himself publishes. Thimme's chronology for the Chiusan urns has few externally dated points of reference but shows a closely worked-out sequence of development; see *Studi Etruschi* XXIII (1954) 25 f., XXV (1957) 87 f. On his findings, rather similar local lids were being employed at Chiusi in the second century B.C. On the other hand, Vessberg's attempt in *Studien zur Kunstgeschichte der römischen Republik* 241 f. to lower the dating of the Volterran lids of this class to the first century B.C. seems rather extreme.

Volterran work of the later third or second centuries B.C.

J. Disney jr., *Museum Disneianum* 199 f., pl. 85; Marsden, *Cat. Disney Coll.* 85 no. 39; Michaelis, *Anc. Marbles* 264 no. 80; Chapman, *Handbook* (2nd ed.) 49.

74 Volterran cinerarium — PLATE 22

Presented by Dr J. Disney. Acquired at Volterra in 1829. Inv.: GR.49*b*.1850.

H. 0·416 m., W. 0·54 m., D. c. 0·26 m. Foraminiferous cream-coloured Volterran tufa. Slightly chipped. Traces of red bands down the outer edges of the relief; red also on the projecting moulding above the relief. The lid is missing.

The bottom of the cinerarium is recessed between two feet of simple shape. Above these a kind of profiled plinth supports the relief frieze which is bounded at the top by a simple concave moulding. The relief shows the deceased man shaking hands in farewell with his wife. He is young and beardless. Both man and wife are dressed after the Greek fashion in chiton and himation. A winged vanth clad in a high-girt chiton and holding the down-turned torch of death is plucking at the young man's arm from behind as she prepares to lead him away. Two wingless figures in the same costume as the vanth are to be seen behind the wife. Their sex is uncertain, but their dress seems feminine. They may represent more benevolent genii, to judge from the way that the foremost appears to be smiting her head in grief. She has her right foot on a low eminence and the flaming torch in her left hand is being taken from her by her companion. This second figure also holds a sword in her left arm. Both of these attributes presumably have some appropriateness to the dead man or to his departure from this life. On an otherwise exactly identical cinerarium in the Museo Archeologico in Florence (inv. 5515) the torch appears to have been replaced by a scabbard; on Florence 5841, in a scene of rather similar type, the vanths hold sword and scabbard as well as torches. For other comparable scenes of leave-taking see G. Körte, *I rilievi delle urne etrusche* III 52 f., pls. 45 f.

On the vexed question of the dating see under **73** above; the reliefs are also discussed in *JHS* LXV (1945) 51 f. It may reasonably be doubted whether this cinerarium could be as early as the third-century-B.C. date to which Fiumi's hypothesis would assign it. Amongst the Chiusan urns the material most comparable with the present example is assigned by Thimme to the second half of the second century B.C.

Volterran work of about the second century B.C.

Bibliography as for **73**.

(G) CLASSICIZING SCULPTURE OF LATE HELLENISTIC DATE

75 Fragment from a base PLATE 26

Transferred from the old University Library. Brought to England by Captain G. Clarke, R.N., and apparently presented to the University by Professor E. D. Clarke. From the Acropolis at Pergamon. Inv.: GR.27.1865.

H. 0·155 m. Medium-grained, greyish-white Asia Minor marble, probably Proconnesian. Right end broken away. Back trimmed off with the point in modern times. Original surface at left end displays point-dressed anathyrosis; light, claw-chiselled anathyrosis on top and bottom surfaces. Surface chipped, particularly at the upper and lower edges, and somewhat corroded by weather. Modern clamp-hole in top. Traces of rust near lower edge in front.

The base broadens steadily all the way down. A band of bead-and-reel ornament at the top is followed by a torus decorated with a double linked guilloche. At the bottom is a broad, concave surface, interrupted by projecting panels of relief. The only one of these preserved on the present fragment shows a three-quarter view of a winged Nike driving a two-horse chariot. A corner fragment also from Pergamon and now in Berlin Museum comes either from the same base or from a second example of identical decoration and dimensions; see F. Winter, *Altertümer von Pergamon* VII. 2. 345 f. no. 439.

Winter assigns both the Cambridge and the Berlin fragments to the period of the Attalids on the grounds of the quality of their execution. If this is justified they must still date to the very end of the period. The reliefs seem already to belong to the classicizing phase of late Hellenistic times and to be harking back to the minor arts of the fourth century B.C. Thus one may usefully compare with the Cambridge fragment K. Schefold, *Kertscher Vasen* pl. 21, A. Furtwängler, *Antike Gemmen* II 47 f. nos. 46, 52–4, pl. 9. The employment of small relief pinakes as a decorative device also savours of late Hellenistic or early Imperial art.

Pergamene work of the mid second century B.C. or later.

Wilkins, *Antiquities of Magna Graecia*, title-page vignette; Clarke, *Marbles* 43 no. 20; Michaelis, *Anc. Marbles* 252 no. 30; Chapman, *Handbook* (2nd ed.) 52; F. Winter, *Altertümer von Pergamon* VII. 2. 345, fig. 439*b*; *AJA* LXIII (1959) 142.

76 Fragment from a head of Aphrodite (?) PLATE 24

Presented by the Cyprus Exploration Fund. From the Temple of Aphrodite in Paphos. Inv.: GR.13.1888.

P.H. c. 0·117 m. Parian marble. Preserved is a fragment from the left side of a female head. Most of the traces of the eye and nose chipped away. Surface bruised and abraded.

The fragment preserves part of a young female head of slightly under life-size. The hair is combed backwards, presumably to a knot at the back of the head, and bound with a narrow fillet which is passed twice round the head after the manner of classical Aphrodite statues such as the Aphrodite of Arles and the Knidian Aphrodite. Over the ear at the side, however, the hair is not confined by the fillets as on the fourth-century figures, but brushed up over them after a common Hellenistic fashion especially frequent in the second century B.C. The combined effect must have been rather similar to that of classicizing Aphrodite statues of the mid–late second century B.C. such as the Melian Aphrodite in the Louvre.

Perhaps mid–late second century B.C.

77 A goddess with Eros PLATE 23

Presented by the Cyprus Exploration Fund. From Paphos. Inv.: GR.14.1888.

P.H. 0·313 m. Moderately fine-grained translucent Parian (?) marble. Broken away are the heads of both figures, the right hand and wrist of the goddess, much of the left forearm and the left hand of Eros and much of the back of the base of the group. Also missing are the goddess's left forearm and the spread wings of Eros; these were fashioned from separate pieces of marble and attached with small dowels. Surface extensively chipped. Traces of adhering mortar against the right sides of the figures.

The goddess wears a chiton, fastened along the forearm to form a sleeve, and, over it, a himation which passes over her left shoulder, encircles her body and is looped over her left forearm. She stands with her right leg slightly flexed and with the upper part of her body turned somewhat to her left. She has long hair falling down behind the back of her neck. This does not hang quite straight, suggesting that her head may have been slightly inclined towards Eros at her right shoulder. Her right hand hung down near her side to which it was attached by a strut. Eros is represented naked. He is carved in one with the right shoulder and arm of the goddess, but is not supported by her and is clearly meant to be understood as hovering in the air just behind her. His left forearm is beside the goddess's neck and his left hand must have been in the vicinity of her ear. Indeed, the most plausible interpretation of the group seems to be that he is whispering in her ear. He has the long, boyish proportions of classical times rather than the more babyish ones much favoured in the Hellenistic period. The group is less elaborately finished at the back and at Eros' feet, which were originally concealed by the goddess's right hand.

This group is not merely a delightfully charming conceit on the part of a classicizing sculptor of late Hellenistic times. It also poses serious problems of its own. As his model for the figure of the goddess, the sculptor has taken a sculptural type that has been attributed, though not without dispute, to the third quarter of the fifth century B.C., tentatively identified as Kore, associated with a contemporary figure of Demeter and assigned to Corinth where copies of both statues have been found. For the type and a list of copies see D. Mustilli, *Il Museo Mussolini* 116 f. no. 5, pl. 74; cf. also *Ann.* IV–V (1921–2) 75 f.; F. P. Johnson, *Corinth* IX 9 f. no. 5; *ActArch* VIII (1937) 132 f.; *RM* LV (1940) 210 f.; G. Lippold, *Griechische Plastik* (*HdA* III. 1) 174 f. In the present small, free copy modifications have been introduced, notably in the taller and slenderer proportions and in the way that the lower edge of the himation is carried higher on the left side. Nevertheless, the sculptor seems deliberately to be making allusion to the so-called 'Kore' figure. Two possibilities suggest themselves. Either the identification as Kore is incorrect and the statue-type in fact represents Aphrodite, to whom Eros holding the apple is an appropriate adjunct, or else one is faced with a much more complex kind of allusion. It is noteworthy that the slender proportions and long hair of the Cambridge statuette seem rather virginal for Aphrodite; also, the fruit held by Eros has a pronounced knob on the top and might conceivably be intended as a pomegranate. If so, the identification as Kore is confirmed and the present dedication to Aphrodite of Paphos is probably intended to symbolize her power over other immortals. Of the two possibilities, the first interpretation is perhaps the more natural.

The execution, with the rather harsh use of the rasp and the running drill on the drapery, is of a kind that seems, on stratigraphical indications from Athens and Delos, to be assignable to *c.* 100 B.C. or not long afterwards.

Classicizing Greek work of the end of the second or early first centuries B.C.

JHS IX (1888) 168, 223 no. 12; Chapman, *Handbook* (2nd ed.) 45; *AJA* LXIII (1959) 143 no. 12.

78 Statuette of Eros — PLATE 24

Presented by the Egypt Exploration Fund and the British School at Athens. From Naukratis. Inv.: GR.24.1899.

P.H. c. 0·143 m. Moderately fine-grained translucent white marble. Head broken away at the base of the neck, right arm at the shoulder, left at the mid upper arm, legs at upper and mid thighs; chlamys broken away behind below left shoulder. Also missing are the wings which were fashioned from separate pieces of marble and attached to small dowels in the shoulder-blades. Traces of purple dye on the chlamys; this has been absorbed into the marble and spread to the adjoining parts. Traces of red paint on the flesh parts. Surface chipped at the chlamys on the left shoulder.

The young god stood with his right leg slightly flexed. His weight was carried on his left leg and, perhaps, his raised right arm, if this last was supported. His left arm is bent forward and has a purple chlamys looped over it and hanging down behind. Apart from this garment, the god is naked. Very little is preserved of his neck. What there is seems not inconsistent with his head's having been turned slightly to the right and bent slightly forward. The surface is well polished, save in the concealed area under his left arm. The pose may be compared with mid-fourth-century representations of the god such as **52.**[1] However, the modelling is harsher and more uncompromising and suggests a self-conscious classicizing creation of late Hellenistic or early Imperial date rather than a copy from some otherwise unknown fourth-century original.

This statuette is important as one of the very few pieces with surviving traces of pigment that indicate that the flesh areas of Greek and Roman male figures in marble were not merely tinted but were painted with an overall reddish wash like their terracotta counterparts. On this question of the use of colour see *Metropolitan Museum Studies* I 25 f.

[1] Loosely comparable for the type is *EA* 739.

Probably classicizing work of late Hellenistic or early Imperial date.

BSA v (1898–9) pl. 14. 8.

79 Female head, probably from a statuette

PLATE 26

Presented by the Egypt Exploration Fund and the British School at Athens. From Naukratis. Inv.: GR.22.1899.

P.H. 0·072 m. Medium-grained white island marble (Parian ?). Broken away under the chin; all the back of the head missing. Repaired at the left cheek. Chipped at hair, brow, nose, lips and chin. Surface weatherworn. Possible faint traces of pigment on eyes and hair (?).

The fragment preserves the front part of a youthful female head. The hair is parted over the brow and combed backwards. It is held in place with a broad fillet. The features of the face are reminiscent of the fourth century B.C., but the softly rendered eyes seem Hellenistic. Probably the head is from a classicizing work of late Hellenistic times, possibly representing Aphrodite. The poor preservation makes it impossible to determine whether an earlier figure is being freely copied. A broadly comparable little head is in New York; see G. M. A. Richter, *Cat. Greek Sculptures, Metropolitan Museum* 89 no. 163, pl. 116.

Probably classicizing work of about late Hellenistic date.

80 Archaizing female head, from a statuette

PLATE 26

Presented by the Egypt Exploration Fund and the British School at Athens. From Naukratis. Inv.: GR.3.1899.

P.H. 0·031 m. Moderately compact creamish-white limestone. Broken away at neck. Surface badly chipped and worn, especially at brow and nose. Traces of black pigment (?) on hair and of pinkish cream on face to sides of nose.

The fragment shows a female head with a plump, round face and two 'Venus-rings' on the neck. The eyes are large and prominently outlined. The hair is parted over the brow and tightly rolled under at the back of the neck. A single lock hangs down in front behind each ear. The texture of the hair is indicated by a series of small, curving nicks. A heavy band encircles the head.

The poor preservation makes it difficult to pronounce on this little head. However, the treatment of the hair and the head-band seems to suggest that it was probably carved no earlier than late Hellenistic times.

Probably archaizing work of late Hellenistic date or slightly later.

81 Caryatid from the Inner Propylaea at Eleusis

PLATES 24–25

Transferred from the old University Library. Presented to the University by Professor E. D. Clarke. From near the Inner Propylaea at Eleusis. Inv.: GR.1.1865.

P.H. c. 2·09 m., H. of cista (at back) 0·705 m., H. of head (in front) 0·5 m. Pentelic marble with heavy fault-lines running more or less vertically. Only the upper part of the figure is preserved, it being broken away completely at the waist. Also missing are the left arm from the end of the sleeve, the entire right arm together with the shoulder, the front of the face, the top part of the cista in front, its two front legs held in the girl's hands and much of the support down the back of the figure which seems also to have served originally to engage it in the wall behind. The surface is also badly chipped at many points, in particular at the girl's right breast and at the lower edge of the cista. At the time of writing the statue is still displayed on the modern base on which it was set in 1803. As a consequence of inaccuracies in this mounting it leans over to the left through an angle of 3½° from the vertical and also is turned very slightly to the left.

When complete this colossal figure represented a young girl standing with both her arms raised to clasp two of the three legs of the sacred cista of the Eleusinian mysteries which she was carrying upon her head. She was one of two caryatid figures standing on either side of the entrance way inside the Inner Propylaea. The upper part of the other statue, itself in a much better state of preservation, is in Eleusis Museum; see H. Hörmann, *Die inneren Propyläen von Eleusis* (*Denkmäler antiker Architektur* I) pl. 50. As the Eleusis caryatid is looking slightly to her right and as her Cambridge sister seems to have had her head turned faintly to her left, one can probably establish their relative positions. The Cambridge statue stood on her sister's right and both bent their gaze on passers-by approaching the gate. A fragment in Eleusis Museum preserves much of the missing right shoulder of the Cambridge caryatid; see Hörmann, *op. cit.* pl. 52*d*. A forearm and elbow in the same museum could belong to either of the two statues.

Although the two statues were created as a pair they were by no means identical. Indeed, their dress differed much more than is usual amongst caryatid figures from the same building. Thus the Eleusis kistophoros (or girl with a cista) appears to have lacked the heavy cloak of her Cambridge sister and certainly wears her over-chiton in a totally different way. The appearance of the Cambridge statue when complete is known to us. Three of the free-standing caryatids from Monte Porzio now in the Villa Albani in Rome are copied from it and show the complete figure quite accurately apart from the head-type and cista; the fourth is a reversed variant based on the Cambridge statue; see *EA* 3260 f., 3267, 3527 f., 3534 f., Hörmann, *op. cit.* figs. 52–5. For the Eleusis caryatid there is no such evidence and the drapery treatment over the lower part of the figure can only be guessed at. Certainly the attempts by Libertini and Hörmann to restore the two kistophoroi as identical by divesting the Villa Albani caryatids of their cloaks and changing the upper part of their drapery to suit the Eleusis figure are manifestly erroneous as well as being ugly.

The Cambridge caryatid has traces of a rectangular, pillar-like support running all the way up her back. It would seem that the statue was not completely free-standing, but was engaged behind over the width of this support. This width is nowhere preserved intact, but may be calculated as being between 0·48 and 0·5 metre. The girl wears a chiton fastened along the shoulders and upper arms by a row of buttons so as to form short, full sleeves. At these sleeves the folds of the chiton are boldly, if somewhat coarsely, channelled with a broad-pointed drill. Over the chiton she is wearing a second linen garment which shall here be designated as an over-chiton rather than a peplos. The Villa Albani caryatids reveal that this was folded double. It is pinned only at her left shoulder and its upper edge trails down across her right breast, bunching heavily because of the double thickness of cloth. Both garments are bound by a broad girdle at the waist and also by two narrower bands fastened under the girdle at the back and pinned at the shoulders. Where these two bands cross between the breasts there is fastened an apotropaic medallion in the form of a Gorgoneion with archaizing spiral-curls. In actual life it would probably be of beaten gold (cf. R. A. Higgins, *Greek and Roman Jewellery* 170 f.). A heavy woollen cloak is pinned at the girl's shoulders and hangs down her back. Little survives of her face. What there is suggests that it resembled the rather soft and plump countenance of her sister in Eleusis rather than the more austerely classicizing features of the Villa Albani caryatids. Like the Eleusis statue she probably wore ear-rings, but these are now broken away. Her hair is parted in the middle over the brow and carried around to the back where it is fastened by a loose band at the nape of the neck. Drill-work similar to that found on the sleeves of the chiton has been used to delineate the irregular waves of the hair.

A small quoit-shaped pad or cushion, rather like that worn by girls carrying water-jars, serves to steady the burden of the cista on her head. The cista itself seems to be represented as if of thin beaten metal, probably silver or bronze, with beaten *appliqué* decoration. In actual life it would be circular in plan, but here it is rather pear-shaped, being rounded in front but much elongated behind where its sides run backwards almost straight to the point where they vanish into the pillar-support. This is clearly due to a device to prevent weakening by excessive undercutting between cista and support. The top of the cista is trimmed level with the point and claw-chisel and appears to have provided a perfectly horizontal bearing surface to take whatever member went immediately under the architrave, perhaps an ovolo and abacus as restored by Hörmann. It seems important, however, to observe that this member must also have been engaged and that the ovolo cannot have been circular in plan as it appears on Hörmann's drawings but must have followed the curious shape of the top of the cista. Although the upper surface of the cista is perfectly horizontal its bottom is tilted backwards through an angle of approximately 6°—the figure being of necessity a mean because of the slight concavity of the under-surface. This backward tilt conforms to a common device found on caryatid figures. It is aimed at throwing the load back on to the crown of the head, as much for structural as for aesthetic reasons. As a result of this refinement the top and bottom of the container are not parallel and a gradual adjustment seems to have been made in its decoration. It, too, has been overlooked in Hörmann's drawings, as well as the circumstance that the vessel is not a simple straight-sided container, but flares outwards slightly all the way up to the top. The two front feet of the cista terminated above in acanthus leaves of which faint traces still survive. It is to be presumed that their lower parts, held in the girl's hands, were in the shape of animal claws. In actual life they would probably be of cast metal. The third foot was not indicated at all, being concealed in the thickness of the pillar-support at the back. The appearance of the complete cista may also be inferred from other representations such as Hörmann, *op. cit.* fig. 34.

Despite the marked differences in the dress of the two caryatids, the decoration of the cistae that they are carrying corresponds quite closely. It is partly symbolic of the sacred role played by the vessels. Michaelis's attempted restoration of the decorative elements on the cista carried by the Cambridge caryatid (*Anc. Marbles* 243, fig. 2) contains many inaccuracies. The bottommost zone, 0·1 m. high at the back, consists of a cable-pattern or guilloche, flanked below, and probably also above, by a 'twist'—a device appropriate to metalwork where it consists of two intertwined strands of wire soldered to the surface. On the Eleusis figure the 'twist' is replaced by plain bands in relief. The next zone is 0·165 m. high at the back. Its centre is occupied by a representation of the *plemochoe*, a vessel which also played an important part in the Eleusinian ritual.[1] It is flanked by stems of acanthus and rosette-like flowers. Above each of the two front legs of the cista there are three ears of corn in this band of decoration. They have large rosettes to either side of them. At the back where the cista meets the pillar-support there are signs of the repetition of this or a similar motif no longer clearly identifiable. The Eleusis statue has narrow bundles of leafy branches at this point. The next zone, 0·14 m. high at the back, consists of a torus in the form of a bound garland or wreath, flanked above and below by bead-and-reel ornament.The bound garland had already become a common motif in architectural decoration. Here there is a difference appropriate to the Mysteries in that, superimposed on the laurel leaves of the garland, there are tiny poppy-heads. The remainder of the decoration is only adequately preserved on the Cambridge statue. A zone, 0·165 m. high at the back, of alternating palmettes and clusters of acanthus leaves is followed by another, *c.* 0·135 m. high, consisting of a Lesbian kymation bounded below, and probably originally also above, by a plain projecting band.

This statue is included at this point because of its strongly classicizing character. It must, however, be frankly admitted that it presents very great difficulties of interpretation. First of all there is the marked difference of dress to be accounted for as between the Cambridge and Eleusis figures—a difference almost unheard-of in a matching pair of Greek caryatids. They seem in fact to have been rather more than a mere architectural decorative feature and to have possessed a kind of individuality of their own. A reason has also to be sought for the substitution of a different head-type on the Monte Porzio copies from the Cambridge statue. In all cases the Monte Porzio statues seem to have had their necks inset, suggesting that the carving of the heads was carried out as a separate operation from the copying of the rest of the figures. At most only two of their heads belonged originally to the statues on which they are now mounted. They seem rather soulless Roman work in a fifth-century-B.C. style. An examination of the hair-detail, no less than considerations of style, shows that they could not possibly be copied from the head of the Cambridge statue. In 1914 a possible solution to the problem was advanced by Svoronos, admittedly for somewhat extraneous reasons, but this has since been generally overlooked; see *Journal international d'archéologie numismatique* XVI (1914) 194 f. Svoronos put forward the hypothesis that the Eleusis and Cambridge statues might be intended as idealized portraits of the two daughters of the dedicator, Appius Claudius Pulcher, possibly inspired by the caryatid portrait-statues of Damophon's two daughters at another Eleusinion, that at Megalopolis (Pausanias VIII. 31. 1). The Republican associations of their father and husbands would then be ample reason for seeking to avoid commemorating them on an Imperial structure such as that at Monte Porzio and thus account for the substitution of a different head-type. It has already been remarked independently that the classicizing hairstyle of the Cambridge and Eleusis figures seems to anticipate that of Augustan female portraits; cf. A. W. Lawrence, *Later Greek Sculpture* 39. Because of the poor condition of the head of the Cambridge statue, the matter must, however, turn on whether or not one is justified in regarding the slight plumpness and other elements of realism present in the face of the Eleusis caryatid as really constituting a portrait. In view of the restraint often found in Greek portraits of the period, this does not seem entirely impossible. Certainly the face is not purely classicizing in character.

The Inner Propylaea, of which these statues in Eleusis and Cambridge formed the chief glory, was vowed by Appius Claudius Pulcher during his consulship in 54 B.C. References in Cicero's letters (*Ad Atticum* VI. 1. 26, VI. 6. 2) suggest that it may have been already under construction in 50 B.C., but the building's dedicatory inscription (*CIL* I 619) reveals that it was not in fact completed until some time after Appius Claudius' death in 48 B.C.

Attic work of the mid-first century B.C.

G. Wheler, *Journey into Greece* (1676) 427 f. and engraving on 428; J. Spon, *Voyage de Grèce et du Levant* (1678–80) II 282 f. and engraving; Les Monceaux in C. le Bruyn, *Voyages* (1725) 492; R. Pococke, *Description of the East* (1743) II. 2. 171; R. Chandler, *Travels in Greece* (1776) 191; Sir Richard

[1] See G. M. A. Richter and M. J. Milne, *Shapes and Names of Athenian Vases* 21 f.; Hörmann, *op. cit.* 67; cf. also *ibid.* fig. 36.

Worsley, *Museum Worsleyanum* I 95 and pl. facing; E. D. Clarke, *Testimonies of Different Authors Respecting the Colossal Statue of Ceres Placed in the Vestibule of the Public Library at Cambridge, July the First, 1803* passim; Idem, *Marbles* 12 f. no. 14, pls. 1, 3, and Flaxman's restoration, pl. 4; Idem, *Travels* 4° III (= II. 2) 772 f., 8° VI 600 f.; S. H. Spiker, *Reise durch England* II 294 f.; Hirt, *Geschichte der Baukunst* II 21; L. Preller, *Demeter und Persephone* 374 f.; Gerhard, *Antike Bildwerke* pl. 306. 4–5; W. M. Leake, *Topography of Athens* (2nd ed.) II, *Demi of Attica* 161 f.; Müller and Wieseler, *Denkmäler der alten Kunst* II 60 f. no. 92, pl. 8; Michaelis, *Anc. Marbles* 242 f. no. 1, figs. 1–2, pl. facing 242; Chapman, *Handbook* (2nd ed.) 63; Sir James G. Frazer, *The Golden Bough* VII (= V. 1) 64 f.; *Journal international d'archéologie numismatique* XVI (1914) 194 f.; *Ann.* II (1916) 207 f.; A. B. Cook, *Zeus* I 173 n. 1, pl. 15; A. W. Lawrence, *Later Greek Sculpture* 39; H. Hörmann, *Die Inneren Propyläen von Eleusis* (*Denkmäler antiker Architektur* I) 10, 47, 64 f., 74 f., 77, 84 f., 90, 99, 105 f., 109, 114, frontispiece and pls. 15, 18, 20–3, 27–9, 33 f., 36, 51, figs. 35, 58; *CAH* VIII 693; *AA* 1933 336, fig. 1; *Die Antike* XVIII (1942) 231, fig. 11; W. B. Dinsmoor, *Architecture of Ancient Greece* (3rd ed.) 286 f.; *Archaeology* VIII (1955) 13; *AJA* LXIII (1959) 143.

(H) A LATE REPUBLICAN ROMAN PORTRAIT

82 Head of a man — PLATE 26

Purchased from funds provided by Sir William Elderton. Formerly at Wilton House. The original provenance of this head is unknown; it is not to be confused with the modern alabaster bust described as of Julius Caesar: Michaelis, *Anc. Marbles* 711 no. 195, J. J. Bernoulli, *Römische Ikonographie* I 163 no. 44. Inv.: GR. 3. 1961.

P.H. c. 0·28 m. Medium-grained Greek marble with vertical faults and showing evidence of heavy weathering. Broken away near the base of the neck, where the surface has been trimmed to fit a Luna-marble bust of about sixteenth- or early seventeenth-century type (much as those used for the Giustiniani Collection), from which it has since been removed. Tip of nose and crown of head broken away, the surfaces being likewise trimmed to take Luna-marble restorations which have also been removed. Minor plaster restorations at the neck and right jaw. The surface has been cleaned, a little harshly in places, over the face and the front of the neck and the tear-duct drillings may have been enlarged in the same process. Chipped at the ears, brows, left cheek, etc. The bust of about sixteenth- or seventeenth-century date on which the head was previously mounted carries the inscription, ΘΕΜΙΣΤΟΚΛῆΣ, *cut probably subsequently and in a disfiguring fashion like those on many others of the Wilton House marbles.*

The portrait shows a man in later middle age and with a purposeful countenance. His head is turned very slightly to his left and also faintly inclined towards the left in relation to the axis of the neck. The crown of the head (or what survives of it) is bald apart from a thin wisp of hair above the middle of the brow. At the back and sides, on the other hand, he still retains a vigorous growth of slightly wavy hair. The jaw is angular, the mouth slightly pouting, with a pattern of folds and wrinkles furrowing the cheeks to either side of it, although their harshness has perhaps been lessened in the modern cleaning. The eyes are somewhat heavy-lidded with 'crow's-foot' creases at their outer corners.

The blend of a forthright realism with the first stirrings of a classicizing restraint would seem to set this vigorous portrait near the end of the Late Republican tradition and date it somewhere in the third quarter of the first century B.C. Any closer assessment must inevitably face up to the vexed question of the identity of the subject, since the Cambridge head shows a striking resemblance to the early posthumous portraits of Julius Caesar without being identical with any one of them. Seen against these, however, it is almost unique in its unconcealed and unashamed display of baldness.[1] Caesar himself indeed showed such a deficiency and it may be glimpsed on some of his coin-portraits, but he is reputed to have been self-conscious about it and to have tried to hide it by growing his back hair long and combing it forward over his bare pate (Suetonius, *Diuus Iulius* XLV). This device is faithfully shown on a few of his marble portraits, including the example from Tusculum which is now generally regarded as an actual contemporary likeness from his

[1] A bald-headed portrait probably intended as a likeness of Caesar figures in M. Milkovich, *Roman Portraits* (*Worcester Art Museum Loan Exhibition, April 6th–May 14th, 1961*) 14 no. 3, with pl. facing. However, the head has a curious inorganic quality which makes one seriously doubt that it is ancient, despite its claimed documentation. The resemblance to Caesar is weakened by these same faulty proportions.

last years (*AA* 1952 123 f., figs. 1–2). Attractive as it may seem to identify the Cambridge head as representing Caesar himself, it must nevertheless be stressed that the matter is far from certain. But, whether Caesar or a private citizen idealized to resemble him, it will not be amiss to consider it briefly against the background of the Caesar-iconography.

Gaius Julius Caesar lived from 100 to 44 B.C. On the complex issues raised by his marble portraits[1] see J. J. Bernoulli, *Römische Ikonographie* I 145 f.; *RM* XLVII (1932) 212 f.; E. Böhringer, *Der Cäsar von Acireale* passim; *PhW* LVI (1936) 412 f.; R. West, *Römische Porträtplastik* I 74 f.; *Oudheidkundige Mededelingen uit het Rijksmuseum van Oudheden te Leiden* XX (1939) 24 f.; *Bull. del Museo dell'Impero Romano* XI (1940) 3 f.; O. Vessberg, *Studien zur Kunstgeschichte der römischen Republik* 138 f.; *Rendiconti della Pontificia Acc. di Archeologia* XX (1943–4) 347 f.; B. Schweitzer, *Die Bildniskunst der römischen Republik* 92, 103 f.; *AA* 1952 123 f.; *Robert Boehringer, eine Freundesgabe* 153 f.; M. Borda, *Iconografia Cesariana* passim; *Kölner Jb für Vor- und Frühgeschichte* IV (1959) 7 f.; *Kunstwerke der Antike, Münzen und Medaillen Auktion* XXII (*Cat.* 13 May 1961) 17 under no. 22. Only a few of the portraits have any claim to be considered as contemporary likenesses. The majority are ancient copies from established posthumous types, different ages of the Imperial period reshaping the dictator's appearance in their own image.

The Cambridge head lacks the part-closed eyes, ironical smile and rounded jaw of the apparently contemporary Tusculum portrait mentioned above and of other slightly later heads related to it. On the other hand, its square jaw, authoritative expression, wide eyes, characteristic shape of mouth and chin and the undulating quality of its hair all find an echo in the Pisa and Chiaramonti heads and the numerous other copies of the same type; cf. E. Böhringer, *Der Cäsar von Acireale* pls. 18 f., 24 f. These seem to be based on a lost original of *c.* 30 B.C., an important work, whether or not it is to be associated with the Temple of the Diuus Iulius in Rome which was dedicated in 29 B.C. The Cambridge portrait, however, seems unmistakably not to be derived from the same original, but to be an independent creation of much the same period. Indeed, in so far as it may claim to take its place amidst the Caesar-portraits, there are several features that conspire to suggest that it may in fact be slightly earlier. Among these may be mentioned the treatment of the hair, the realistic rendering of the baldness, and the traces, all but obliterated in the modern cleaning, of harsh diagonal wrinkles against the sides of the neck. These last could go straight back to the Tusculum portrait and the contemporary coin-types. The unique position of the Cambridge head and the manner and quality of its execution might seem then to imply that it is an original work, most probably of the period *c.* 40–30 B.C. It would appear at least to have been profoundly influenced by the changing likeness of the deified Julius and there is the possibility that it may have been intended as a somewhat unorthodox portrait of him. Complete certainty on this issue does not seem attainable because of the idiosyncrasies shown by the Cambridge head and because it is difficult to discount the effect of the over-working associated with the modern cleaning. This seems to have been confined to minimizing the damage at the nose, mouth and chin. To judge from the adjacent areas where the original surface has survived, the recutting was not very deep and there seems to be no clear evidence that it has significantly modified the character of the head. Nevertheless, a little consideration of the expression of the face suggests that much has been lost in the process.

Roman work of the third quarter of the first century B.C.

R. Cowdry, *A Description of the Pictures, Statues, Busto's, Basso-Relievo's and Other Curiosities at the Earl of Pembroke's House at Wilton* (1751) 45; J. Kennedy, *A Description of the Antiquities and Curiosities in Wilton House* (1769) 112; C. Newton, *Notes on the Sculptures at Wilton House* 31; Michaelis, *Anc. Marbles* 715 no. 233; *Cat. Christie* 3 July 1961 33 no. 146; *The Times* 25 October 1961 6; *Annual Report of the Fitzwilliam Museum Syndicate* 1961 pl. 1.

[1] On the coin and gem portraits see now *Antike Kunst* II (1959) 27 f., III (1960) 81 f.

VI

ANCIENT COPIES FROM HELLENISTIC ORIGINALS

83 Young satyr (originally Pan?) playing the flute PLATES 28–29

Presented by Dr J. Disney. Probably acquired in Italy. Inv.: GR.2.1850.

H. 0·501 m. Medium-grained Proconnesian (?) marble. Restored in plaster are a part of the right shoulder, the lower end of the flute beyond the left hand, and a section of the garland on the right side of the head; a modern dowel-hole in the right hip has been filled with plaster. There is evidence of at least three attempts to repair the right arm which had been broken at the shoulder. At first it seems to have been reset in approximately its original position with the aid of a metal support to the right hip. Subsequently the splintered area at the shoulder was ruthlessly cut back, with the consequence that the elbow was twisted outwards in an ugly fashion. Today the arm has been returned to its original position, as revealed by the breaks under the armpit, but this has necessitated the restoration in plaster of the part removed in the previous recutting. The lower part of the flute was at one stage supplied by an ancient fragment representing the limb of a tree, but this has now been replaced by the plaster restoration. The fingers of the right hand and the little finger of the left have also been broken away in this vicinity; the surface has been trimmed to take modern marble restorations, but these had already been removed more than a century ago. Traces of a golden-brown patina on the hair, garland, base and flute. The garland and base also show remains of a dark coating, possibly of pitch. Over this on the garland there are faint vestiges of gold leaf. Other such traces of gold also occur on the hair, the inner side of the original part of the flute (but not on the extraneous fragment formerly used to restore the rest of it) and on the base. It is not certain that all of these are in situ; *those on the base quite possibly are not. It is also not clear just when the gold was applied, but, in view of its relationship to the restored areas and the general good preservation of the statuette, it may well be ancient.*

The copyist has added the diminutive tail of a horse, making the figure that of a youthful satyr. At the date at which he was working the other features such as the emergent horns on the brow and the little pouches of tissue on the sides of the neck under the pointed ears would not have seemed inappropriate to a satyr; but in the much earlier period to which the statuette's prototype would seem to have belonged these details befit Pan, although artistic whimsey was then rife. He is shown seated on a rock, playing his flute. His legs are crossed and his torso is thrust back almost to the point of being off-balance. This is merely because he is caught in a momentary pose as he moves his whole body with his playing. His non-human pedigree is portrayed above all else by the delightfully animal and mischievous character of the face. His tousled hair is bound with a massive garland of pine. The figure has a completely three-dimensional quality; yet, despite its many crossing axes, it also possesses a simple unity in that the eye and mind are led unerringly to the flute, its music and the thought behind the music in the expression of the player. Flesh, rock and hair are distinguished by their different surface textures. In addition, a line cut with the running drill separates the feet and buttocks from the rock on which they rest.

This statuette is clearly intimately related to the so-called 'Skopaic satyr'—in actual fact a standing figure of the young Pan playing the same kind of flute, whose common ascription to Skopas gains some support from the close resemblance of its hips, legs and feet to those of that artist's Pothos. For lists of examples of the type see W. Klein, *Praxiteles* 212, H. Riemann, *Kerameikos* II 108 f. under no. 160; its date probably falls in about the third quarter of the fourth century B.C. Despite the wide difference in pose, no other work so closely resembles the head-type and body treatment of the Cambridge statuette. As a consequence it seems desirable to begin by considering whether this figure is any more than a copyist's free variant of the Skopaic type. It is first of all essential to stress that at no point, with the possible exception of two curls in front of the left ear, is it exactly copied from the Skopaic statue. Secondly, and much more important, if one may attribute the tail and possibly the form of the garland to the copyist, the style seems otherwise perfectly consistent in suggesting an only slightly later date than that of the Skopaic Pan. Finally, there are the high quality and organic unity of the Cambridge statuette which hardly smack of a mere copyist's confection. In general, then, it seems not unreasonable to assume that it is copied from an otherwise unknown creation by an artist of the same school, probably working in about the last quarter of the fourth century B.C. As compared with the earlier statue, Pan has now lost his timid and fey look. His cheeks are puffed with blowing and his eyes are sly and mischievous. In this late fourth-century setting, his face now also claims comparison with those of the young satyr dressed in a pig-skin and of another of his kind with his cloak filled with fruit. The latter figure also has something of the sense of movement that pervades the Cambridge statuette. The hairstyle already looks forward to the third-century satyr of the 'invitation group'.[1] The Skopaic positioning of the legs has been abandoned. The new type, seated on a low rock, is rather to be compared with a young satyr in the Vatican, G. Lippold, *Kat. vaticanischen Museums* III. 2. 150 no. 68, pl. 70. The execution of the Cambridge statuette suggests that it is a copy of early Imperial date; a small work of this kind would be appropriate, e.g., to a fountain in the peristyle of a house.

Probably a copy of early Imperial date from an original of about the last quarter of the fourth century B.C.

J. Disney sr., *Cat. Hyde* 3 no. 19; J. Disney jr., *Museum Disneianum* 53, pl. 26; *AZ* v (1847) 158; *GGA* 1849 447 f.; Marsden, *Cat. Disney Coll.* 83 no. 2; *AA* 1864 169; Michaelis, *Anc. Marbles* 255 no. 33; Chapman, *Handbook* (2nd ed.) 54.

84 Reclining river god

PLATE 27

Purchased. Dredged up from the Tiber in the early nineteenth century. Formerly in the possession of the painter, J. M. W. Turner. Inv.: GR. 1. 1887.

H. 0·504 m. Fine-grained Luna (?) marble. Broken away are both arms from a little below the shoulders and the left leg from just above the knee, together with the end of the plinth and the cloak lying on top of it. The lower part of the right leg is also missing; this was worked from a separate piece of marble and attached by a dowel, 0·012 m. in diameter. Also broken away are parts of the god's hair and most of the 'sceptre' of reed in his left arm. His nose is very awkwardly restored in marble. Surface chipped at the hair, right cheek, etc. Repaired at breaks at the neck and at the top of the thighs under the hips. As a result of his long sojourn in his familiar element, the front part of the god's head and the inside of his left thigh have been riddled with termite-like burrows made by under-water creatures. Over the face these holes have been filled with plaster without otherwise restoring the surface; a detail on Plate 27 shows the appearance of the head before it was so treated. The underside of the plinth preserves a small dowel-hole, 0·019 m. in diameter, for the mounting of the figure and also a much larger hole under the hips towards the end of the plinth. It is 0·031 m. in diameter and 0·119 m. deep and still shows traces of the reamer which completed its cutting. It was clearly intended to receive a cylindrical metal bar relieving the base of the weight of the comparatively unsupported chest and head. In addition to these ancient drillings there are two modern dowel-holes underneath from a previous mounting of the figure on a marble slab. The surface has been corroded by moisture.

The god is shown reclining naked on top of a small garment, perhaps a short cloak, the edge of which appears on top of the plinth between his thighs. His left leg lies flat on the ground, his right is sharply bent at the knee. His left arm was probably bent forward at the elbow and his left forearm and elbow probably rested on some low object or attribute behind him. However, the elaborate arrangement for easing the weight of the upper part of the body and the termination of the plinth under the lower part of the back would suggest that this support was not a structural member. Probably it was carved from a separate block of marble. In his left arm the god also held a staff or sceptre of reed. This was largely free-standing, but it can be seen where it has been broken away from the outer side of the arm. Also, the end of one of its long, blade-shaped leaves is preserved, curving down behind his left shoulder. A garland of the same kind of reed encircles the god's head. The surface is slightly chipped at his raised right knee, but the broken area seems rather small to conceal a point of attachment for his right hand. More probably his right forearm was bent forward across his body and the hand held some further attribute. His hair hangs rich and lank down to his shoulders where it clings as if wet. His mouth is open and twisted down at the left corner as if he were speaking or singing. Both rows of teeth are indicated. His eyes stare into the distance. The centrally placed pupils are slightly hollowed but do not

[1] Satyr dressed in a pig-skin: for lists of examples see W. Klein, *Praxiteles* 212, H. Riemann, *Kerameikos* II 109 f.; for the head-type see *EA* 3741, M. Bieber, *Die antiken Skulpturen und Bronzen, Cassel* 26 no. 33, pl. 27, E. Paribeni, *Cat. Sculture di Cirene* 118 no. 334, pl. 156. Satyr with his cloak filled with fruit: e.g. *EA* 3483 f., 3559 f. (where a list of duplicates is given in the text). 'Invitation group' satyr: A. W. Lawrence, *Later Greek Sculpture* pl. 31*a*.

seem to have been drilled. The back of the figure has been less fully finished and shows traces of the claw-chisel and the gouge. The drill and flat chisel have been used in the undercutting of the hair.

This figure is clearly a decorative Roman work that may once have adorned a fountain, but it possesses a certain presence and it appears likely that it may reflect an earlier statue-type not too inconsistently. The face recalls a late Classical and early Hellenistic divine head-type adapted for portraits of Alexander the Great. The rather over-emphatic musculature of the youthful body also suggests the early Hellenistic period. Figures in this kind of posture had long been developed to meet the requirements of pedimental sculpture, as seen, e.g., in the so-called Kephissos from the Parthenon. However, in this case, the pose seems exactly to have mirrored that of a Hellenistic statue-type of the reclining Nile-god; see *Antike Plastik (Festschrift W. Amelung)* 25 f., C. Watzinger, *Ausgrabungen in Alexandria (Expedition Ernst von Sieglin)* II. I. B. 111 f. no. 98, pl. 43. To be sure, the cloak under the Cambridge god does not cover his legs and he holds his reed 'sceptre' in his left hand instead of the right which was thus probably free to clasp the horn appropriate to a river god; but the position of the body, arms, legs and head seems to have been the same. The flabby forms of the Nile-god type are probably a concession to the native Egyptian tradition. The date at which it was first created is difficult to determine with any precision. Uncertainty also surrounds the somewhat similar pedimental figures from Samothrace, although it now seems more likely that these are of the second century B.C.[1] In any case, the more austere forms of the Cambridge god seem much earlier and it may well be that he represents an antecedent version in the same tradition.

Roman decorative work of Imperial date apparently based on a Hellenistic (Alexandrian ?) statue-type of about the third century B.C.

Chapman, *Handbook* (2nd ed.) 35.

85 Statuette of Aphrodite PLATE 27

Bequeathed by Sir Robert H. Greg. From Egypt. Inv.: GR.2.1954.

P.H. 0·216 m. Medium-grained Proconnesian (?) marble. Head broken away at the neck, arms missing from near the shoulders, legs from the knee and a little above it; also broken away are the support against the left leg and the lock of hair falling behind the right shoulder. On the back of the figure are patches of stain from decayed vegetable matter.

This statuette represents the *anadyomene* or Aphrodite emerging from the sea in which she has been born and wringing out her wet hair. The type is the same as that of **86** under which both statuettes will be discussed in detail together. The present example has much heavier proportions than **86** and these strike something of a classical note. The back of the figure is less well finished than the front and somewhat ill shaped about the hips.

A small free copy of late Hellenistic or early Imperial date from an Alexandrian original probably of the third century B.C.

AJA LXIII (1959) 143 no. 29.

86 Statuette of Aphrodite PLATE 27

Bequeathed by Sir Robert H. Greg. From Egypt. Inv.: GR.3.1954.

P.H. 0·241 m. Fine-grained white marble, possibly Pentelic (?). Legs broken away above the knees, arms at the shoulders, head at the base of the neck; also missing are most of the support against the left leg and of the lock of hair falling behind the right shoulder.

This statuette is of the same type as **85** although it displays the more elongated proportions often found in later Hellenistic times. Both figures show the goddess standing with her right leg slightly bent and with her weight on her left foot. The many more complete examples of the same type reveal that both her hands were raised to her hair to wring it out. Both statuettes preserve the end of the long locks of hair gripped in her right hand where they fall behind her right shoulder.

There are many statuettes extant showing the goddess in this pose.[2] The vast majority of them are from Egypt, where the type is also copied in bronze and terracotta figurines. It has, as a consequence, been very reasonably assumed that the original from which they are derived was a cult statue in that country, most probably in Alexandria. The small votive figures themselves are a very imperfect guide to the date and style of this lost original which they tend to

[1] A. Conze, *Archaeologische Untersuchungen auf Samothrake* 15 f., 24 f., pls. 35–6; *ÖJh* XXXIX (1934–5) 1 f.; *Hesperia* XXI (1952) 40 f.

[2] E.g. M. C. C. Edgar, *Cat. Greek Sculpture, Cairo* 11 no. 27454, pl. 6; Труды Госуд. Музея (Pushkin Mus.) 1960 47; *JHS* XXVIII (1908) 12 no. 13, pl. 9; *RA* ser. 4, I (1903) 233 f., pl. 5, 388 f., pl. 6; G. M. A. Richter, *Cat. Greek Sculptures, Metropolitan Museum* 153 f., especially no. 155; *Ars Antiqua, Auktion* II (*Cat.* 14 May 1960) 25 no. 55, pl. 25 (it has since been established that the Eros does not belong and is from another group); Sir E. A. Wallis Budge, *Some Account of the Egyptian Antiquities in the Possession of Lady Meux* 353 no. 1311, pl. 26; etc. Cf. also *Mon. Piot* XIII (1906) 117 f., pl. 10; *NdSc* 1899 207 fig. 2; G. Kaschnitz-Weinberg, *Sculture del Magazzino del Museo Vaticano* 127 no. 270, pl. 58.

reinterpret in the idiom of their own day; compare, for example, the differences in proportions between **85** and **86** above. The type, however, is otherwise rendered with remarkable consistency. The support against the goddess's left leg takes the form of a dolphin on some of the statuettes, symbolizing the sea from which she is stepping; a few have an Eros in this position, but one of the most elaborate examples, now in Dresden, has the figure of a triton; this last forms so satisfying a group with the goddess that it has been persuasively argued that the original cult statue also had a triton in this position.[1] In a recent study entitled *Die kauernde Aphrodite* R. Lullies has come to the conclusion that the naked Aphrodite-type under consideration dates from the mid second century B.C. or slightly later. On the other hand, he assigns a related half-draped type in exactly the same pose to the mid third century B.C.; see D. Mustilli, *Il Museo Mussolini* 38 under no. 8, Lullies, *op. cit.* 78 f. Unfortunately, Lullies does not seem to be comparing like with like. In the case of the half-draped Aphrodite he is assigning a stylistic date to the original on the basis of its best copies; but with the naked *anadyomene* he is dating not the original but the time at which the Dresden copy was executed. Of this type there are no mechanically exact copies, but only free versions which, as we have seen, adhere to the pose of the original but vary its style. These little votive statuettes are, admittedly, mostly conceived frontally, but a few are as three-dimensional as the half-draped type, e.g. *RA* ser. 4, I (1903) pl. 5. Both statue-types are clearly very intimately connected and the half-draped type seems almost meaningless unless it had the naked *anadyomene* to serve as prototype. It thus seems probable that the naked type itself must go back to an original of the third century B.C. A closer dating is not easy as no valid conclusions can be based on the variable modelling and head-types, whether of the goddess herself or of the Dresden or Cyrene tritons. Nevertheless, the use of the figure of the triton in this way to indicate the surrounding sea seems akin to Eutychides' employment of the river god, Orontes, in his Tyche of Antioch, at least suggesting the possibility that the original might date from early in the third century B.C.

A small free copy of about late Hellenistic date from an Alexandrian original probably of the third century B.C.

ILN 2 April 1955 607; *AJA* LXIII (1959) 143 no. 28.

87 Herakles as a child PLATE 28

Presented by the Cyprus Exploration Fund. From Cyprus (exact find-spot and year of acquisition not recorded). Inv.: GR.S.4.

P.H. c. 0·225 m. Very hard-textured, extremely fine-grained white marble with a faint reddish-brown veining. Head and neck broken away; right arm missing from just above elbow, left from somewhat higher up, taking with it much of the animal skin originally looped over the forearm; right leg broken away below the knee, left from just above the knee; also broken away is the attribute (cornucopia ?) held against the outer side of the left upper arm; likewise missing is the object (club ?) originally fashioned from a separate piece of marble and attached by a metal pin to the side of the right leg at the level of the knee. The surface has been badly chipped and flaked, especially over the front of the body, the knees, the right hip, the small of the back and the spinal groove.

The figure is that of a child with short, chubby limbs. Small folds of fat appear at the armpits, on the inside of the legs above the knees and in a layer along the iliac crest. The young hero stands with his weight on his left leg, the right being extended somewhat to the side and being bent backwards slightly from the knee. His spine is arched, with shoulders thrust back and pelvis and abdomen pressed forward. His left arm was bent at the elbow and carried a lion's skin draped over it, as may be seen more clearly on better-preserved related works. These also tend to confirm the indications of the preserved attachments in suggesting that his other attributes were a cornucopia in his left arm and a club against his right leg. There is a quaint inconsistency in having the child already carry the spoils of the Nemean lion and of Acheloos. Where the original surface is preserved it has been worked to a beautiful, even finish and the quality of the modelling is of a very high order.

The Cambridge statuette seems clearly related to the Brunswick child Herakles type in the same pose and represented with cornucopia, lion's skin and club; see *EA* 4174–5, 4178, H. Stuart Jones, *Cat. Museo Capitolino* 275 f. no. 3, pl. 64. The Brunswick Herakles seems certainly a parody, in child form, of the late-fourth-century adult version of the hero of the New York type; cf. *EA* 4833 f. (where duplicates are listed in the text), G. M. A. Richter, *Cat. Greek Sculptures, Metropolitan Museum* 121 f. no. 121, pl. 93. Its original was probably one of the numerous child

[1] *AA* 1894 29; *BSA* IX (1902–3) 221, fig. 1; G. Dickens, *Hellenistic Sculpture* fig. 25; *JEA* XI (1925) 183, pl. 20 *right*; *AA* 1933 428; *From the Collections of the Ny Carlsberg Glyptothek* II (1938) 34; R. Lullies, *Die kauernde Aphrodite* 67, 81, figs. 43–4. Cf. also E. Paribeni, *op. cit.* 102 no. 274, pl. 134.

statues of the third century B.C. by artists such as Boethos. The Cambridge statuette differs mainly from the Brunswick and New York types in that it does not have the upper part of the lion's skin drawn over its head and shoulders. It may thus be rather a parody of the early-third-century Ludovisi Herakles which adopts exactly the same pose but shows the hero as a muscular young man; this statue seems also to be represented on coins of Herakleia in Lucania, perhaps the city where it was originally set up; see P. W. Lehmann, *Statues on Coins of Southern Italy and Sicily in the Classical Period* 7 f., pl. 1. 5–7; cf. also Louvre 3083, *Cat. sommaire des marbres antiques* 33, pl. 17. However that may be, the Cambridge Herakles seems rather to have followed the Brunswick type in the matter of the subsidiary attributes of club and cornucopia and their respective positions; as we have already seen, the two types seem to have been interrelated. Other copies of the Cambridge type seem to be lacking. Certainly, a poorly executed torso in Rome fails to carry conviction as being of the same boy; see H. Stuart Jones, *Cat. Palazzo dei Conservatori* 242 no. 59, pl. 88. Under the circumstances and in view of its fine quality, the Cambridge Herakles might thus be considered an original; but its small scale and its find-place far from the statue it was parodying both suggest that it is rather a copy, although its execution very probably still falls within the Hellenistic period. The original from which it is derived should be either contemporary with, or later than, that of the related Brunswick type.

Although the versions just considered are very rare, the theme of Herakles as a child was a popular one with Roman copyists as well. Much commoner is the variety listed by O. Waldhauer in *Die antiken Skulpturen der Ermitage* II 64 under no. 187; note also the related type of Eros as Herakles grouped by D. Mustilli in *Museo Mussolini* 72 under no. 14.

Probably a copy of late Hellenistic date from an original of about the third century B.C. or slightly later.

88 Herm of a Hellenistic ruler PLATE 30

No record of source or date of acquisition.[1] This herm has been in the Museum for many years in another Department. Inv.: GR.S.3.

H. 0·173 m. Rather pale giallo antico. *Restored in alabaster are left side of head and right shoulder of herm. Somewhat chipped, notably at the ram's head (?) under the right edge of the helmet. Surface somewhat weathered and showing traces of a brown incrustation. It has been partly cleaned in modern times.*

The herm bears the head of a young man with rather forceful features, heavy brows and deep-set eyes. The face is full, even slightly plump; the crease in the flesh under the chin and the Venus-rings on the neck have been exaggerated in the modern cleaning, but do, in fact, seem to have ancient authority. The lips are slightly parted. On his head the young man wears a royal Macedonian helmet. To either side of the plume it has ram's horns in relief. These are the attributes of Zeus Ammon and in wearing them in this way the dynast is associating himself with the godhead and following a tradition established by his predecessor, Alexander the Great, whom his portrait faintly resembles in other respects as well. Attached to the underside of the brim of the helmet over the ears of the young ruler there appear to be further coiled horns. Better-preserved examples of the same herm-type suggest that these belonged to small representations of down-turned rams' heads. The ends of the diadem hang down on to the shoulders from behind them. The helmet is also fitted with cheek-pieces set close against the face. Over his chest the young king wears protective armour closely resembling an aegis. It is not certain how far this is intended as a further usurpation of a divine attribute. In any case, in actual practice this would have been produced after the fashion of a common type of mail consisting of overlapping, scale-like plates of metal.

In the text to *EA* 3940 f. R. Herbig has assembled twenty other examples of the same type; for earlier discussions of these herms see *RA* ser. 4, VIII (1906) 3 f.; *JHS* XXVIII (1908) 12 f.; *Rendiconti dei Lincei* ser. 6, II (1926) 49 f.; B. Ashmole, *Ancient Marbles at Ince Blundell Hall* 48, under no. 111. All of the known examples are small decorative works like the Cambridge herm; they were apparently produced by Italian copyists in about the first century A.D.—a dating now confirmed by a further copy from Pompeii in Pompeii Museum. Attempts to identify the young ruler as Alexander the Great have not been particularly successful. To judge from the popularity of his portrait with Italian copyists, he was probably a Macedonian king especially well known to the Romans. Little more can be said for sure. Herbig has tentatively suggested an identification as Pyrrhus. Ashmole has remarked on an interesting resemblance to the head of Philip V as it is copied on Roman denarii of the beginning of the first century B.C.; see *BMC*

[1] Probably not to be equated with J. Disney sr., *Cat. Hyde* 47 no. 228, as this is not mentioned in J. Disney jr., *MS Cat.*, and had probably been disposed of.

Coins of the Roman Republic II 277 nos. 532 f., III pl. 93. 18. Some resemblance also exists to a portrait in Naples, A. Hekler, *Greek and Roman Portraits* pl. 71 *b*. But, as no certain identification seems yet possible, let it here suffice to describe the subject as a Hellenistic ruler probably of the third or earlier second centuries B.C.

Decorative work of about the first century A.D. based on a Hellenistic portrait of the third–second centuries B.C.

89 Statuette of Artemis PLATE 30

Purchased. Inv.: GR.1.1906.

P.H. 0·208 m. Medium-grained Parian marble with a golden-brown patina. Head broken away at base of neck, right arm from a little below the shoulder, both legs from just under the knees; much of the support at the back of the figure also broken away. Also missing are the left arm and the quiver behind the goddess's right shoulder; both of these were originally fashioned from separate pieces of marble and attached by small metal dowels or pins.

The goddess is represented as hastening forward. She is clad in a high-girdled chiton with a long overfold and the drapery is blown back against her limbs. A strap over her right shoulder served to carry her quiver. Her legs were carved in the round and the lower part of the figure was strengthened by a support at the back. The rear surface has been left roughed out with the gouge.

This little statuette is clearly derived from the so-called Artemis Rospigliosi, a Hellenistic statue-type assigned by Kramer to the later third century B.C. but whose date Beschi has recently proposed to lower to the mid second century B.C. On the type see *JdI* XLIII (1928) 269 f.; Kramer in *AM* LV (1930) 237 f.; *RM* LIV (1939) 234; G. Lippold, *Griechische Plastik* (*HdA* III. 1) 336; Beschi in C. Anti (ed.), *Sculture greche e romane di Cirene* 255 f. The Cambridge statuette is not an exact copy, but one of a small group of variants which change the pose by advancing the left leg instead of the right; one may also cite:

(1) Louvre: *AM* LV (1930) 247, fig. 2.

(2) Ostia Museum 1118.

(3) Leningrad: O. Waldhauer, *Die antiken Skulpturen der Ermitage* III 56 no. 304, fig. 51.

(4) Cyrene: E. Paribeni, *Cat. Sculture di Cirene* 71 no. 162, pl. 95.

(5) Pergamon: *AM* LV (1930) 249, fig. 3.

(6) Apollonia: *Rendiconti della Pontificia Acc.* XXIII–XXIV (1947–9) 86 f., fig. 2.

(7) Paros: *EA* 1332.

(8) Alexandria: A. Adriani, *Repertorio d'arte dell' Egitto greco-romano*, ser. A, I 38 no. 52, pl. 39.

This variant type marks a return to the earlier leg position of the Artemis of Versailles. The beginnings of the modified version are somewhat obscure, but may quite well have fallen in middle or late Hellenistic times. The Cambridge Artemis is a poor copy of Imperial date.

A modified version of Imperial date based on a Hellenistic statue variously assigned to the late third and mid second centuries B.C.

VII
SCULPTURE OF IMPERIAL ROMAN DATE

(A) CLASSICIZING SCULPTURE OF IMPERIAL DATE

90 Head of a young man — PLATE 30

Bequeathed by C. B. Marlay. Provenance unknown. Inv.: GR.9.1912.

P.H. c. 0·269 m. Fine-grained white marble with a golden-brown patina; although it shows greyish veinings, the texture and fault-lines of the marble suggest that it is Pentelic rather than Italian. Broken away at the base of the neck, where the surface has been cut level to fit a modern bust from which the head has since been removed. Restored partly in Luna and partly in Proconnesian marble are portions of nose, lower lip and chin. The surface has been lightly cleaned over much of the face and neck and at the lower edge of the hair over the brow.

The head is turned to the right. In addition, the abrupt conflict between head and neck angles and the wrinkles present at the right side of the neck would seem to suggest that the shoulders were set somewhat obliquely—perhaps, for example, as in Brunn-Bruckmann 346. The face is that of a young man with a somewhat brooding expression. The lips are lightly parted. The eyes are turned upwards—and also slightly inwards, although this last circumstance is probably due to an accidental incompetence. A deep furrow runs across the brow which bulges above and beneath it.

The face finds its closest parallels in work of the early Hellenistic period, mainly of the late fourth and early third centuries B.C. The hair, on the other hand, finds no counterpart in this period nor in the classicizing phase of late Hellenistic times when such types tended to be revived. Instead it appears to approximate to a hair-style of Julio-Claudian times. The row of small curls over the brow resembles a style worn by Drusus the Younger, Germanicus and Tiberius, but the tightly massed small locks over the rest of the head may indicate a somewhat later date, quite probably into the second quarter of the first century A.D. The head is essentially an ideal likeness with little about it to suggest a portrait, but the up-turned eyes represent a device adopted from the time of Alexander on to represent a princely mortal in communion with the divine; see H. P. L'Orange, *Apotheosis in Ancient Portraiture* 39 f. There is, nevertheless, nothing of the mild individuality commonly met with in Greek portraits of early Imperial date, as witness the examples recently assembled by G. Hafner in *Späthellenistische Bildnisplastik*. It is only possible to assume that here an ideal type has been used in lieu of a portrait.

Probably Greek work of the first half of the first century A.D.

AJA LXIII (1959) 143 no. 18.

91 Statuette of Aphrodite — PLATE 31

Transferred from the old University Library. Presented to the University by Professor E. D. Clarke. From Kurşunlu Tepe (the ancient Skepsis) in the Troad. Inv.: GR.2.1865.

P.H. 0·462 m. Medium-grained Proconnesian (?) marble with a faint golden-brown patina. Broken away are the body of the goddess from the level of her hips, the back edge of her peplos where it must have hung down under her left arm, and the upper part of the archaistic statue against her left side; this latter figure is missing from somewhat above the knees. The surface is also badly chipped at many points. The break at the goddess's hips has been cut level in modern times and fitted with a lead-set dowel to take a restoration; the top of the drapery behind her left hip and the edge of her abdomen have also been recut at the same time. This restoration would seem to have been made after the statuette had left Clarke's hands. It had already been removed by the time that the figure was seen by Michaelis.

The goddess stands with her weight on her right foot. Her left knee is bent and her left foot rests on a slightly higher part of the base. She has apparently been wearing her Doric peplos with the open side to her left. Now, unpinned from her shoulders as she undresses, it has been allowed to slip down to her waist and the top of her thighs. The top corner of the garment at the back appears to have been looped over her missing left arm; in front, it trails down over her flexed left leg against the small statue at her side. Sandals are summarily indicated on the goddess's feet. The support in the form of a statue against her left side appears to have represented a female figure wearing a chiton and, over it, a himation. Both garments seem to have been shown in an archaistic fashion with a heavily bunched central fold from which, in the case of the himation, subsidiary curving folds radiate to both sides. When complete, this figure would have reached almost to Aphrodite's hip and the goddess is probably to be interpreted as originally resting her left forearm on top of its head. This statue-support is represented as standing on a round base, in shape not unlike the round altars, **71** and **72** above.

Lethaby's misguided attempt to interpret this figure as a copy of the Melian Aphrodite is best passed over in silence. The Cambridge statuette is not, in any case, a copy at all, but an original creation in its own right. This is clear from technical considerations. The sculpture was never fully finished and the abundant surviving indications show that the whole of the primary work was done with the point without the aid of control drillings. Nevertheless, in his task of producing an entirely new figure, the artist has contented himself with making a judicious blend of already existing statue-types. In particular he has drawn heavily on a much-copied statue to which some scholars have given the name of Aphrodite Potnia. For examples of the type see *EA* 1542, 2081 f., 2596 f., 3716, 5020; for discussions of it see B. Ashmole, *Ancient Marbles at Ince Blundell Hall* 20 f. under no. 36, *JdI* LVI (1941) 156 f., G. Lippold, *Griechische Plastik* (*HdA* III. 1) 298 f. This type he seems to have blended with a second variety of Aphrodite in a similar pose but clad in a high-girt chiton as well as a himation and having a support in the form of an archaistic statue set against her left side; e.g. C. Anti, *Il Regio Museo Archeologico, Venezia* 88 no. 12, *Burlington Fine Arts Club, Cat. Ancient Greek Art* (1904) 28 no. 42, pl. 31, Michaelis, *Anc. Marbles* 544 no. 11. Other statuettes apart from the Cambridge example adapt this use of an archaistic support-statue to a figure of the goddess naked to the waist. They adopt a similar pose but dispose the drapery somewhat differently. Notable are a statuette in the Palazzo Doria in Rome, *EA* 2288, and another in the Museo Nazionale in Naples, *AZ* XXXIX (1881) 131 f., pl. 7. The Cambridge Aphrodite might, in view of its conservative technique and slender proportions, still claim to be considered as a classicizing product of late Hellenistic times, but its closest parallel is that provided by the vividly coloured statuette in Naples, cited above, which is probably already of the first century A.D.

Asia Minor work of the first century B.C.–first century A.D.

Clarke, *Marbles* 38 f. no. 16; Idem, *Travels* 4° II (=II. 1) 127 n. 2, pl. facing 30, 8° III 162 n. 1; *AA* 1864 172; Michaelis, *Anc. Marbles* 244 f. no. 2; Preuner, *Über die Venus von Milo* 39; Chapman, *Handbook* (2nd ed.) 45; *JHS* XXXIX (1919) 207 f.

92 Hekateion PLATE 31

Purchased with funds provided by Sir William P. Elderton. Provenance unknown. Inv.: GR.1.1960.

H. 0·328 m. Luna marble with traces of a brown incrustation. Modern marble restorations of the forearms of all three figures of the goddess and of the edge of the base, including the left foot of one of the figures, have been removed. The group has been slightly chipped, e.g. at the stephanai of the goddess. Over the greater part of two of the figures the surface has been cleaned in modern times; one of these two has also had her chin recut.

The three young female figures grouped about a central column form a kind of trinity representing different aspects of the goddess, Hekate. Amongst the classicizing Hekateia this is by no means an advanced example and the three figures of the goddess are not yet distinguished by different dress or attributes. Also, their half-lowered forearms, when complete, probably all held short torches in their hands. All three figures are dressed in chitons, fastened along the upper arms to form sleeves. Over these they appear to be wearing a somewhat heavier garment, probably a peplos; it has a deep over-fold and is girdled at the waist, the girdle being carried higher in front under the breasts. All the figures also have shoes on their feet and stephanai in their hair. The hair itself is parted in the middle over the brow and carried round towards the back of the head. Two locks are allowed to hang down on to the shoulders from behind each ear. The facial type is best judged from the one head that has not been cleaned. It is round and full; the eye treatment still faintly echoes Hellenistic practice. Two of the figures stand with their right leg slightly flexed and their weight on their left foot; the third reverses the procedure, flexing the left leg. As a result they exactly counterbalance each other, mirroring each other's movements on all sides save one.

On the ancient Hekateia see *Archäologische und epigraphische Mitteilungen aus Österreich* IV (1880) 141 f., V (1881) 1 f.; E. Schmidt, *Archaistische Kunst in Griechenland und Rom* 47 f.; T. Kraus, *Hekate* 84 f. Unfortunately, all of these studies have confined themselves to the archaistic type of Hekateion, which is much commoner in Greece itself, and have quite neglected this classicizing variety of which, nevertheless, many examples are known, especially in the west. The earliest extant Hekateion of this type seems to be a group, probably of Hellenistic date, from Cyrene; see E. Paribeni, *Cat. Sculture di Cirene* 72 f. no. 167, pls. 96–8. The Cambridge example probably represents an early Imperial stage of about the first century A.D.; it is close in style to an early Imperial grave relief at Corinth: F. P. Johnson, *Corinth* IX 125 no. 259. Certainly it seems much earlier in appearance than the second-century-A.D. Hekateion in the British Museum dedicated by P. Aelius Barbarus, a freedman of Hadrian, on which see *A Description of the Ancient Marbles* X pl. 41, *CIL* VI 9089, A. H. Smith, *BMC Sculpture* III 83 f. no. 1714.[1] Thereafter the type tends to grow excessively slender and the different figures acquire a welter of distinguishing attributes: e.g. W. Amelung, *Kat. vaticanischen Museums* I 435 f. no. 181, pl. 45, H. Stuart Jones, *Cat. Palazzo dei Conservatori* 228 no. 33, 285 f. no. 1, pls. 85, 114, Villa Borghese 767 (wrongly restored), etc.

The origin of the classicizing Hekateion is obscure. Kraus seems to regard it as a creation of Roman times whereas he treats the highly variable, archaizing Attic Hekateia of classical and Hellenistic date as being ultimately derived from the fifth-century-B.C. group by Alkamenes on the Acropolis. But the most reliable evidence for the appearance of this group is probably that provided by an Attic coin in a series showing major statues in Athens; the representation is very crude, but from the few details that can be made out it is clear that the figures of the goddess are wearing stephanai, not poloi, and holding short torches instead of long ones.[2] These two features are the hallmark of the classicizing type and never occur on the archaizing Hekateia. The archaizing variety may thus have embarked early on a divergent development of the kind already noted under **45–7**. The relationship of the ordinary classicizing type to the Roman Hekateion in Berlin in a style reminiscent of Alkamenes still seems uncertain, as also the significance of the Berlin group; see *RM* IV (1889) 74, C. Blümel, *Kat. Berlin* IV 37 no. K 174, pl. 65. The remaining Hekateia, whether classicizing or archaizing, do not seem in any strict sense copies so much as free creations adapting a traditional type. The two varieties may be somewhat interrelated. Thus the classicizing Cambridge group may show faint links with the archaizing type in the locks of hair falling on the shoulders, the wearing of a chiton and peplos and the bunching of the folds of the latter between the legs.

Probably carved in Italy in about the first century A.D.

JHS and BSA Archaeological Reports 1961–2 47 no. 1, fig. 1.

93 Head of Dionysos, from a frontal herm (?)

PLATE 32

Presented by G. D. Hornblower. From Egypt, where it is reputed to have been found 'in a Roman villa in the Nile Delta'. Inv.: GR.3.1936.

P.H. 0·184 m. Medium-grained Proconnesian (?) marble, much worn by weather and showing patches of a yellowish-brown incrustation. Broken away at the neck and the right side of the head. Although somewhat re-trimmed in modern times, the back of the head had, already in antiquity, been dressed roughly flat with the point. In the middle there is a lead-lined rectangular dowel-hole, 0·02 × 0·014 m., presumably for attachment to a flat surface behind.

The head is that of a bearded god with an august and serene countenance. He wears a broad fillet across his brow. Above, his hair is parted over the centre of the brow and apparently carried outwards and upwards over a second band encircling his head somewhat higher up. The details of hair and beard are somewhat summarily shown.

Other examples of the same head-type are known from Egypt, e.g. C. Watzinger, *Ausgrabungen in Alexandria (Expedition Ernst von Sieglin)* II. 1. B. 94 f. nos. 81 f., especially figs. 31, 33; M. C. C. Edgar, *Cat. Greek Sculpture, Cairo* 7 no. 27441, pl. 3. Because of the diadem across the brow it has usually been identified as representing Dionysos. The style is broadly that of the mid–late fifth century B.C. Comparable is L. Curtius, *Zeus und Hermes* 54 f., Typus B, especially as seen in the more superficial copies such as F. Poulsen, *Kat. over antike Skulpturer, Ny Carlsberg Glyptotek* 356 no. 516, *Billedtavler* 39. However, as no copies of the type of the Dionysos-head itself seem to be known from outside of the Egyptian area, it seems quite probable that the original was itself no more

[1] The initial '*P(ublius)*' of the name seems to be faintly legible on the stone, although not so read by the *CIL* or by Smith.

[2] *Journal international d'archéologie numismatique* IX (1906) 299, pl. 13. 15; *Festschrift Hugo Blümner* 485 f., fig. 1. 1; E. Schmidt, *Archaistische Kunst in Griechenland und Rom* pl. 24. 4; M. Thompson, *New Style Silver Coinage of Athens* 390 no. 1268, pl. 142. A figure of the archaistic type seems to appear on the coin, Thompson, *op. cit.* 385 no. 1245, pl. 139, but is not identifiably triune.

than a classicizing creation of late date. Certainly there is little sensitivity in the modelling of the face and the rendering of the nose, in particular, seems excessively harsh and uncompromising.

Probably carved in Egypt in early (?) Imperial times.

AJA LXIII (1959) 143 no. 16.

94 Head of a goddess PLATE 32

Transferred from the old University Library. Presented to the University by Professor E. D. Clarke. From Kurşunlu Tepe (the ancient Skepsis) in the Troad. Inv.: GR.9.1865.

P.H. c. 0·313 m. Medium-grained translucent Parian (?) marble. Only the head and neck preserved. Broken away are the nose and the ends of the knot of hair on top of the head. Chipped at mouth, chin and hair, also at right ear. The back part of the head is not indicated at all; instead, the back surface has been trimmed roughly flat, but hardly level enough for the immediate juxtaposition of a further piece of marble. At the right side of the head, near the lower edge of this flat surface and extending down into the nape of the neck, there is a deep narrow cutting containing lead and intended for the attachment of a substantial metal support in the form of a bar, c. 0·048 m. wide and 0·0035 m. thick. Between this cutting and the edge of the right ear the surface has been chamfered back in antiquity, as if to allow space for some attribute or upward projection in the block forming the shoulders of the figure. The back of the neck has been left at the point-dressed stage and was apparently not meant to be visible. The surface shows patches of brown incrustation.

The evidence of the flat surface at the back of the head runs counter to that of the depth of the cheeks in suggesting that the head was turned slightly to the left. The neck is stretched forward and the face is a little shallow in depth in relation to its other dimensions. The goddess has her long hair parted in the middle and bound with a fillet. At the sides it is carried up over the fillet and tied in a knot at the crown of the head. At the right side a small wisp of hair has escaped and hangs down in front of the right ear. The corners of the mouth are lightly drilled. There is a faint Venus-ring on the neck.

The arrangements for anchoring the head from behind suggest that, although virtually free-standing, it was placed in some relief-like setting. In view of the way that the neck is stretched forward, this may well have taken the form of a relief medallion. The coiffure is met with on many statue-types but the appearance of the head is especially reminiscent of two Hellenistic works, the Aphrodite of Doidalsas and the Artemis Rospigliosi; on the first see R. Lullies, *Die kauernde Aphrodite* passim, on the second see under **89** above. If the foregoing interpretation as a relief medallion is the correct one, then the identification as Artemis would seem the more likely, as some attribute such as, perhaps, a quiver would appear to have been set against the right side of the head where it served to conceal the anchoring metal bar. For medallions of this kind see M. Cagiano de Azevedo, *Le antichità di Villa Medici* 55 no. 42, pl. 11, *Belleten* XXII (1958) 231, fig. 48. The type is also well attested in metal emblemata, e.g. R. A. Higgins, *Greek and Roman Jewellery* pl. 52 and, closer for the head angle, *BCH* LXXXIII (1959) 649 fig. 36, P. Amandry, *Collection Hélène Stathatos* pls. 38–9.

Asia Minor work probably of early Imperial date.

Clarke, *Marbles* 48 no. 26; Idem, *Travels* 4° II (=II. 1) 127 n. 2, pl. facing 130, 8° III 162 n. 1; Michaelis, *Anc. Marbles* 247 no. 9; Chapman, *Handbook* (2nd ed.) 57.

95 Janiform herm PLATE 32

Presented by Dr J. Disney. Probably acquired in Italy. Inv.: GR.20.1850.

H. 0·28 m. Luna marble, with a somewhat corroded surface and a yellowish patina. Restored in marble are the right corner of the breast of the herm of Dionysos, the tip of the god's nose and a leaf and a bunch of berries on his garland. Largely broken away are other modern restorations of Dionysos' garland, of a cluster of berries on that worn by the silen and of the left corner of the silen's chest. The silen's ears, probably originally partly concealed under the garland, have been completely recut in a forward position. Also recut are the lower vertical edges of the herm, which must originally have been slightly larger. The surface has been somewhat chipped at many points. The underside affords a relieving surface and a dowel-hole for attachment to the shaft of the herm. The sockets for the projecting slabs at the shoulders have been sealed with marble by the modern restorer.

Dionysos is shown wearing a fillet across his brow with its loose ends trailing on to his shoulders. At the sides it is concealed under his garland, but the locks of hair hanging down over the god's ears are perhaps to be understood as looped over the same head-band. He wears a garland of ivy with clusters of berries. Bunches of grapes hang down from the garland behind his ears. The god's eyes are heavy-lidded and his lips are parted. The corners of the mouth are deeply drilled. The bald-headed silen likewise wears both a fillet and an ivy garland. His beard is divided by coarse channelling cut with the running drill and the corner of his right eye is disfigured by over-deep drilling.

The Dionysos-head takes its place amongst the endlessly variable Roman types showing the god similarly bedecked and garlanded, e.g. W. Amelung, *Kat. vaticanischen Museums* I 510 no. 298, pl. 53, G. Lippold, *ibid.* III. 2. 254 no. 29, pl. 118, 266 no. 46, pl. 122, *EA* 2137, 2382, 3443 f., 3964, 4931 f., etc. The head of the silen may be loosely compared with figures of silens with wineskins such as O. Waldhauer, *Die antiken Skulpturen der Ermitage* I 38 f. no. 20, pl. 15. However, neither it nor the head of Dionysos is in any true sense a copy; instead, both seem free decorative creations of a classicizing artist of Imperial times.

Poor work, probably carved in Italy in the first–second centuries A.D.

J. Disney sr., *Cat. Hyde* 47; J. Disney jr., *Museum Disneianum* 25, pl. 13; *AZ* v (1847) 158; *GGA* 1849 444; Marsden, *Cat. Disney Coll.* 84 no. 22; Michaelis, *Anc. Marbles* 258 no. 51; Chapman, *Handbook* (2nd ed.) 44.

96 Janiform female herm PLATE 32

Presented by Dr J. Disney. Found at Cumae in 1824 by Henry Tufnell, who gave it to Disney in 1835. Inv.: GR.7.1850.

P.H. 0·585 m. Fine-grained, greyish-white Italian (?) marble which has flaked badly at the surface. Broken away is the double-faced head of the herm. The bottom-most 0·015 m. of the shaft appears to have been slightly recessed to fit a socketed base. Whatever traces there may have been of an ancient dowel to secure it in position have been obliterated by a large modern dowel-hole in the underside. Surface chipped and badly worn by weather.

The lower part of the shaft of the herm is of square section and tapers towards the bottom where it was presumably fitted into a base carved from a separate block of marble. The janiform female torsos in which it terminates above are almost identical. They each wear a sleeved chiton and, over this, a himation carried up obliquely over the left shoulder after the fashion of late archaic korai. The lower edge of the garment is schematized as a typically archaistic 'swallow-tail' of zigzag folds. Their hands clasp its hem to each side. Undulating rows of curls, stylized after the archaic fashion into the form of beads, fall on to their shoulders. Between the forearms of these figures there have been cut out sockets of trapezoidal shape, tapering towards the top. In view of their position these cannot possibly be connected with the projecting shoulder-slabs commonly found on herms. Instead, it seems clear that the present herm, like others identical with it, functioned as a vertical support for a low railing which was fitted into these sockets between the arms.

Almost identical are a group of archaistic female herms carved in *rosso antico*, e.g. H. Stuart Jones, *Cat. Palazzo dei Conservatori* 301 f. no. 9, pl. 119, F. Poulsen, *Kat. over antike Skulpturer, Ny Carlsberg Glyptotek* 54 no. 40, *Billedtavler* pl. 3. Poulsen cites further examples in the Museo Nazionale Romano in Rome and in Palermo. A janiform herm of Luna marble in the Palazzo Doria in Rome is even closer to the Cambridge example in all respects save in that it has substituted classicizing heads for the usual archaistic type. The only examples with a dated context are those in the Palazzo dei Conservatori, which come from the baths of Neratius Cerealis who was consul in A.D. 358. But, as remarked to the authors by Professor Toynbee, this seems a definite instance of the re-use of earlier decorative sculptures in the fourth century A.D. So far as one may judge from style and technique, the monuments in question would seem assignable to the later first or first half of the second centuries A.D.

Later first or early–mid second centuries A.D.

J. Disney jr., *Museum Disneianum* 61, pl. 29; *AZ* v (1847) 158; *GGA* 1849 444 f.; Marsden, *Cat. Disney Coll.* 84 no. 35; Michaelis, *Anc. Marbles* 257 no. 38; Chapman, *Handbook* (2nd ed.) 48.

97 Statuette of Asklepios (?) PLATE 33

Presented by Dr J. Disney. Acquired in Italy (?). Inv.: GR.1.1850.

P.H. 0·32 m. Medium-grained Proconnesian (?) marble. Head and right arm missing; the modern restorations of these members had already been removed before the statuette was inherited by Disney. Restored in marble are the rear part of the right foot and the drapery over the left elbow. Repaired at a break through the left leg, a little above the ankle, and the upper part of the containers for rolls set behind it. The surface of the top of the base appears to have been recut in the vicinity of the right foot. Surface slightly chipped and showing isolated black smudges.

The statuette shows a male figure standing with his weight on his left leg, his right foot being set somewhat backwards and to one side. He is dressed in a himation and wears sandals on his feet. As a support against his left ankle are set *scrinia* or book-containers. His left hand, where it emerges from the looped folds of the himation, has its thumb and first two fingers extended, its other two fingers bent, in a motif recalling that found on **58**. Iconographic parallels suggest that this figure also is to be identified as a votive statuette representing Asklepios. Certainly the recut area beside the right foot seems best to be interpreted as concealing the point of attachment of the snake-entwined staff of the god.

Closest to the Cambridge statuette seems a figure of Asklepios in Rome: W. Amelung, *Kat. vaticanischen Museums* I 777 f. no. 684, pl. 84. It is doubtful, however, whether the Cambridge Asklepios may be called a strict copy of the same type. Its artist seems to have been confused by the drapery over the left hand and has vastly simplified the folds below, giving a falsely early effect. One may also note resemblances to other similar representations of the same god which show, however, a different treatment of the left arm, e.g. Naples, Museo Nazionale 8645, Venice, Museo Archeologico MA 82 (*EA* 2531). The Asklepios in Venice is also of interest as affording a further statuette of the god with a similar book-container-support against the left ankle. As has been seen, the Cambridge figure does not seem to be a true copy but a classicizing work of Imperial times. The style and quality of the carving and the form of the profiled base both appear to suggest a date in the second century A.D.

C. second century A.D.

J. Disney jr., *Museum Disneianum* 51, pl. 25; *AZ* v (1847) 158; *GGA* 1849 447; Marsden, *Cat. Disney Coll.* 86 no. 50; Michaelis, *Anc. Marbles* 255 no. 32; Chapman, *Handbook* (2nd ed.) 52.

98 Torso of a statue of Dionysos (?)

PLATE 33

Presented by the Cyprus Exploration Fund. Found at Salamis in Cyprus in an area that subsequent exploration has shown to have been occupied by a second-century-A.D. gymnasion-complex. Inv.: GR.2.1891.

P.H. (as mounted) 1·04 m. Moderately coarse-grained white island marble (Parian or Naxian ?). Head broken away at the neck, right arm at the shoulder, right leg from mid thigh, left from just below hip. Also lost are the left wrist and hand which were worked in a separate piece of marble and attached with a dowel of 0·019 m. diameter. (The left hand of this statue and the lower part of the right leg with the tree-support against it, as described in JHS XII (1891) 131, failed, for reasons unknown, ever to reach Cambridge.) There also appears to have been deliberate ancient damage, the genitals having been hacked away with the point. Modern repairs at left arm and back. An ancient iron pin at the edge of the lock of hair to the right of the neck may have played some role in an ancient repair. The statue has been tolerably finished at the back apart from behind the shoulders, around the rear part of the main mass of hair and over the back surface of the chlamys. At these points a rough preliminary dressing with the gouge has sufficed. The surface has been corroded by weather and shows stains and root marks.

The statue is over life-size. It represents a young male figure standing with his weight on his right leg, the left having been apparently bent. The very top of a support is preserved against the outer side of his right thigh. The now lost fragment going below showed this to have taken the form of a tree-stump (see above). His head was turned to the left. Curling locks of hair hang down on to his chest from either side of the neck, whilst at the back the main hair-mass appears to have been gathered into a great knot at the nape of the neck. This hair-style could hardly be appropriate to any others save the gods, Dionysos and Apollo. That Dionysos is the likelier possibility is revealed by other details. Against the god's right buttock there survive traces of a strut with its front surface showing indentations apparently in the form of claws. One may only surmise that the god may have been trailing an animal skin from his right arm or may possibly have been flanked by a panther. He wears a chlamys, fastened with a clasp, hanging over his left shoulder and looped over his left arm, which is bent forward at the elbow.

Statues of essentially this type were used extensively in Roman times as a vehicle for Imperial portraits; cf. W. Amelung, *Kat. vaticanischen Museums* I 742 no. 637, pl. 79. Especially close to the Cambridge torso are portrait-statues of Hadrian and Antoninus Pius; see O. Deubner, *Das Asklepieion von Pergamon* 43 fig. 32, J. Sautel, *Vaison la romaine* 104 f., with text-figs., *Ragguaglio delle Arti* I (1954–8) 74. The origins of this body-type have been sought in a fifth-century-B.C. figure of Diomedes and the fourth-century Hermes Farnese.[1] The bodies actually used for fourth-century-B.C. portrait-statues may equally have been a source of inspiration, e.g. *FD* IV pl. 68. However that may be, the type was considerably modified at Roman hands and acquired a distinctly Roman flavour especially noticeable in the treatment of the folds of the chlamys. The Cambridge statue is unusual in showing a hairstyle appropriate to a deity such as the young Dionysos. It is possible that a young

[1] G. Lippold, *Kopien und Umbildungen griechischer Statuen* 180 f., 184 f. The related statuettes of Hermes (see below) favour the Hermes Farnese as a source of inspiration.

Imperial personage may have been portrayed in the guise of the god (cf. **109**), although the poor finish of the hair-knot at the back speaks somewhat against the statue's having carried a portrait head. Statuettes of exactly the same type in Istanbul, used to represent Hermes, show, however, that this Romanized kind of figure was still able to be employed for ideal representations of divinity; see G. Mendel, *Cat. Constantinople* II 78 f. no. 316, 112 f. no. 375.[1] To judge from the related portrait-statues, the most likely date for the Cambridge figure would seem to fall in the second–third quarters of the second century A.D.—a conclusion that accords well with the context where it was found.

C. second–third quarters of the second century A.D.

JHS XII (1891) 131 no. 12; Chapman, *Handbook* (2nd ed.) 61; W. Amelung, *Kat. vaticanischen Museums* II 135 under no. 53; *Archaeology* VIII (1955) 13; *AJA* LXIII (1959) 143 no. 22.

99 Eros—support-figure from a statuette of Aphrodite

PLATE 33

Transferred from the old University Library. Presented to the University by Professor E. D. Clarke. From Egypt. Inv.: GR.5.1865.

P.H. 0·399 m. Moderately coarse-grained white marble (perhaps Proconnesian ?). The entire figure of Aphrodite is missing, as also the top part of the drapery to Eros' right in the area where it may originally have made contact with the goddess's left hand. Also broken away are the left forearm and hand of Eros, the neck of the alabastron that they were holding, and the edge of the plinth on all sides save for the part under Eros' feet. Eros' left arm has been drilled to take a modern restoration which has subsequently been removed. Surface somewhat worn and corroded by weather.

Behind Eros there is faintly indicated what may be a knotty tree-stump, but this may serve as no more than a filling element, as the drapery seems not so much supported by it as held from above, perhaps in the left hand of the adjacent figure of the goddess. If this interpretation is correct, then, like the Knidian Aphrodite, she may have been represented in the act of laying aside her clothing in readiness for her bath, although it is to be observed that drapery of a similar kind sometimes serves as a support for statuettes of the Egyptian anadyomene-type discussed under **85** and **86** above; cf. *AA* 1903 109 fig. 3. However the matter may be, the little Eros on the Cambridge support is shown gazing up at his mother in rapt admiration and holding a bottle of perfume in readiness for her *toilette*, as he prepares to shoulder the tumbled garments. He shows the chubby, babyish forms met with from Hellenistic times on. Nevertheless, it is doubtful if he is closely copied from an earlier work. The little god's nearest kin seem rather to be found on sarcophagus-reliefs of the second century A.D. The drapery folds likewise fail to carry conviction as being of earlier inspiration and probably the whole support is simply a classicizing creation of Imperial times, although the missing figure of Aphrodite may have conformed to an earlier type.

C. second century A.D. (?).

Clarke, *Marbles* 54 no. 34; Idem, *Travels* 4° III (=II. 2) 47, 8° V 70 f.; Michaelis, *Anc. Marbles* 246 no. 5; Chapman, *Handbook* (2nd ed.) 45.

100 Head of Artemis, from a statue

PLATE 33

Presented by Dr J. Disney. Provenance uncertain.[2] Inv.: GR.30.1850.

P.H. c. 0·243 m. Medium-grained Parian (?) marble. Broken away at the base of the neck. Restored in Italian marble are the tip of the nose and the crown of the head, the latter restoration failing to supply the top of the large folded mass of hair at the back of the head. The ancient, flat, dressed surface at the top of the head shows that the upper part was also originally either carved from a separate piece of marble or else modelled in stucco. Parts of the left side of the face and of the left eye have been restored in tinted plaster. Chips are missing from the hair, stephane and top end of the bow. The bow itself has a hollowed rectangular socket in its underside to provide for its continuance in a separate piece of marble. Traces of adhering plaster on the right side of the head, but these are not in situ *and may be from an extraneous source.*

The fragment preserves the head of a goddess, turned somewhat to her left. She wears a stephane in her hair and has her long locks parted in the middle over her brow and carried backwards across the top of her ears, apparently to be looped up against the back of her head. A wisp of hair is shown hanging down in front of her right ear and there may originally also have been a corresponding curl before her

[1] Cf. also bronze statuettes such as D. K. Hill, *Catalogue of Classical Bronze Sculpture in the Walters Art Gallery* 17 f. no. 28, pl. 8.

[2] The suggestion of von Bothmer and Vermeule that this head may be of Egyptian origin derives support of a kind from Disney's proposal (*MS Cat.* 56) to equate it with a memorandum dated to February 1753; '*La testa di Cleopatra, opera greca, in grande, il naso moderno.*'

left ear, where the surface is now badly damaged. The upturned pupils of the eyes are rendered as a slight hollow just under the lids and the irises are outlined. On the left side the upper edge of the drapery is preserved against the bottom of the neck. Towards the back part of the right side of the neck there appears to be represented the end of a long horn, pressed against the lower edge of the hair and continuing obliquely down behind the body. In view of the way that this is carried across the back it seems almost inescapable that it represents the tip of a composite bow. This attribute identifies the goddess shown as Artemis. The workmanship is somewhat superficial and the hair is rather perfunctorily finished.

One may broadly compare the Artemis-type, *EA* 2014, 2742, M. Wyndham, *Cat. Antiquities in the Possession of Lord Leconfield* 82, pl. 52, although the Cambridge head seems neither a copy nor a variant of this type. It is, in fact, very much closer to an unmistakably Roman creation: H. Stuart Jones, *Cat. Museo Capitolino* 328 no. 24, pl. 82. Once again there are differences, of which the most notable is in the presence of the bow, and the individual cast of the face might faintly reflect the likeness of an Antonine empress; cf. the Faustina, **116** below. In *AJA* LXIII (1959) 142, Dr von Bothmer and Dr Vermeule have advanced the suggestion that the Cambridge head may be of Egyptian provenance—an attractive hypothesis on technical grounds, although it is to be noted that the closest parallels for the type itself do not seem to be of Egyptian origin.

C. mid–late second century A.D.

J. Disney sr., *Cat. Hyde* 3 no. 17; J. Disney jr., *MS Cat.* 56; Marsden, *Cat. Disney Coll.* 84 no. 16; Michaelis, *Anc. Marbles* 260 no. 61; Chapman, *Handbook* (2nd ed.) 52; *AJA* LXIII (1959) 142.

101 Statuette of Fortuna (?), restored with non-joining ancient head PLATE 34

Presented by Dr J. Disney. Found in 1825 near Tivoli in the so-called Villa of Quintilius Varus. Restored in Rome under the supervision of Vescovalli. Inv.: GR.5.1850.

a Head of a goddess

P.H. c. 0·129 m. Luna marble with a brownish incrustation. Nose restored in marble. An original stephane has been harshly recut to the shape of a crown; its ancient surface survives at only two points towards the top, which reveal that its outer surface sloped back much more markedly. It was also much less shallow behind, as shown by the recut hair of the top of the head. At the back the originally free-standing head has been adapted to fit the modern restorer's veil. The surface of the flesh has been cleaned.

The goddess wore a stephane. Her hair is parted in the middle and carried round towards the back of the head. Curling wisps of hair hang down in front of each ear. As the left cheek is somewhat deeper than the right, the head may originally have been intended to be seen turned somewhat to the right. The upturned pupils of the goddess's eyes are indicated by shallow hollows under the eyelids. Her mouth is rendered in the same fashion as that of **102**, with deep drillings in the corners and a subtle cutting suggestive of the tongue pressed against the upper teeth in speech. A faint Venus-ring on the neck seems to have been obliterated by the modern restorer.

Probably copied from the same type are the heads of *EA* 1505, G. Lippold, *Kat. vaticanischen Museums* III. 1. 103 f. no. 535, pl. 10. But these heads, too, do not belong to the bodies on which they are now mounted and the appearance of the original figure remains uncertain. The heads themselves appear to be classicizing Roman work.

C. second century A.D.

b Statuette of Fortuna (?)

*H. as restored (without plinth) 0·647 m. Luna (?) marble with a golden-brown patina and with brown incrustation on the back. Restored in marble are the middle part of the neck, the veil over the back of the head, the right arm from above the elbow, including the adjacent edge of the chiton, the left hand and wrist with the adjoining part of the himation, the whole of the sceptre, the left foot with the adjacent hem of the chiton, and small parts of the himation at the right edge, between the legs and to the left of the left knee; also the four legs of the stool and the rear left corner of its top. The ancient head (***a*** *above) does not belong. The statuette is set in a rectangular modern plinth. Minor parts of the drapery are restored in plaster. An ancient dowel-hole in the left upper arm indicates the position of a second point of support for the attribute originally held in the left hand.*

A female figure is shown seated upon a cushion on a simple, backless throne and with her feet resting on a footstool set at a slightly oblique angle in relation to the front of the throne. She is dressed in a chiton and a himation and has sandals on her feet. The chiton is girdled high under her breasts and buttoned along her upper arm to form a sleeve. The himation is worn draped across her lap and carried up behind over the back of her head where it serves as a veil.

A statuette of Fortuna in the Vatican seems identical in all respects with the Cambridge figure and is of the same scale; see W. Amelung, *Kat. vaticanischen Museums* I 880 f. no. 215, pl. 113. It holds a cornucopia in the left arm in a position that accords well with the evidence of the dowel-hole on the Cambridge example, which, in any case, has this arm in the wrong position for grasping the full-length sceptre of Demeter, in whose likeness it has been restored. This identification as Fortuna seems strengthened by further examples of the same type, e.g. Amelung, *ibid.* no. 216, pl. 113, G. Kaschnitz-Weinberg, *Sculture del Magazzino del Museo Vaticano* 63 f. no. 115, pl. 28, and the altar relief, O. Benndorf and R. Schöne, *Die antiken Bildwerke des lateranischen Museums* 134 f. no. 216; but similar figures, although without veils, also appear on gems as representing Demeter and a modified variant of the type in Rome is employed for Terra Mater; cf. G. M. A. Richter, *Cat. Engraved Gems, Metropolitan Museum* 352 nos. 347 f., pl. 45, H. Stuart Jones, *Cat. Palazzo dei Conservatori* 127 f. no. 1, pl. 45. Indeed Arndt has proposed associating this manifestly later type with a fifth-century-B.C. image, apparently of Demeter, although no clear chain of evidence of the kind observed under **45–46** above seems to link the two varieties.[1] The present type is also met with in many related variant forms and is, in addition, adapted as a vehicle for female portrait-heads.[2] Whatever its remoter origins, it clearly filled an important place in the repertoire of classicizing sculptors of Imperial times.

C. first–second centuries A.D.

J. Disney jr., *Museum Disneianum* 63 f., pl. 30; *AZ* v (1847) 158; *GGA* 1849 447 f., 450 f.; Marsden, *Cat. Disney Coll.* 83 no. 4; Michaelis, *Anc. Marbles* 256 no. 36; S. Reinach, *Répertoire de la statuaire* II 245. 5; Chapman, *Handbook* (2nd ed.) 47; P. Arndt, *La Glyptothèque Ny-Carlsberg* 109; *AJA* LXIII (1959) 142.

102 Head of Aphrodite (?) PLATE 35

Transferred from the Museum of Archaeology and Ethnology. Formerly Beldam Collection. Inv.: GR.38.1952.

P.H. c. 0·135 m. Pentelic (?) marble. Broken away at the neck; tip of nose and hair-knot at back of head also broken off. Chipped at various points, including chin and right brow. Recut behind neck and at lower part of back of head. A small recut area towards the back of the head might possibly also conceal the junction of a strut to a raised left hand. The surface has been cleaned.

The goddess wears a diadem in her hair which is parted in the middle and carried back across the top of the ears to a knot at the back of the head, now broken away. A single coiled lock hangs down from behind each ear. There is no certain evidence that the pupils of the eyes were indicated plastically. The mouth, however, is rendered in the same way as that of **101 a**, the corners being deeply drilled and the tongue being shown pressed against the upper teeth as if in speech. The cheeks are full and a deep Venus-ring is to be seen on the neck.

On typological grounds it would seem most likely that the head is from a figure of Aphrodite, perhaps of the *anadyomene*-type; cf. E. Paribeni, *Cat. Sculture di Cirene* 105 no. 287, 108 nos. 290 f., pls. 137, 142, *5000 ans d'art égyptien* (*Exhibition, Brussels, March–June, 1960*) 32 no. 87, fig. 52, etc. Its date is presumably much the same as that of **101 a.**

C. second century A.D.

103 Head of a god PLATE 34

Presented by Dr J. Disney. Acquired for the collection at the Hyde by exchange in 1761. Inv.: GR.16.1850.

Restored H. 0·47 m. P.H. c. 0·345 m. Pentelic marble. Restored in Italian marble are the greater part of the herm, the back of the head, the tip of the nose, much of the lock of hair hanging down behind the left ear and part of that looped over the head-band above the left eye. The surface of the flesh has been cleaned. Small fragments are missing from the ears, hair, moustache and end of the beard. Minor restorations of the right ear and hair in plaster.

It is extremely doubtful if there is any justification at all for the modern mounting of this head as a herm. The ancient part appears to preserve a curving original vertical surface at the bottom of the back of the neck and extending out towards the shoulders. At

[1] P. Arndt, *La Glyptothèque Ny-Carlsberg* 108 f., pl. 68. This has been related to *EA* 472, H. Stuart Jones, *Cat. Palazzo dei Conservatori* 16 f. no. 5, pl. 6. The identification of the goddess has been based on coin-types such as *BMC Coins of the Roman Empire* I pl. 36. 4, III pl. 64. 11. However, figures of this type are more commonly met with on Imperial coins as representing Fortuna or Concordia.

[2] E.g. the unveiled related Demeter- or Fortuna-type, commonly met with, such as O. Waldhauer, *Die antiken Skulpturen der Ermitage* III 52 no. 296, fig. 45; the related veiled Fortuna-type with a different arrangement of the himation over the knees, e.g. *EA* 1412; the related portrait-type, such as H. Stuart Jones, *Cat. Museo Capitolino* 131 f. no. 56, pl. 22; and the rather similar Fortuna figures which do, however, advance the other foot like the Cybele-type considered under **45** and **46**: *EA* 400, 3668, G. Kaschnitz-Weinberg, *Sculture del Magazzino del Museo Vaticano* 64 no. 116, pl. 29. In origin, the figures under consideration may be in some way related to this Cybele-type. Certainly, because of their close similarity, the two varieties are commonly found blended together, e.g. G. Mendel, *Cat. Constantinople* II 74 no. 311.

both sides this ancient member has been cut off short to fit the modern herm, but it seems definitely to suggest that the head was originally either mounted as a bust or inset in a statue. That it is probably from a statue seems to be established by the circumstance that the head was obviously intended to be seen from its right side. This is shown by the deep drill-work in the beard on that side and in front, as compared with the shallow and cursory cutting to the left, and by the way that the right cheek is much deeper than the left and that the hair-parting over the brow is set somewhat to the right of centre. Probably the whole figure was set at an angle to the viewer, since the head seems to have been turned only very slightly to the left in relation to the axis of the body. The right shoulder was raised, the left lowered. The god's long hair is combed outwards so that it radiates in undulating waves from a point at the crown of the head. It is held in place with a heavy head-band of round section. Over the brow the hair is parted slightly to the right of centre and, after being looped twice round the head-band as a double lock to either side, it hangs down as two heavily undercut spiral curls in front of each ear. Behind the ears two further tresses, one on each side, descend on to the chest. The rest of the hair was carried backwards to some massive knot or loop at the back of the head, of which the weak modern restoration gives a very imperfect idea. The features are rendered in a distinctly individual style. Characteristic are the deep undercutting of the brows, the shallow, broad eyes of an almost archaic appearance, the delicate nostrils and the full, sensuous lips.

The Cambridge head seems completely pervaded by the spirit of the fifth century B.C. and yet to stand strangely apart from the actual works of that period. The way that the god wears his hair looped up over the head-band may, it is true, be compared with mid-fifth-century-B.C. heads such as L. Curtius, *Zeus und Hermes* 58 f., type C, and an Asklepios-type known from gems, e.g. G. M. A. Richter, *Cat. Engraved Gems, Metropolitan Museum* 80 no. 343, pl. 45. But the widely spaced loops terminating in spiral curls seem quite outside the range even of the formalizations of the end of the archaic period although completely in character with Roman creations in a classical style. Although a sculpture of about the second quarter or middle of the fifth century B.C. may have served as the inspiration for the Cambridge head, the very eclectic nature of the work argues that it is a free classicizing creation of Imperial date rather than a true copy. The extensive use of the running-drill in the beard favours a date in the mid–late second century A.D. for its execution. As the body in which the head was inserted was probably, for technical reasons, draped, an identification as Dionysos would seem the most likely, although no certainty is possible. Interestingly comparable in material, character and scale is a seated draped Apollo in the Vatican with a similarly inserted head and which seems similarly ill at ease with the style that it affects; see W. Amelung, *Kat. vaticanischen Museums* II 592 f. no. 395, pl. 51.

C. mid–late second century A.D.

J. Disney sr., *Cat. Hyde* 9 no. 48; J. Disney jr., *Museum Disneianum* 17, pl. 9; *AZ* V (1847) 157; *GGA* 1849 441; Marsden, *Cat. Disney Coll.* 84 no. 32; Michaelis, *Anc. Marbles* 258 no. 47; A. Furtwängler, *Über Statuenkopien im Altertum* 48 f. (= *Abh. bay Ak.* XX. 3. 572 f.), pl. 9; Chapman, *Handbook* (2nd ed.) 57; *AJA* LXIII (1959) 142.

104 Statuette of Sarapis standing

PLATE 35

Purchased. From Egypt. Inv.: E.87.1900.

P.H. 0·072 m. Mottled dark and light green stone (serpentine ?). Feet broken away at ankles, right hand above the wrist; attribute against side of right arm also broken off. The left arm and the modius are also missing; these were carved from separate pieces of stone and attached by dowels. Traces of gold leaf over surface.

The god wears a sleeved chiton and, over it, a himation which is looped over the left shoulder but leaves the right free. Around his hair is a heavy fillet. Hair and beard are rendered as masses of tight spiral curls. The head is rather large for the body and curiously broad-featured. The body, on the other hand, is over-shallow in depth. Chest and navel are rendered visibly through the drapery. The attribute broken away from the god's right arm was most probably a cornucopia. To judge from related representations, his missing left arm was raised and held a sceptre.

This version of the god, Sarapis, is somewhat remote from the type of **55–57**; it is, however, broadly related to a number of bronzes collated by Michaelis in *JHS* VI (1885) 298 f. The wide-featured, rather foreign-looking character of the face may be matched in other representations of the same god from Egypt, e.g. F. Poulsen, *Kat. over antike Skulpturer, Ny Carlsberg Glyptotek* 585 no. 869, *Billedtavler, Tillaeg* II pl. 15. It is not clear whether the coiled spiral curls are to be interpreted as an archaistic feature or a reflection of Antonine fashion. In any case, a date in about the second century A.D. may not be far from the truth.

C. second century A.D. (?).

105 Head of a bearded god (?) PLATE 35

Purchased. Provenance unknown. Inv.: GR.95*b*.1906.

P.H. 0·09 m. Fine-grained white marble (Pentelic ?). Broken away at base of neck. Tip of nose and end of beard chipped away.

The fragment preserves a somewhat crudely executed, bearded male head with large, deep-set eyes. The face is no longer young and shows sagging cheeks. The surface of the flesh has been partly polished, but the back part of the hair has been simply roughed out with the point. But, as there is no trace of attachment behind and as the back of the neck appears to have been worked in the round, it seems likely that the head is from a votive statuette rather than from a high relief. The treatment of the hair and beard still faintly recalls divine types created for deities such as Zeus and Asklepios in the fourth century B.C. The poor execution may be compared with provincial work such as L. Robert, *Hellenica* X (1955) 104, pl. 14.

C. second–third centuries A.D.

106 Head of the young god, Dionysos (?) PLATE 35

Presented by Dr J. Disney. Acquired in Italy (?); certainly Disney's claim that it had come originally from the Athenian Acropolis seems distinctly doubtful. Inv.: GR.17.1850.

P.H. of the ancient part c. 0·316 m. Moderately coarse-grained white island marble (Parian or Naxian ?). Mounted on a modern marble bust. Only the head and upper part of the neck are ancient. The large, looped knot of hair at the back of the head has been for the most part broken away, the surface at this point and in the vicinity of the lock of hair descending on to the left shoulder having been extensively recut in modern times. Surface of the marble weatherworn.

The head is turned slightly to the right and also inclined somewhat to the right in relation to the axis of the neck. Appropriate adjustments have been made in the planes of the face, which are by no means symmetrical. Over the lower part of the head and in front the god wears his hair parted in the middle over the brow and carried around across the top of the ears to what seems originally to have been a large looped knot at the back, from which a single long tress appears to have hung down on to each shoulder. A small wisp of hair curls forward in front of each ear. The hair is bound with a fillet worn low across the brow. At the crown of the head, however, the hair, now sadly corroded by weather, seems only to have been roughed out with the point, perhaps implying that this part of the head was not meant to be visible. Above the long hair rendered in detail at the front and sides there is a distinct hollow and it is possible that the head, which is probably from a statue, was intended to be seen decked with a garland. Heavy drill-work is visible on the mouth, nostrils, tear-ducts and ears; worm-like channels cut with the running-drill divide the hair at the sides of the head.

Although the present work bears a faint resemblance to certain Bacchic female head-types of the mid–late fourth century B.C.,[1] it almost certainly in fact belongs to the endlessly variable type of classicizing representation of the god, Dionysos, himself, recently studied by Schefold in *ÖJh* XXXIX (1952) 92 f. In the present case, the coarse drill-work on the hair would seem to preclude a date before the second half of the second century A.D. The harsh and angular modelling of the face may possibly suggest a later date still.

Second half of the second–third centuries A.D.

J. Disney sr., *Cat. Hyde* 7 no. 27; J. Disney jr., *Museum Disneianum* 19, pl. 10; *AZ* V (1847) 157; *GGA* 1849 446; Marsden, *Cat. Disney Coll.* 83 no. 8; Michaelis, *Anc. Marbles* 258 no. 48; Chapman, *Handbook* (2nd ed.) 57.

107 Support in the form of a herm of the young Dionysos PLATE 35

Transferred from the old University Library. Presented to the University by Professor E. D. Clarke. From the vicinity of the Erechtheion on the Athenian Acropolis. Inv.: GR.8.1865.

P.H. 0·446 m. Thessalian verde antico. *The lower part of the herm and the bottom of the support behind it broken away, the latter being partly restored in plaster to provide a standing surface. Repaired at a break under the capital at the level of the top of the head of the herm. Surface badly pitted and chipped, notably at the nose, hair and brows of the herm. In the top of the capital is a circular socket for attachment, 0·048 m. in diameter and 0·019 m. deep.*

A herm of the young Dionysos is shown frontally in high relief against the approximately rectangular shaft of a support intended to serve, e.g., as a furniture-leg. The herm is treated in a classicizing style and has a garland of ivy leaves about the head and a fillet

[1] E.g. *EA* 2119–20 and the head from the south slope of the Acropolis and its copies, Brunn-Bruckmann 174*a*, C. Blümel, *Kat. Berlin* V no. K 251, pls. 71–2, etc.

across the brow. The wavy hair is parted in the middle and apparently carried round to a knot at the back of the head whence heavy locks descend from behind the ears on to the chest and others hang down the back. The herm has sockets to receive the rectangular projecting slabs at its shoulders. A pentagonal capital is set above, somewhat forward of the shaft of the support and back from the brow of the herm, so that its weight is shared by both. Its front surface is decorated with bead-and-reel ornament and with a symmetrical scroll pattern, possibly representing taeniae.

A head of the young Dionysos of a closely similar type occurs on a herm in Rome; see H. Stuart Jones, *Cat. Palazzo dei Conservatori* 248 no. 97, pl. 97. The soft forms, imprecise cutting and neglect of right angles shown by the Cambridge support are in part due to the difficult material in which it is worked, but are probably also indications of late date.

C. third century A.D. (*?*).

Clarke, *Marbles* 39 f. no. 17; Idem, *Travels* 4° III (=II. 2) 496, 8° VI 240 f.; S. H. Spiker, *Reise durch England* II 295; Michaelis, *Anc. Marbles* 247 no. 8; Chapman, *Handbook* (2nd ed.) 53.

(B) ROMAN PORTRAITS

108 Head of the Emperor Domitian

PLATE 36

Presented by Dr J. Disney. Presumably acquired in Italy. Inv.: GR. 14. 1850.

P.H. c. 0·309 m. Medium-grained greyish-white Proconnesian (?) marble. Broken away at the base of the neck, the surface being trimmed in modern times to fit an armour-clad bust to which the portrait did not belong and from which it has now been removed. This bust was ancient, but had been so extensively recut in modern times that no traces of the original surface survived anywhere save at the back. Greater part of nose broken away, the surface at the break being dressed to take a marble restoration that has since been removed. Chipped, more especially at the back of the head and at the edges of the ears. Surface harshly cleaned in modern times.

The head is turned very slightly towards the left. The hair radiates from a point high up at the back of the head whence it is combed and trimmed in such a way as to give the impression of a series of waves of small, lightly curling locks. For the outermost of these over the brow the strands of hair are rather longer and crimped up in the middle into a kind of formal garland of curls stretching from ear to ear. The outermost of these hang down in front of the ears and curve slightly forward at the ends. The corners of the mouth are lightly drilled.

Titus Flavius Domitianus lived from A.D. 51 till 96 and was Emperor from A.D. 81 to 96. On his portraits see J. J. Bernoulli, *Römische Ikonographie* II. 2. 52 f.; R. West, *Römische Porträtplastik* II 18 f.; Matz in *RM* LIV (1939) 145 f.; Götze in *MdI* I (1948) 141 f.; B. M. Felletti Maj, *Cat. Museo Nazionale Romano, i ritratti* 83 f. under nos. 149 f. Despite its harsh cleaning, the present head seems an unmistakable portrait of the Emperor in his later years. The treatment of the waves of curls over the back part of the head is distinctly unusual, but otherwise this piece may be closely compared with portraits of the Emperor such as that at Naples, Bernoulli, *op. cit.* pl. 18, A. Hekler, *Greek and Roman Portraits* pl. 196*b*. The Emperor is shown wearing the crescent of crimped curls ove rthe brow, as regularly from about A.D. 84, on Matz's analysis of the coin-portraits.

C. mid 80's–mid 90's A.D.

Memoirs of Thos. Hollis, Esq. 820; J. Disney sr., *Cat. Hyde* 7 no. 28; J. Disney jr., *Museum Disneianum* 13, pl. 7; Marsden, *Cat. Disney Coll.* 84 no. 19; Michaelis, *Anc. Marbles* 257 no. 45; Chapman, *Handbook* (2nd ed.) 44; J. J. Bernoulli, *Römische Ikonographie* II. 2. 11.

109 Colossal head of Antinous

PLATE 36

Bequeathed by C. S. Ricketts and C. H. Shannon. Found in 1769 in Hadrian's villa at Tivoli, it subsequently formed part of the collection at Lansdowne House. Inv.: GR. 100. 1937.

P.H. of ancient part c. 0·41 m. Luna marble. Only the head and neck are ancient. Restored in marble are the bust, the nose, parts of the lips and chin, part of the curl against the right cheek, two of the clusters of berries on the ivy garland and parts of several of the ivy leaves, four of them entirely. Repaired at the other two clusters of ivy berries and at the curls against the left cheek. A few very minor restorations have also been made in plaster. The surface has been badly worn by weather and there are rust stains from some of the iron pins holding the restorations.

The young favourite is represented in the guise of the youthful Dionysos. Across his brow he wears a fillet or 'mitra'. At the sides this is concealed by the rich hair, of which the topmost locks are gathered into a small knot at the crown of the head. The main mass of the hair is carried round to the back of the neck where it is coiled into a loop and bound with the fillet, which hangs down to either side of it. Above, a garland of ivy is worn in the hair. The head is bent forward and turned slightly to the left and the youth's gaze is directed downwards. Indeed, the face seems to have been intended to be seen somewhat from below and this, no less than the large scale, favours the view that the head was originally set not on a bust but on a colossal statue. The obliquity of the neck may possibly suggest that the left shoulder was a little higher than the right. The pupils of the eyes are not indicated plastically. The eyebrows are bold and heavy and rendered as a series of parallel transverse striations as on the head of Aelius Verus, **110** below. The hair and the ivy garland are boldly undercut, the hair showing signs of the extensive use of the running-drill and of a succession of small gouges. The clusters of ivy berries are made to stand out by virtue of being undermined by a network of small drillings.

Antinous, the young favourite of the Emperor Hadrian, lived from A.D. 110 to 130. On his portraits see *MA* XXIX (1923) 161 f.; A. Holm, *Das Bildnis des Antinous* passim; R. West, *Römische Porträtplastik* II 128 f.; *ÖJh* XLI (1954) 62 f. The deep cutting of the hair and the angle of the head of the Cambridge example suggest the Antinous Braschi in the Vatican (West, *op. cit.* pls. 35, 38), but the flat massing of the hair over the brow also recalls the Antinous Mondragone in the Louvre (*ibid.* pl. 38). The execution of such a deified portrait is most likely to fall in the later years of Hadrian's reign, between A.D. 130 and 138, although a somewhat later date is by no means excluded.

Probably second quarter of the second century A.D.

Mentioned in letters of 16 July and 6 August 1772, from Gavin Hamilton to the Earl of Shelburne, later first Marquess of Shelburne; Michaelis, *Anc. Marbles* 453 no. 64; A. H. Smith, *Cat. Ancient Marbles at Lansdowne House* 29 no. 64; H. Winnefeld, *Die Villa des Hadrien* (*JdI Erg* III) 159; *MA* XXIX (1923) 192 no. 80; F. Poulsen, *Greek and Roman Portraits in English Country Houses* 78 no. 63 and pl. facing; *Cat. Christie* 5 March 1930, 16 no. 18, 81; R. West, *Römische Porträtplastik* II 136 no. 2, pl. 38.

110 Head of Aelius Verus, from a relief

PLATES 36–37

Presented by Dr J. Disney. Probably acquired in Italy, but, if so, the head seems likely to have been brought there from further afield. Inv.: GR.32.1850.

H. c. 0·39 m., H. of head c. 0·32 m. Medium-grained white island marble (Parian ?). The unit of head and neck, carved separately for attachment to a relief, is preserved almost entire. Broken away are the tip of the nose, whose modern restoration has long since been removed, and the lower left edge of the neck. The base of the neck has been shaped for insertion in a socket. The back of the head has been dressed perfectly flat, with anathyrosis and sockets for horizontal metal pins to attach it to the relief-ground behind. Surface chipped and worn by weather, especially on top of the head. Pupils of eyes retouched in modern times. Faint traces of red pigment in the hollows of the beard.

The head was shown turned at a three-quarter angle towards its left. It was also inclined distinctly forwards and outwards towards the spectator, the depth of relief being markedly greater at the top of the head than at the neck. It thus seems clear that it was intended to be viewed from below and, assuming that the relief-ground was vertical, was probably placed in some kind of high architectural setting. The hair and beard are rendered as a mass of short, curling locks. Over the front and right side of the head the running-drill has been freely used to separate these curls, but only to a shallow depth and with negligible undercutting. Elsewhere the point and chisel seem to have sufficed. The eyes are shaded by heavy eyebrows indicated by transverse striations. The pupils may not originally have been shown plastically at all. The moustache covers the corners of the mouth in a somewhat unfortunate fashion.

Aelius Verus lived from A.D. 86 to 138; he was adopted by the Emperor, Hadrian, as his successor in A.D. 137, but died before the Emperor in the following year. According to Spartianus, at his death monuments were decreed to him throughout the Empire. His likeness is securely identified by coin-types; on his marble portraits see Bernoulli, *op. cit.* II. 2. 134 f., West, *op. cit.* II 141 f. (the latter work being somewhat undiscriminating). The Cambridge head may be closely compared with the statue and bust in the Louvre: Bernoulli, *op. cit.* pl. 43, West, *op. cit.* pl. 42, fig. 159. To judge from its style and execution it was probably produced somewhere in Greece or the eastern provinces of the Roman Empire. The technique of working the head separately for attachment to a relief recurs on portraits of Domitian from Pergamon and Antoninus Pius from the Roman Forum: F. Winter, *Altertümer von Pergamon* VII. 2. 231 no. 280, Beiblatt 30, M. Wegner, *Das römische Herrscherbild* II. 4, *Die Herrscherbildnisse in antoninischer Zeit* 140, pl. 6*c–d*. Its purpose in the present case is uncertain. One possibility is that the head of Aelius Verus was a replacement inserted on an earlier relief 'adapted' as a memorial to him. But, without excluding the possibility that the head was set on a historical relief, its great depth at the top and extreme shallowness at the bottom would seem rather to suggest that it was specially carved for insertion on a bust cut in shallow relief against a medallion-like ground.[1]

C. second quarter of the second century A.D.

J. Disney sr., *Cat. Hyde* 8 no. 38; J. Disney jr., *MS Cat.* 52; Marsden, *Cat. Disney Coll.* 84 no. 27; Michaelis, *Anc. Marbles* 260 no. 63; Chapman, *Handbook* (2nd ed.) 44; Bernoulli, *Römische Ikonographie* II. 2. 139, 216 (confused with another head?); *AJA* LXIII (1959) 142.

111 Head of a Roman PLATE 38

Presented by Dr J. Disney. Reputed to have been found in 1824 at a farm about three miles from the Porta Maggiore, Rome; bought by Disney in Rome in 1827. Inv.: GR.34.1850.

P.H. of ancient part 0·26 m. Luna (?) marble. Only head and upper part of neck ancient. Restored in marble are the bust, the nose and most of the lips, moustache and bearded chin. Eyebrows chipped and lower edge of right eye damaged. Cleaned at some parts of the face and neck and some of the hair over the brow.

The head is turned slightly towards the right. The rich, curling hair is combed down over the brow, where traces of seven control-drillings are still visible marking the divisions between the main curls. Over the back of the head the hair is rendered as a mass of small, tightly coiled curls. The irises of the eyes are outlined and the pupils indicated by an oblique, semi-circular drilling. The poor preservation has clearly robbed the head of much of its character. The treatment of the hair over the brow suggests a date in Hadrianic times. Also, although the tightly coiled curls at the back of the head may look forward towards a style of Antonine times, they can as well be paralleled in late portraits of the Emperor Hadrian himself, e.g. M. Wegner, *Das römische Herrscherbild* II. 3. pl. 9*d*. The identity of the man portrayed is unknown.

It seems likely that there has been confusion on the part of Michaelis and his successors between this head and a further, apparently non-existent portrait, Michaelis, *Anc. Marbles* 260 no. 65, Chapman, *Handbook* (2nd ed.) 40. Although Michaelis claims to have been unable to find the present head in Cambridge, it has in fact been in the Museum since 1850, whereas there appears never to have been any additional portrait answering to the description of Michaelis no. 65.

C. second quarter of the second century A.D.

J. Disney jr., *Museum Disneianum* 35, pl. 18; *AZ* V (1847) 158; *GGA* 1849 445; Michaelis, *Anc. Marbles* 267, 333; *AJA* LXIII (1959) 142 (where apparently confused with **205**, Michaelis, *op. cit.* 259 no. 57). (Possibly also to be equated with Marsden, *Cat. Disney Coll.* 84 no. 30; Michaelis, *op. cit.* 260 no. 65; Chapman, *Handbook* (2nd ed.) 40.)

112 Head of the Emperor Antoninus Pius (?) PLATE 38

Bequeathed by C. B. Marlay. Provenance unknown. Inv.: GR.8.1912.

P.H. 0·36 m. Luna marble, the surface badly worn and covered with a brown patina. Broken away at the neck, where the under-surface has been trimmed in modern times, presumably to fit a bust. Minor chips missing from hair, beard and left ear.

The head appears to have been turned slightly to the left. The running-drill has been very extensively and skilfully used in both the hair and the beard. The upturned pupils of the eyes are indicated with shallow lunate drillings. This is not one of the most typical of likenesses of Antoninus Pius, but it does seem possible that a portrait of that Emperor may, in fact, have been intended.

Publius Aurelius Antoninus lived from A.D. 86 to 161 and was Emperor from A.D. 138 till 161. His marble portraits are discussed in the following: Bernoulli, *op. cit.* II. 2. 139 f.; M. Wegner, *Das römische Herrscherbild* II. 4, *Die Herrscherbildnisse in antoninischer Zeit* 15 f., 125 f.; *Arti* II (1940) 340 f. The damaged hair over the brow of the Cambridge head appears broadly to have conformed with that of an official portrait-type that seems to have been mainly current in the earlier half of the Emperor's reign and which Wegner has named the Formia Type. The Cambridge portrait may, in fact, instructively be compared with the type-example, the head from Formia in the Museo Nazionale Romano: Wegner, *op. cit.* pl. 3, B. M. Felletti Maj, *Cat. Museo Nazionale Romano, i ritratti* 106 no. 203. The vigorous use of the drill in the beard and hair of the Cambridge example may argue against a date much earlier than the mid-second century A.D. and might possibly favour assigning it to a somewhat later period.

C. mid-second century A.D.*, or possibly later.*

AJA LXIII (1959) 143 no. 8.

[1] The authors are fortunate in having been able to have the views of Mrs I. Scott Ryberg on this head. She stresses its Greek appearance.

113 Pasticche formed with elements from three portraits of the second century A.D. PLATE 38

Presented by Dr J. Disney. Presumably acquired in Italy. Inv.: GR.9.1850.

a Upper part of the head of a man

P.H. c. 0·17 m. Medium-grained, white island marble (Parian ?). Missing below the level of the cheek-bones. Lower part of the head supplied with fragment, **b**. *The nose, the lower part of the ears and the hair immediately behind them restored in marble (see* **b**). *Brows restored in plaster and cement. Hair over brow much damaged. Surface of flesh cleaned; recut at top of cheeks and edge of nose. Chipped and weatherworn.*

The hair over the brow has suffered badly, but seems originally to have been in very high relief and carefully chiselled. The eyebrows must have overhung much more markedly than their present restoration would suggest. The eyes themselves show outlined irises and drilled pupils.

The way that the hair is worn low over the brow recalls portraits of the Emperor, Lucius Verus, although the actual detail of the hair does not seem to conform to any known portrait-type.

C. third quarter of the second century A.D. (?).

b Part of a head of the Emperor Antoninus Pius

P.H. c. 0·23 m. Luna marble, showing a yellowish-brown patina. Preserved from the level of the upper part of the cheeks to the base of the neck. Restored in marble are the nose, tip of the beard and the lower part of the ears together with the hair behind them, including an extensive area towards the back of the head on the left side. Traces of the original right ear and the hair at the left side of the back of the head filed away to receive these restorations more appropriate to **a**. *Restored in plaster and cement are parts of the cheeks, hair, etc. Top of head has been supplied by the fragment,* **a**; *mounted in the bust,* **c**, *the back of the neck having been recut to fit it and the drapery against the left side of the neck having been filed away at the back in order to approximate to the original part of the cloak surviving on* **c**.

Despite its sorry state, enough survives of this fragment to make it reasonably clear that it originally formed part of a tolerably careful portrait of the Emperor Antoninus Pius. On his portraits see under **112** above. The head was turned somewhat to the left. Against the left side of the neck there survive traces of drapery.

Second–earlier third quarters of the second century A.D.

c Male bust

P.H. of ancient part 0·38 m. Medium-grained Proconnesian marble with a brownish patina. Restored in marble are the drapery in front of and to the left of the left shoulder, the index plate and the base. The traces of a cloak on top of the left shoulder are original and the modern restoration in front is not fully consistent with these in that it also echoes the edge of the drapery preserved on the fragment, **b**, *mounted above.*

The bust probably carried a portrait-head of the second century A.D., but certainly not that now mounted on it.

C. second century A.D.

J. Disney sr., *Cat. Hyde* 4 no. 22; J. Disney jr., *Museum Disneianum* 3, pl. 2; Marsden, *Cat. Disney Coll.* 84 no. 21; Michaelis, *Anc. Marbles* 257 no. 40; Chapman, *Handbook* (2nd ed.) 47; J. J. Bernoulli, *Römische Ikonographie* II. 2. 145 no. 58; M. Wegner, *Das römische Herrscherbild* II. 4, *Die Herrscherbildnisse in antoninischer Zeit* 126.

114 Head of the Emperor Marcus Aurelius, mounted on an ancient bust of later date PLATE 38

Presented by Dr J. Disney. From Alexandria. Prior to its acquisition for the collection at the Hyde, in the Palazzo Barberini, Rome. Disney (*MS Cat.* 26) quotes a memorandum of 26 February 1753: *un busto di Marco Aurelio il quale era portato d'Alessandria undici anni fa.* Inv.: GR.10.1850.

a Head of the Emperor Marcus Aurelius

P.H. c. 0·345 m. Medium-grained Proconnesian marble. Only the head is preserved. Nose and middle part of the neck restored in marble. The hair is slightly worn and chipped.

The running-drill has been employed with restraint in articulating the curls over the front part of the head. At the back only the chisel has been used and the coiled locks present a simple and conservative appearance. The beard, likewise, shows traces only of chisel- and point-work. The irises have been outlined, the pupils and corners of the eyes drilled, the former in a heavy lunate form that only just stops short of being a complete circle, with highlights left above.

Marcus Aurelius Antoninus lived from A.D. 121 to 180 and reigned as Emperor from A.D. 161 till 180. On his portraits see Bernoulli, *op. cit.* II. 2. 162 f.; Wegner, *op. cit.* 33 f., 166 f. The present example follows a version probably current from about the beginning of the Emperor's reign and to which

Wegner has given the name, the Type of Terme 726. As might be expected from its provenance, it is closest to Greek examples of the type such as Wegner, *op. cit.* pl. 31.

Alexandrian work, probably still of the third quarter of the second century A.D.

b Toga-clad bust

P.H. of ancient part 0·485 m. Luna marble with isolated patches of brown patina. Restored in marble are the index tablet and base and much of the neck, above which is set the earlier head, **a** *above; small parts of the folds of the toga also restored in marble. Surface chipped.*

The bust appears to be careful Italian work. Probably the Alexandrian provenance applies only to the head, **a** above, which was not mounted until it had been brought to Rome. Busts of this type were extensively used with male portraits of the second and third quarters of the third century A.D.

Second–third quarters of the third century A.D.

Memoirs of Thos. Hollis, Esq. 835; J. Disney sr., *Cat. Hyde* 5 no. 45; J. Disney jr., *Museum Disneianum* 5, pl. 3; *AZ* v (1847) 157; *GGA* 1849 445; Marsden, *Cat. Disney Coll.* 84 no. 26; Michaelis, *Anc. Marbles* 257 no. 41; Chapman, *Handbook* (2nd ed.) 55; J. J. Bernoulli, *Römische Ikonographie* II. 2. 171 no. 66; M. Wegner, *Das römische Herrscherbild* II. 4, *Die Herrscherbildnisse in antoninischer Zeit* 171; *AJA* LXIII (1959) 142.

115 Head of the Emperor Marcus Aurelius

PLATE 39

Presented by Dr J. Disney. Presumably acquired in Italy, but in that case, like the preceding portrait, it had probably been brought there from further afield. Inv.: GR.33.1850.

P.H. c. 0·312 m. Moderately coarse-grained white island marble (Parian ?) with traces of a deep brown incrustation. Only head and upper part of neck preserved. Tip of nose broken away and break trimmed level to take a restoration since removed. Possible traces of minor reworking on eyebrows and beard. Top of head worn by weather.

The running-drill has been used with moderation in the beard, but the tightly curled hair seems mainly worked with the gouge and chisel. The irises of the eyes are outlined and the pupils marked with lunate drillings. The modern restorer is perhaps largely to blame for the heavy treatment of the eyebrows.

On the portraits of Marcus Aurelius see under **114 a** above. The present example seems to be a somewhat crude provincial work, but even so it shows a remote derivation from Wegner's Type of Terme 726. The main hair elements over the brow seem to have been moved somewhat towards the right, but, in general, the artist is concerned to give an impression rather than follow a model exactly. The head may be compared with a portrait in Jerusalem (Wegner, *op. cit.* pl. 33) and others from Egypt (*ibid.* 283).

Eastern provincial work of the third or early last quarter of the second century A.D.

J. Disney sr., *Cat. Hyde* 9 no. 21; J. Disney jr., *MS Cat.* 30; Marsden, *Cat. Disney Coll.* 84 no. 28; Michaelis, *Anc. Marbles* 260 no. 64; Chapman, *Handbook* (2nd ed.) 40; J. J. Bernoulli, *Römische Ikonographie* II. 2. 235 no. 58; *AJA* LXIII (1959) 142.

116 Head probably of the Empress Faustina the Younger

PLATE 39

Presented by Dr J. Disney, who purchased it in London in 1823. Inv.: GR.27.1850.

P.H. 0·32 m. Medium-grained, translucent, creamish-white marble (Parian ?). Only head and neck preserved. End of nose restored in marble. Traces of rust beside nose. Blotchy stains over the surface, perhaps from oil.

The surface has been well polished, bringing out the translucency of the marble. The irises of the eyes are very faintly outlined and there are light lunate drillings to mark the pupils. The head is decked with a diadem and is turned very slightly towards the left. The long hair in front is parted over the middle of the brow and carried round in two evenly waved masses on each side to a coiled 'bun' at the back of the head. From a little in front of the ears these lower tresses are lightly coiled upon themselves. A short spiral lock is looped over the bottommost of them at each side to hang behind each ear. Behind the diadem the hair has only been roughed out with the gouge. The attempts to assign this head to the Severan epoch have been most unhappy; it does in fact find its closest analogies in the portraits of Faustina the Younger and it seems probable that it was actually intended as a likeness of that Empress.

Annia Galeria Faustina, the daughter of the Emperor Antoninus Pius and Faustina the Elder, lived from *c.* A.D. 130 to 175. In A.D. 145 she married the future Emperor, Marcus Aurelius. On her portraits see Bernoulli, *op. cit.* II. 2. 189 f., Wegner, *op. cit.* 48 f., 210 f. Among her likenesses, the treatment of the hair over the brow and other details shown by the Cambridge head are much the same as on the Type of Louvre 1144 which Wegner regards as typologically datable to the 160's; see Wegner, *op. cit.* pl. 36. For the diadem one may compare a coin portrait-type (*ibid.* pl. 63 *n*) which he assigns to the same period. Interesting correspondences also exist with the portrait-statue, B. M. Felletti Maj, *Cat. Museo Nazionale Romano, i ritratti* 119 f. no. 236.

C. third quarter of the second century A.D.

J. Disney jr., *Museum Disneianum* 43, pl. 22; Marsden, *Cat. Disney Coll.* 84 no. 29; Michaelis, *Anc. Marbles* 259 no. 58; Chapman, *Handbook* (2nd ed.) 40; J. J. Bernoulli, *Römische Ikonographie* II. 2. 133; *AJA* LXIII (1959) 142.

(C) MISCELLANEOUS SCULPTURE IN THE ROUND

117 Small statue of the Egyptian god, Bes, from a fountain PLATE 39

Presented by A. E. Gregory. In the eighteenth century formed part of the collection at the Palazzo Verospi, to judge from Saint-Non's engraving, for reference to which the authors are indebted to Mr E. C. Chamberlain. Inv.: GR.1.1818.

H. 0·595 m. Luna marble. Restored in marble are the bridge and tip of the nose, the lower lip and teeth and both hands resting on the knees. Repaired at the lion's-head spout. Part of the bottom of the plinth broken away at the back. Minor recutting on beard (see below).

The god is shown squatting on his haunches and with his hands resting on his knees. He is dressed in a lion's skin with the mane drawn over his own head and with the fore-paws hanging over his shoulders down on to his chest. The back paws and tail trail about his buttocks. The surface of this skin garment is for the most part left smooth and the detailed texture of the pelt is only indicated over the mane and fore-paws. This is mostly shown by shallow curving incisions, but on the mane at the left side of the head an abortive start was made with a deeper and bolder cutting with the running-drill. About his waist the god wears a string of large beads as a kind of loose-fitting belt. Around his neck hangs a charm in the shape of an animal's head. Egyptian monuments show that this should, in fact, be the lion's head amulet, but it seems clearly to have been misinterpreted by the Italian craftsman as a wolf's head. The irises of the god's eyes are boldly outlined and the pupils are marked by deep lunate drillings. The figure is squatting on a plinth of more or less cylindrical shape which has been hollowed with the point underneath to take some sort of hydraulic installation. On the front of the plinth there is a spout in the shape of a lion's head. A hole, 0·008 m. in diameter, communicates with this from behind in the hollowed interior of the base. This channel divides into three in the thickness of the wall so that the main jet issues over the centre of the lion's tongue and the two others pass out to either side of his fangs.

In all the main essentials this representation of Bes follows its Egyptian prototypes reasonably closely, but there are many curiosities of style and detail that make it quite certain that it was produced in Italy, not in Egypt. The large numbers of Egyptian glazed pottery figures of the god from Pompeii testify to his wide popularity in Italy already in the first century A.D. A marble figure from the Alban Hills now in the Museo Barracco in Rome, itself probably an Alexandrian import, is almost exactly identical with the Cambridge statuette; see *Cat. del Museo di Scultura Antica, Fondazione Barracco* 21 no. 60. It differs in having the eyes painted and in showing a faint vestigial indication of the lion's head over the god's brow. It represents the god with his tongue stuck out over his chin and, in view of the general correspondence in type, suggests that the lower lip of the Cambridge figure has been wrongly restored, also. If so, the original curving surface between the hanging ends of the moustache, immediately under the restored area, should be part, not of the beard, but of the tongue. Certainly the incisions on its surface to indicate hair seem, in large part at least, to be due to modern recutting. The treatment of the eyes of the Cambridge statuette suggests that it is most likely to date from the later part of the second or earlier part of the third centuries A.D., an impression perhaps strengthened by the conflicting techniques found on the mane of the lion's skin. For a Bes of different type cf. W. Amelung, *Kat. vaticanischen Museums* I 728 no. 621, pl. 78.

Probably later second–earlier third centuries A.D.

R. de Saint-Non, *Recueil de griffonis de vues et paysages, fragments antiques et sujets historiques gravés . . . d'après différents maîtres de l'École Italienne et de l'École Française* pl. 43 (or at least so numbered in the set in the Fitzwilliam Museum); *Cat. Fitzwilliam Collection* (ed. of 1826 and 1833) 21 no. 3; Comte F. de Clarac and A. Maury, *Musée de sculpture antique et moderne* IV 277 no. 1755 *c*, pl. 730; *Handbook to the Marbles, Casts and Antiquities in the Fitzwilliam Museum* (1855) 58 no. 6; *Visitor's Guide to the Fitzwilliam Museum* (1868) 53; S. Reinach, *Répertoire de la statuaire* I 419.

118 Sandalled left foot, from a statue

PLATE 40

Circumstances of acquisition not recorded, but most probably presented by the Cyprus Exploration Fund in the later nineteenth century.[1] Inv.: GR.S.5.

P.H. 0·215 m., of which between 0·083 and 0·111 m. is made up by the plinth. Moderately coarse-grained white island marble (Parian or Naxian ?). Broken away above at the ankle; rear part of foot missing; plinth broken away on all sides. Toes chipped.

All that is preserved is part of the sandalled left foot of a statue of distinctly more than life-size and probably representing a male figure, to judge from the absence of drapery traces over the foot. The sandal is fastened with a bow. The leather of its uppers is indicated by coarse rasp work which forms an effective contrast with the polished smooth surface of the flesh. The way that the toes are rendered and the careful workmanship suggest a date in early Imperial times.

Early Imperial (?).

Chapman, *Handbook* (2nd ed.) 38.

119 Right hand, from a statue

PLATE 40

Transferred from the old University Library. Presented to the University by Professor E. D. Clarke. From Paphos. Inv.: GR.7.1865.

Max. dimension 0·25 m. Pentelic (?) marble. Broken away at wrist; tips of fingers missing. Traces of cement adhering to palm. Lead-lined dowel-hole at base of thumb.

The fragment preserves the greater part of the right hand from a colossal statue, almost twice life-size. The rough drill- and point-work showing on the palm was probably concealed, the hand being fairly tightly closed, probably about some staff-like object. The arm and hand would seem to have been carved in a separate piece of marble from the adjacent member or support to which they were attached by the dowel at the base of the thumb. The veins of the back of the hand are boldly treated, suggesting that the statue was male, but the fingers are insensitively rendered as cylindrical members separated by flat grooves.

Probably of Imperial date.

Clarke, *Marbles* 55 no. 38; Idem, *Travels* 4° II (=II. I) 335, 8° IV 44; Michaelis, *Anc. Marbles* 247 no. 7; Chapman, *Handbook* (2nd ed.) 38.

120 Club, from a statue (?)

PLATE 40

Transferred from the old University Library. Presented to the University by Professor E. D. Clarke. From Athens. Inv.: GR.11.1865.

P.H. 0·39 m. Medium-grained Proconnesian (?) marble. Broken away at bottom; upper part of club missing, an iron pin in the broken upper surface being apparently a relic of an ancient repair. Surface chipped.

The fragment preserves the lower part of a knotty wooden club broadening towards the end. Contrary to Michaelis's findings, the surface under its thicker end shows a definite ancient break. The fragment most probably comes from a statue of Herakles in which the club served as a support, standing more or less upright with its end resting either on the plinth or on some low object beside the hero. It is, however, just possible that the club was carved alone as a votive offering to Herakles like the example in the Vatican, W. Amelung, *Kat. vaticanischen Museums* I 371 no. 95 D, pl. 38.

Of Imperial date (?).

Clarke, *Marbles* 53 no. 33; Michaelis, *Anc. Marbles* 247 no. 11; Chapman, *Handbook* (2nd ed.) 37.

(D) RELIEFS FROM THEATRE BUILDINGS

121 Comic mask, from a decorative relief

PLATE 40

Transferred from the old University Library. Presented to the University by the Rev. R. Walpole. Found in the ruins of the ancient theatre at Stratonicea in Caria. Inv.: GR.10.1865.

P.H. 0·267 m. Medium-grained, greyish-white Asia Minor marble, containing isolated fragments of shell. The mask has been cut in modern times from a relief decorating

[1] It had probably not yet come to the Museum at the time of Michaelis's visit, but had already been received by 1898, when it is described by Chapman (*Handbook* (1st ed.) 36).

an architectural member of a somewhat concave profile, curving forward towards the top. A small part of the original under-surface of the block is preserved at the bottom. The hair at the mask's left side has been broken away and chips are missing elsewhere from the nose, hair and beard. An orange-brown incrustation covers areas of the eyes, eyebrows and beard, but there are no clear indications of ancient pigment.

The relief represents an actor's mask as worn in performances of the New Comedy of Menander and his successors. It has been carved with the flat chisel, occasionally aided with the gouge and point, and it is not certain that it was ever completely finished. The mask has a roll of hair over the brow and a short, trumpet-shaped beard. One eyebrow is raised and the other furrowed and lowered. Amongst the mask-types described by Pollux, it approximates either to that of the Leading Old Man or to that of the Leading Slave; see C. Robert, *Die Masken der neueren attischen Komoedie* (25th *hall. Winckelmannsprogramm*) passim. Miss A. Simon has listed it as an old man, but Professor T. B. L. Webster, in correspondence with the Museum, has stated that he considers it much more likely to represent a slave, to judge from such details as the shortness of the beard.

Two marble representations are closely similar in type, a mask from the Kerameikos and a relief in Mantua; see A. Brueckner, *Maske aus dem Kerameikos* (57th *berliner Winckelmannsprogramm*) 32 f., pls. 4–6; A. Levi, *Sculture greche e romane del Palazzo Ducale di Mantova* 47 no. 80, pl. 51; M. Bieber, *History of the Greek and Roman Theatre* (2nd ed.) figs. 253, 266. For the use of such masks in relief decoration one may also compare the frieze from Pergamon, F. Winter, *Altertümer von Pergamon* VII. 2. 314 f. no. 404. Professor Webster regards the Cambridge mask as probably still being essentially Hellenistic in form. On technical grounds, however, it is doubtful if its execution can fall any earlier than Imperial times, to which period have also been assigned the Kerameikos and Mantua examples.

Probably of Imperial date.

Clarke, *Marbles* 40 f. no. 19; S. H. Spiker, *Reise durch England* II 295 f.; Michaelis, *Anc. Marbles* 247 no. 10; Chapman, *Handbook* (2nd ed.) 38; J. R. A. Nicoll, *Masks, Mimes and Miracles* 61, fig. 58; A. K. H. Simon, *Comicae Tabellae* (*Die Schaubühne* XXV) 193 n. 48; T. B. L. Webster, *Monuments Illustrating New Comedy* (*Bull. Inst. Classical Studies, London Univ., Suppl.* XI) 168 no. XS 1 (where Stratonicea apparently confused with Stratonike in north Greece).

122 Relief fragment with part of a male figure PLATE 40

Transferred from the old University Library. Presented to the University by Professor E. D. Clarke. Found outside the entrance to the Acropolis in Athens. Inv.: GR.25.1865.

P.H. 0·34 m., H. of relief 0·15 m. max., preserved depth 0·27 m. Pentelic marble. Top surface of block preserved. Broken away on both sides and underneath, with the consequence that the lower parts of both arms of the figure are missing, together with the whole of the body from a point a little below the waist; head and neck also broken away. The whole of the back of the block has been cut down in modern times. Modern clamp holes in top and bottom.

The relief shows a male figure wearing a chlamys which is fastened on his right shoulder by a pin with a disc-shaped boss. His head would seem to have been turned to his left and, to judge from the part of the relief-ground from which it has been broken away at the back, probably bent somewhat forward towards the left as well. Traces of a strut on his right arm may suggest that a staff or similar object was held against it. The top of the block is faintly channelled near its front edge.

This relief appears to be Imperial work of about the second century A.D. Clarke's attempt to recognize in it part of a metope of the Parthenon is certainly quite unwarranted; but, nevertheless, it seems likely that it may be attributed with tolerable certainty to a major monument. A close check has revealed an identity of proportions, depth of relief, tooling and surface treatment with the figures of the Phaidros Bema in the Theatre of Dionysos in Athens. On these reliefs see J. N. Svoronos, *Das athener Nationalmuseum* 232 f., pls. 61–4; A. B. Cook, *Zeus* I 708 f., pl. 40 (at end); R. Herbig, *Antike griechische Theaterbauten* VI, *Das Dionysos-Theater in Athen* II, *Die Skulpturen vom Bühnenhaus* 36 f. About half of the frieze, consisting of four scenes relating to the career of the god, Dionysos, remains in position on the front of the stage. Of the other half only fragments survive, many of which have been gathered together by Mrs S. Karouzou in the National Museum in Athens.[1] It is not possible in all cases to tell with certainty whether they are from the Phaidros Bema or from another relief of the same scale and date. But with the Cambridge fragment there is little room for doubt. It will be observed that, when intact, the top of the head of the figure in relief must have projected quite distinctly

[1] The authors are deeply indebted to Mrs Karouzou for allowing them access to this material in Athens.

above the upper surface of the block. This projection is a peculiarity of the reliefs of the Phaidros Bema. It appears to arise from the circumstance that they had been remounted and, in their new position, had to be lowered in height to match other elements. This was achieved by cutting down the tops of the frieze blocks and inserting the crowning moulding behind the upper parts of the heads of the figures in relief. Herbig has dated the reliefs towards the middle of the second century A.D.

C. mid second century A.D.

Clarke, *Marbles* 45 no. 22; Idem, *Travels* 4° III (=II. 2) 475, 8° VI 213; *AA* 1866 301; Michaelis, *Anc. Marbles* 252 no. 28; Chapman, *Handbook* (2nd ed.) 45.

(E) VOTIVE MONUMENTS

123 Votive relief to Asklepios and Hygieia

PLATE 41

Transferred from the old University Library. Presented to the University by Professor E. D. Clarke. From Athens. Inv.: GR.14.1865.

H. 0·545 m., H. of relief 0·035 m. max., depth 0·143 m. max. Pentelic marble. Faces of figures broken away, as also the right arm and much of the snake-entwined staff of Asklepios. Modern clamp-hole in top.

The sides, top and bottom of the stele have been dressed level with the claw-chisel; the back has simply been roughly worked with the point. The relief is set in a plain, roughly rectangular framing, without architectural pretensions and lacking the upwards taper noted on **64**. Represented are the god, Asklepios, and the goddess, Hygieia. Asklepios is shown wrapped in a himation and leaning upon his staff, about which a snake is coiled. Hygieia is dressed in a chiton and a himation and holds a phiale in her right hand.

The chief interest of the Cambridge relief lies in the circumstance that both deities are represented in the form of famous Attic statue-types. The widely copied figure of Asklepios may go back to the cult image of the Asklepieion in Athens; if so, its original should date to *c.* 420 B.C.; see K. A. Neugebauer, *Asklepios* (78th *berliner Winckelmannsprogramm*) 3 f., G. Lippold, *Griechische Plastik* (*HdA* III. 1) 191; for a contrary view, see *JdI* XLVI (1931) 29. The figure of the goddess approximates to that of the Hope Hygieia, which derives from an original of the later first or second quarters of the fourth century B.C.; see *JdI* XIX (1904) 55 f., *BSR* X (1927) 1 f., Lippold, *op. cit.* 253. On the Cambridge relief she lacks the snake appropriate to this type—an omission that has been ingeniously explained by the circumstance that it already appears coiled around the staff of Asklepios! The execution of the Cambridge stele cannot be closely dated. A similar kind of plain framing about a relief has already been noted in late Hellenistic work (see under **64**), but the irregular shape shown by that of the Cambridge stele would seem to indicate a date no earlier than Imperial times. On the other hand, the tooling still seems fairly early, with scant use made of the drill.

Attic work, probably of about early Imperial date.

Clarke, *Marbles* 37 f. no. 15; Idem, *Travels* 4° III (=II. 2) 529, 8° VI 285 f.; Michaelis, *Anc. Marbles* 249 no. 16; *JHS* V (1884) 89 n. 4; Chapman, *Handbook* (2nd ed.) 46; *BSR* X (1927) 6, pl. 5, fig. 33; *Forschungen und Fortschritte* X (1934) 109 f., fig. 1; U. Hausmann, *Kunst und Heiltum* 107 f., fig. 20; G. Lippold, *Griechische Plastik* (*HdA* III. 1) 253 n. 1; *AJA* LXIII (1959) 142.

124 Votive altar to Zeus and Helios

PLATE 41

Presented by the Rev. H. S. Cronin, Professor W. M. Ramsay and G. A. Wathen. Bought at Fassıllar, to the east of Beyşehir (perhaps the ancient Misthia), in Lykaonia.[1] Inv.: GR.182.1902.

H. 0·222 m. max., max. depth 0·115 m. Hard, pale brown limestone. Chipped, e.g. at the noses and chins of the heads in relief. Traces of red pigment on the rayed crown of Helios, the drapery and the right front edge of the altar.

The small votive altar is rectangular in shape, with its faces slightly recessed to suggest the outline of a crowning at the top and of a base on feet at the bottom. Its back is left plain. In the top there is a round hollow with a conical projection in the centre, so that it approximates in shape to a phiale mesomphalos. On the front there are crude reliefs representing the upper parts of the two gods. Their heads appear to be garlanded. Zeus is shown bearded and

[1] It had formerly been proposed to locate the ancient Misthia at Fassıllar; for a discussion of the question cf. H. Swoboda, J. Keil and F. Knoll, *Denkmäler aus Lykaonien, Pamphylien und Isaurien* 12 f. More recently A. S. Hall has suggested that Beyşehir itself is a more likely site for Misthia; see *Anatolian Studies* IX (1959) 119 f.

holding a bunch of grapes and a sheaf of wheat in his right hand. His companion, Helios, is identified by his rayed crown. On the projecting base beneath them is incised the inscription:

Καυμενω

This admits of no ready interpretation in terms of orthodox Greek forms. Possibly a dual participle of unusual formation is intended, signifying '*the two burning ones*'. Such an epithet would be appropriate both to the sun-god and to Zeus, if viewed as god of lightning, perhaps akin to the Phrygian Zeus Bronton.[1]

However that may be, the attributes of grapes and sheaf of wheat identify him as an old Anatolian agricultural god, sometimes styled Zeus Phatnios or Zeus Megistos, whose antecedents may take one back to the deity on the İvriz relief; cf. *JHS* LXVIII (1948) 8, fig. 6. He appears on other monuments of Imperial date from the same region, e.g. *MAMA* I 5 no. 7*a*, VII I no. 1, pl. 1; cf. also H. Swoboda, J. Keil, F. Knoll, *Denkmäler aus Lykaonien, Pamphylien und Isaurien* 13, fig. 6, L. Robert, *Hellenica* X (1955) 107 f., pl. 44. There are also other examples showing him associated with Helios, e.g. *MAMA* I 4 no. 5. The date of the Cambridge altar probably falls in the second–third centuries A.D.

Local provincial work of the second–third centuries A.D.

JHS XXII (1902) 112.

125 Altar (?) to Cybele PLATE 41

Bequeathed by G. A. Warren. Provenance unknown. Inv.: GR.5.1938.

H. of preserved lower member 0·43 m. max., W. 0·425 m., D. 0·336 m. Luna (?) marble. The top, which was carved from a separate block of marble and attached by metal dowels in the corners, is completely missing. The body of the monument has been assembled from fragments with minor plaster restorations; missing are the upper right corner of the front and the lower right corner of the right side. Surface chipped. The damaged bottom of the relief of the pine tree shown on the right side has been recut in modern times. Traces of whitewash and other modern stains.

The preserved lower part of this monument consists of a marble box whose hollow interior measures 0·27 m. × 0·18 m. × 0·27 m. deep. It is somewhat like a cinerarium in form, but uninscribed and, to judge from the arrangements for the attachment of its top, meant to be kept permanently sealed. The receptacle shows signs of having been deliberately smashed in antiquity. It seems quite probable that it may have contained relics sacred to the cult of Cybele. To judge from analogous monuments, the whole, when complete with its permanently fastened lid, may well have taken the form of a small altar. The monument has a prominent projecting plinth topped by a heavy moulding. Above this at the back there is a simple rusticated surface dressed with the claw-chisel. The other three sides are decorated with reliefs. On the front of the monument is represented the goddess Cybele herself, distinguished by her greater height, flanked by an antithetical pair of her priests or Galli. The goddess wears a chiton and, over it, a himation which is drawn up over the back of her head as a veil. Under the veil she appears to be wearing a garland with a central medallion. In her left hand she holds an oinochoe and an open bowl, possibly containing fruit, whilst her right hand grasps a branch and a pomegranate. The pomegranate has associations with the dead and it is to be noted that the two Galli are both represented as mourning, doubtless for the dead Attis. They wear girdled chitons, cloaks and Phrygian caps. On the right side is carved a representation of the goddess's sacred pine tree hung with musical instruments used in her worship—a pair of cymbals, a tympanon, engraved with a laurel garland, and a double pipe of the kind in which the longer member is curved at the end (cf. the piping maenad on the elephant on **161**; for the component pipes shown hanging separately cf. *JHS* LXXX (1960) pl. 8. 1). The relief on the left side shows part of a procession carrying a sacred bier. The bier is oblong in shape, decorated with a scroll pattern on the side and borne on two poles. These are carried by four Galli dressed in trouser-like *anaxyrides*, girdled sleeved chitons and Phrygian caps. On top of the bier are set the richly ornamented sacred throne and footstool of the goddess. Upon the seat of the throne against a shell-shaped wicker background is displayed a basket with a conical lid—the *cista mystica* of the cult. The throne is flanked by an antithetical pair of figures (probably statues) of Galli on low pedestals. They are dressed in *anaxyrides*, girdled sleeved chitons, Phrygian caps and cloaks. With their raised arms they appear to steady a long cross-beam resting on supports, possibly in the shape of lion's paws, on top of the arms of the throne. To this beam are fixed clusters of pine branches. A long branch of laurel is fastened to each end of the bier.

It has been argued by Dr Tillyard that the basket thus prominently carried in procession may have contained the genitals of Galli, or emasculated priests,

[1] *RE* s.v. *Bronton*; *JdI* XXXIV (1919) 77 f.; A. B. Cook, *Zeus* II 835; *MAMA* V, introd. 35 f.

after their ritual act of castration on the *Dies Sanguinis*, 24 March; see *JRS* VII (1917) 288. The other scenes strengthen the view that some allusion is being made to this season of the year, the prominence of the pine suggesting that the *Arbor Intrat* ceremony was already over and the mourning for Attis that his annual resurrection had not yet taken place. Possibly these inferences may give some clue to the contents of the receptacle inside the Cambridge altar, but no definite conclusions seem yet possible. Von Bothmer and Vermeule have dated this monument, with surprising precision, to the first quarter of the second century A.D., presumably because the hair-styles of the Galli have been interpreted as Trajanic. It is doubtful, however, if the crudely indicated curls over their brows and covering their ears can be dated closely at all. They seem equally possible in the later part of the second or early third centuries A.D., a period to which, on other indications, this monument would seem more plausibly assignable. For the figure of Cybele one may compare *EA* 3794, F. Poulsen, *Kat. over antike Skulpturer* 61 no. 53, *Billedtavler* pl. 4; for the Galli in procession, S. Reinach, *Répertoire des reliefs* III 321. The pine tree recurs, with little modification, on a Cybele altar of A.D. 295, but this shows a figure-style that is markedly later than that of the Cambridge monument; see *EA* 3599, 3605.

Perhaps later second–early third century A.D.

JRS VII (1917) 284 f.; *CAH* XII 423, Plates V 158*b*; *AJA* LXIII (1959) 143 no. 7.

126 Small shrine, originally supporting Malīkat's 'lamp' PLATE 42

Bequeathed by C. F. Tyrwhitt Drake. From Ḳanawât, the ancient Kanatha, in Syria.[1] Inv.: GR. 1. 1874.

P.H. 0·542 m., W. and D. c. 0·434 m. Coarse grey Syrian basalt of a hard and markedly foraminiferous texture. The base and the lower part of the walls of the shrine are broken away, also one of the back corners of the crowning moulding under the edge of the roof and the greater part of the four small grooved projections set above the corners of the flat roof itself. Also missing are the hinged door of the shrine and the metal structure of the 'lamp' standing on its roof. Chipped at many points, including the edges of the door-frame, the rayed crown of the bust of Helios and the nose of that of Selene on the sides and the tips of the large acanthus leaf at the back. There seem to be traces of a powdery white plaster over parts of the mouldings and reliefs and evidence of a coating with red ochre.

This monument preserves the greater part of a small, monolithic shrine whose hollow interior presumably originally housed a statuette of the deity to which it was dedicated or some similar sacred object. Its form, with a flat roof and a hinged door, resembles an Egyptian shrine-type, but it is decorated with degenerate Greek architectural ornament, at some points misapplied. The top and sides of the door-frame show an egg-and-dart motif, set upside-down, perhaps under the influence of the Egyptian tongue-pattern. The door itself had only a single leaf, hinged on the right side where its upper socket is still preserved. Above the door-frame is set a panel of double guilloche which extends up to a foliate ornament around the underside of the flat roof. This seems to be a weak and late derivative of the Greek acanthus-and-palmette motif. It extends around all four sides of the shrine. Under it, at the sides and back of the monument, appear an egg-and-dart moulding, again upside-down, and an elongated bead-and-reel motif. On the right side of the shrine there is displayed a relief-bust of Helios. His head is crowned with the rays of the sun and he wears a chiton fastened at his shoulders by pins with large, round bosses. On the left side of the monument are preserved the head and part of the crescent moon of a corresponding bust of Selene. The back wall of the shrine is decorated with a splendid acanthus leaf in bold relief. Above the leaf there is roughly incised the inscription:

Λ̣ύχνος Μαλειχάθ̣
ου

Malichathos' lamp.

Malichathos is simply the Greek form of the common south Syrian man's name, Malīkat; see, e.g., E. Littman and others, *Princeton University Archaeological Expedition to Syria* III. A. 369 no. 777, 376 no. 784, 429 no. 797/9. The 'lamp' that Malīkat had dedicated is probably to be identified in the structure, apparently largely of metal, that originally stood on the roof of the shrine. Conjectures as to its form must be based on the evidence of the surviving stone elements. On top of the centre of the roof of the shrine there is a projection in the shape of a bowl, 0·23 m. in diameter and 0·115 m. deep, part of whose bottom has since been broken away. It appears that this may have masked a hemispherical metal pan whose handle may have passed through a round hole of 0·025 m. diameter in the right side of the bowl and whose rim may have been steadied in position by a clamp on its front side. The holes for these attachments are still

[1] *Syria* XI (1930) 272 f.

fully preserved. The main structure, however, seems to have stood above and to have been considerably higher. Four large, rectangular sockets, one of them still containing lead, occur on top of the roof of the shrine, one in the middle of each side. The most plausible interpretation seems to be that these carried the four legs of a tall, metal stand. The projecting bosses on top of the four corners of the roof seem to have had their lower edges grooved to receive metal rods. If the interpretation given is the correct one, these could well have been stays, one on each side of each of the four legs of the stand.

It is not known to what deity this monument was dedicated. On the Syrian cult of the Sun and the Moon cf. M. Nilsson, *Geschichte der griechischen Religion* II 491, pls. 8. 1, 9. 1. However, the reliefs of Helios and Selene might merely play a subsidiary role as they do on many Mithraic monuments, e.g. the Syrian example, M. J. Vermaseren, *Corpus Inscriptionum et Monumentorum Religionis Mithriacae* I 76 no. 88, fig. 33. The reliefs themselves are difficult to date. The main elements of their style had already been formed under Nabatean influence by the late first century B.C., as witness the sculptures from Siʿ, H. C. Butler, *Princeton University Archaeological Expedition to Syria* II. A. 365 f., especially figs. 330 f. The reliefs on the Cambridge shrine are later as may be seen from their softer, more classicizing forms, but their dating must rest on other criteria. The letter-forms of the inscription are also only an approximate guide, but are most likely to fall between the later second and the fourth centuries A.D. The degenerate forms shown by the architectural ornament, e.g. the inverted egg-and-dart, seem unlikely much before the third century A.D. Certainly, the spiky-tipped acanthus leaf on the back of the shrine appears to find its best parallels in the third century A.D., e.g. on the Arch of Galerius at Salonica, *Mostra Augustea della Romanità* pl. 68.

Outstandingly fine local Syrian work of about the third century A.D.

R. F. Burton and C. F. T. Drake, *Unexplored Syria* I 166 and frontispiece; *Proceedings of the Society of Biblical Archaeology* XIII (1891) 286 f., 438; Michaelis, *Anc. Marbles* 248 no. 14; Chapman, *Handbook* (2nd ed.) 61, and pl. facing.

(F) OSCILLA

127 Oscillum with reliefs of two masks and of a satyr PLATE 42

Presented by Dr J. Disney. Presumably acquired in Italy. Inv.: GR.41.1850.

Original diam. c. 0·31 m. Luna marble. Small part of the circumference of the disc preserved. Otherwise badly broken away at the edges. Assembled from two joining fragments. Surface worn and pitted by weather.

This is a much-damaged oscillum, a species of decorative marble disc with reliefs on both sides that was hung from the architrave between the columns of a colonnade. On the present example the relief on one side is distinctly higher. It shows two masks set side by side against a flat ground. The foremost mask seems characterized by its heavier features as male; its hair-style and attributes suggest that it represents the youthful Dionysos. A fillet is worn across the brow, an ivy garland about the head. The hair is gathered into a looped knot at the back, with spiral curls hanging down at the sides. The second mask is shown to be feminine by the smaller and more delicate features and by the sakkos worn over the hair and knotted after the fashion of the fifth century B.C. Probably Ariadne is represented. The other side of the oscillum shows the figure of a young satyr dancing. Here the relief is much shallower and partly cut into the ground which, as a consequence, acquires a distinctly convex surface. The satyr has a skin cloak looped over his bent left arm and he holds a thyrsos in his left hand. In front a roaring panther gazes back up either at the satyr or at some object such as a bunch of grapes that he once held in his missing right hand. The carving is sketchy but bold, the effect almost impressionistic.

On oscilla see F. G. Welcker, *Alte Denkmäler* II 122 f.; *RA* ser. 2, XLII (1881) 92 f., 129 f., 193 f., 273 f.; Daremberg and Saglio, *Dictionnaire des Antiquités* I 1258 f., IV 257; *JdI* XXXIV (1919) 161 f., XXXVI (1921) 33 f.; *Archiv für Religionswissenschaft* XXIV 25; etc. For dating the present example, it is to be observed that the treatment of the back muscles, hair and animal skin of the young satyr is close to an oscillum in Naples, probably assignable to about the middle or third quarter of the first century A.D.; see B. Maiuri, *Museo Nazionale di Napoli* 164. The rendering of the Dionysos mask and the general character of the relief of the satyr may also be compared with a double-sided relief in Munich which has been tentatively assigned to the late first century A.D.: T. Schreiber, *Hellenistische Reliefs* pl. 100, *EA* 2962–3.

Probably mid–late first century A.D.

J. Disney jr., *Museum Disneianum* 69, pl. 33; Marsden, *Cat. Disney Coll.* 86 f. no. 67; Michaelis, *Anc. Marbles* 261 no. 72; Chapman, *Handbook* (2nd ed.) 41; *JdI* XXXVI (1921) 41 n. 63.

128 Oscillum with reliefs of a satyr and a silen making offerings PLATE 42

Presented by Dr J. Disney. Presumably acquired in Italy. Inv.: GR.39.1850, GR.40.1850.

Diam. 0·258 m. Luna marble. Small area at the top in the vicinity of the suspension hole restored in plaster. The two sides of the oscillum have been sawn apart in modern times and mounted for display individually.

Both sides of the oscillum are decorated with very shallow reliefs, partly cut down into the background which assumes a somewhat convex appearance as a consequence. The more elaborately finished side shows a satyr with an animal skin flapping from his shoulders advancing towards a rock-altar. In his left hand he holds a small *liknon* or winnowing-fan, an implement that had assumed an important role in Dionysiac cult. His outstretched right hand grasps an indistinct object, perhaps rightly identified by Miss Harrison as a bundle of twigs. The rock-altar is rendered after a fashion commonly met with in early Imperial reliefs. The scene on the other side is much more superficially treated. It shows a bald-headed, pot-bellied silen clad in a loin-cloth. He is holding a much larger *liknon* out over another rock-altar. The object protruding from the top of the *liknon* has, on the analogy of kindred representations, hitherto been interpreted as a phallos. This may well be right, but it shows an unmistakable snake-like head turned back towards the silen!

On oscilla and their use see under **127**. The present example is similar in execution to **127**, but lacks its pervading Hellenistic spirit. The incidence of kindred reliefs on candelabra suggests that it might be a little later. For the figure of the satyr one may also compare the oscillum, G. Kaschnitz-Weinberg, *Sculture del Magazzino del Museo Vaticano* 197 nos. 440–1, pl. 78.

Probably about later first–earlier second centuries A.D.

J. Disney sr., *Cat. Hyde* 9 no. 46, 10 no. 50; J. Disney jr., *Museum Disneianum* 77, pl. 37; *AZ* V (1847) 159; *GGA* 1849 451; Marsden, *Cat. Disney Coll.* 86 nos. 52, 54; Michaelis, *Anc. Marbles* 261 nos. 70, 71; S. Reinach, *Répertoire des Reliefs* II 444. 1–2; Chapman, *Handbook* (2nd ed.) 38; *JHS* XXIII (1903) 318 f., figs. 15, 16; *JdI* XXXVI (1921) 40 n. 61.

(G) OTHER RELIEFS OF A NON-FUNERARY CHARACTER

129 Relief fragment showing a yoked ox PLATE 43

Presented by Mrs W. H. Thompson. Provenance unknown. Inv.: GR.1.1886.

P.H. 0·39 m. Luna (?) marble with a brown patina and incrustation and with isolated root-marks. The original back of the slab is preserved and also part of its original right edge, showing anathyrosis for the attachment of a further slab of relief and part of a dowel-hole for this purpose towards the top. Broken away above, below and to the left. Right horn of ox also missing; this was carved from a separate piece of marble and attached with a dowel. The face of the relief has been partly cleaned in modern times, mainly around the outlines of the ox and his yoke. The surface of the marble shows isolated deep pitting.

The comparatively thin relief slab has a smooth-dressed back. The present fragment preserves the head and neck of an ox. He has a heavy dewlap and the treatment is strong and muscular. On his shoulders rests a yoke. The angle at which this is set makes it reasonably certain that the pole at its bottom edge is one of a pair of shafts—i.e. only a single animal is harnessed between shafts and the load drawn is much more likely to be a cart or similar vehicle than a plough. Although the relief is quite bold it is completely tied into the background, the only free-standing element being the missing right horn.

This fragment probably comes from a relief representing a pastoral scene of a kind not infrequently met with in the decorative art of Imperial times. Too little survives for it to be dated with any precision, in particular as the heads of the cattle on many of the comparable reliefs are largely the work of the modern restorer. One may, however, compare T. Schreiber, *Die hellenistischen Reliefbilder* pls. 9 (heads restored), 53, 74, 80 (head restored), 109. In general the Cambridge relief does not seem a particularly late example of this genre. The limited emergence of the figure from its ground and the restrained use of the drill in the hair over the brow of the ox are both of a kind associated with work still of the first century A.D. or of the earlier part of the second.

Perhaps mid-late first or early second centuries A.D.

Chapman, *Handbook* (2nd ed.) 37; *AJA* LXIII (1959) 143 no. 3.

130 Bearded head of a god or daimon (?)

PLATE 43

Purchased. Provenance unknown. Inv.: GR.95*a*.1906.

P.H. c. 0·119 m. Pentelic marble with traces of a brownish incrustation. Broken away at the neck. Chipped at the tip of the nose and on the hair to the left side of the head. The remains of the relief-ground appear to have been trimmed away from the back of the head in modern times. Possible traces of red pigment on hair and beard.

The fragment preserves a head with a curling beard and rich, long hair. The face has a certain grandeur, suggesting that no mere mortal is represented, but there is also a kind of animality, perhaps savouring less of a god than of a giant or centaur. The traces of the original relief-ground show that the head was turned at a three-quarter angle to the right. There is also a marked divergence between head and neck angles. The cheek muscles are powerfully and asymmetrically treated. The mouth is open revealing the upper teeth. In general the effect is that of a figure in violent motion, as perhaps in a battle scene. The detail of the hair and beard is very carefully but extremely shallowly carved.

A distinctly Hellenistic spirit seems to pervade the head (cf. A. Schober, *Istanbuler Forschungen* II, *Der Fries des Hekateions von Lagina* pl. 22); but this is probably to be ascribed to the Hellenistic tradition persevering into Imperial times that has already been noted under **90** above; for the treatment of the flesh and the purely linear handling of the furrowed brow seem to show that this piece is unlikely to be any earlier. The head seems rather small in scale to be from one of the earlier Attic sarcophagi of Imperial date, but it is probably about contemporary with them (cf. **156** f.).

C. second century A.D.

131 Relief of a dancing maenad (?)

PLATE 43

Presented by Dr J. Disney. Presumably acquired in Italy. Inv.: GR.47.1850.

P.H. c. 0·249 m., H. of relief c. 0·02 m. max. Pentelic (?) marble. The fragment has been trimmed to a rectangular shape in modern times, only a small part of the bottom surface seeming original and even this having been re-trimmed at a different angle. Back also sawn away in modern times. The surface has been harshly cleaned and the damaged left leg has been distorted by recutting.

A young woman is shown dancing towards the left. She is wearing a girdled chiton with an overfold and with both hands she is grasping a cloak fluttering above her head. In front of her, at the top left corner of the relief, there may be the edge of the floating garment of an adjacent figure. The relief may never have been fully finished. There are extensive traces of the drill in the folds of the drapery.

Most probably a dancing maenad is represented, as, e.g., on *EA* 3637 and the altar in the British Museum, *A Description of the Marbles* IX pl. 40. 2, A. H. Smith, *BMC Sculpture* III 392 f. no. 2498. But, although no crescent is shown in the hair, attempts have also been made to identify the figure as Selene, whom it otherwise resembles in type; cf. C. Robert, *Die antiken Sarkophagreliefs* III. 1. 53 f. If a goddess is intended, the figure might equally be Iris, as on the frieze at Ostia, *AA* 1938 658 f., fig. 19, R. Calza, *Il Museo Ostiense* 29 no. 148, 54. The scale seems too small for the fragment to be from the wall of a sarcophagus and too large for a sarcophagus-lid relief. Probably it filled an architectural role like the Ostia frieze or adorned an altar like the British Museum example; at least, it is of interest to note that both of these are likewise carved in Greek marble. The figure wears a hair-style popular in Hellenistic times (cf. **76**), but the way that the relief is executed suggests that it probably dates to the second century A.D.

C. second century A.D.

J. Disney jr., *Museum Disneianum* 75, pl. 36; *AZ* V (1847) 159; *GGA* 1849 453 f.; Marsden, *Cat. Disney Coll.* 86 no. 62; *AA* 1864 170 f.; Michaelis, *Anc. Marbles* 264 no. 78; Chapman, *Handbook* (2nd ed.) 56.

(H) GREEK GRAVE-RELIEFS

132 Kioniskos of Euklidas PLATE 43

Transferred from the old University Library. Presented to the University by Professor E. D. Clarke. From Athens. Inv.: GR. 19. 1865.

H. 1·073 m., H. of relief 0·04 m. Fine-grained bluish Hymettan marble with vertical faults. The lower part of the shaft is dressed back with the point for insertion in a socketed base of the usual type. Underside recut in modern times. Surface chipped, particularly at the head of Euklidas.

This monument is a kioniskos or miniature column, the standardized type of Attic grave-stone in Hellenistic times after the sumptuary laws of Demetrios of Phaleron had forbidden the erection of more elaborate memorials. The present example, which appears to represent a survival into the succeeding period, differs from the basic type in being decorated with a relief. The figure of the dead man, Euklidas, is shown in a shallow niche hollowed out with the gouge and framed by an archway. He is wrapped in a himation draped tightly round him and swathing his arms in the manner characteristic of the Lateran Sophokles—a type widely used on Attic grave-reliefs of Imperial date. Long hair falls on to his shoulders. His head seems to have been slightly turned and inclined towards his right. Beneath the niche a bounding, curly-tailed dog is carved in outline. The inscription over the arch reads as follows:

Εὐκλίδας Εὐκλίδου
Ἑρμιονεύς
Euklidas, son of Euklidas, from Hermione.

The broad letter-forms find their most abundant parallels in the first half of the first century A.D. and this is the probable period to which the monument should be assigned, although a slightly later date is perhaps not entirely to be excluded.

The Hellenistic kioniskoi clearly continued to be made in Attica in early Imperial times and examples such as this, with figures in relief, are to be seen as overlapping in date with the beginnings of the revival of funerary relief-stelae; cf. A. Conze, *Die attischen Grabreliefs* IV 29. For the type of the figure in relief one may compare Conze, *op. cit.* IV 24 no. 1821, 65 f. nos. 1989 f.; for similar additions in shallow outline below see *ibid.* 40 no. 1887, 80 no. 2053; for the dog, cf. also *ibid.* 79 no. 2050.

Attic work of about the first half of the first century A.D.

R. Chandler, *Inscriptiones Antiquae* II 105; Clarke, *Marbles* 10 f. no. 12; Idem, *Travels* 4° III (=II. 2) 530 f., 8° VI 287 f.; S. H. Spiker, *Reise durch England* II 295; *CIG* I 839; *AA* 1864 172; Michaelis, *Anc. Marbles* 250 no. 21; S. A. Koumanoudis, Ἀττικῆς Ἐπιγραφαὶ Ἐπιτύμβιοι 1654; *IG* III 2410; Chapman, *Handbook* (2nd ed.) 40; A. Conze, *Die attischen Grabreliefs* IV 23 f. no. 1820, pl. 387; *JHS* LXII (1942) 14 no. I. 3; *IG* II–III² 8499; *AJA* LXIII (1959) 142.

133 Grave-stele of Aphrodisia PLATE 44

Presented by the Friends of the Fitzwilliam Museum. From the Piraeus. Inv.: GR. 5. 1919.

H. as mounted 0·955 m. Pentelic marble. Minor chips missing, including the tip of the nose of Aphrodisia. Mounted on a modern base. Bottom corners of stele restored in plaster. Repaired at the crowning acroterion. There is a dowel-hole in the lower part of each side, perhaps for attachment to a kerbing or to other monuments in a family plot. Four more dowel-holes, all containing lead, occur in the upper part of the stele, all at the same level; two are in the face of the relief to either side of Aphrodisia's head and one occurs in each side of the stele.

The relief is set in an architectural frame, flanked by antae, and with architrave, pediment and acroteria above. Aphrodisia stands facing the front, clad in a chiton and a himation and with shoes on her feet. She is in the act of throwing the end of her himation over her left shoulder and shows the characteristic pose and drapery motif of the smaller statue of a girl from Herculaneum—a type much favoured by the sculptors of Attic grave-reliefs in this period. Her hair is worn in a fashion popular in early Antonine times, although deriving ultimately from the Hellenistic 'melon-style'. It is carried up in a series of broad coils to a plait wound round the top of the head. Her long-haired servant-girl gazes sadly up at her. She is shown on a smaller scale and clad in a sleeved chiton with a long, girdled over-fold. To Aphrodisia's right there appears a lyre, apparently represented as hanging upon the wall of the naïskos. Presumably it symbolizes the lady's musical interests. The dowel-holes to either side of her head and in the edges of the stele most probably served for the attachment of hooks for carrying garlands. On the architrave of the naïskos is incised the inscription:

Ἀφροδεισία ἡ καὶ Ἐπίλαμψις Ἀφροδεισίου
Λευκονοέος θυγάτηρ.

Aphrodisia, also called Epilampsis, daughter of Aphrodisios of the deme, Leukonoe.

The distinctive letter-forms suggest a date in the second quarter or middle of the second century A.D.; see *Berytus* X (1952–3) 56 n. 4. The face and sides of the stele have been dressed, somewhat unevenly, with the gouge and flat chisel; the back has simply been roughed out with the point. There are clear traces of the running-drill on the relief.

For the type see A. Conze, *Die attischen Grabreliefs* IV 43 f. nos. 1901 f., *JHS* XXVIII (1908) 18 no. 23, pl. 12, etc. Aphrodisia's family are also known from other inscriptions of the second century A.D.; see *IG* III. 2. index 333. To judge from hair-style and letter-forms, the date of the present stele probably falls in the second quarter or middle of the second century A.D.

Attic work of the second quarter or middle of the second century A.D.

S. Reinach, *Répertoire des reliefs* III 530. 4; A. Conze, *Die attischen Grabreliefs* IV 49 no. 1930, pl. 413; *Annual Report to the Friends of the Fitzwilliam Museum* 1919 I no. I, fig. on 4; *IG* II–III² 6725; *JHS* LXII (1942) 14 no. I. 6; *Berytus* X (1952–3) 56 n. 4, 62 n. 2, 70 n. 5, 86 n. 3, 87 n. 7; *Archaeology* VIII (1955) 13; *AJA* LXIII (1959) 143 no. 24.

134 Memorial to Amarantos PLATE 44

Lent by the Master and Fellows of Trinity College. From Smyrna (?).

P.H. 0·347 m., P.W. 0·175 m. Medium-grained Proconnesian (?) marble with yellowish stains on the surface. Assembled from three fragments. Right side and bottom broken away; rebated part of left edge also missing. The relief and the inscription show traces of red pigment which may be ancient.

The monument consists of a thin slab of marble of a maximum thickness of *c.* 0·035 m. which appears originally to have had its vertical edges rebated to fit in grooves and which may have served to close a niche in a columbarium. It carries the following inscription in letters of the second–third centuries A.D.:

Διονυσ[ό]
δωρος Ἀμ
αράντῳ ἀ
δελφῷ μ[ν]
είας χάριν.

Dionysodoros (set it up) to his brother, Amarantos, in remembrance.

The inscription is framed with incised lines above and below. Later than these lines and apparently added as an afterthought is a shallow relief cut down into the polished surface of the stone. It shows a dog and a horizontal trident. A heavy base-line has been added below. Although this relief was clearly not envisaged when the stone was dressed the surface discoloration and incrustation seem to show it to be ancient. Most probably it is of the same date as the inscription. The back of the slab has simply been shaped with the point.

Probably carved in western Asia Minor in the second–third centuries A.D.

Classical Journal XXX 134; H. J. Rose, *Inscriptiones Graecae Antiquissimae* 399 no. 8; *CIG* II 3269; *JHS* LXII (1942) 16 no. VII. *b.* 3.

135 Grave-stele of Aristeas PLATE 44

Transferred from the old University Library. Presented to the University by Professor E. D. Clarke. Found 'on a small, rocky island near the mouth of the harbour of La Scala in Patmos'. Inv.: GR.21.1865.

P.H. 0·635 m. Pentelic (?) marble, with a faint golden patina. Broken away are the tang at the bottom, the upper right corner and the greater part of the crowning and lateral acroteria. Surface chipped and worn, in particular over the faces of the relief figures. Rear edges damaged. The original point-dressed back of the stele has been rubbed smooth by wear. Modern clamp-hole in top; modern dowel-holes in underside.

The top of the stele is in the form of a pediment, decorated with a rosette and originally carrying crowning and lateral acroteria. Below, the stele broadens slightly in width from top to bottom. A corresponding and, indeed, somewhat enhanced widening is revealed by the sunken relief panel which thus shows an optical adjustment similar to that remarked on **63** and **64**. The deceased, Aristeas, is shown reclining on a couch after the familiar fashion of the funerary banquet scenes of the hero-reliefs; cf. **36**, **61** f. He is beardless with close-cropped hair and wears a sleeved chiton and a himation. A papyrus roll in his left hand suggests literary interests or may represent his will. In front of him are his pet dog and a round table laden with indistinct objects which might either be items of food or further rolls of papyrus. On the form of the table-legs see **181**. His wife sits on the couch at his feet, clad also in a chiton and a himation. The latter garment she is drawing behind her head as a veil in a gesture probably ultimately derived from Attic grave-reliefs of classical date; cf. **28**. Her feet rest on a footstool. Behind Aristeas stands another female figure similarly clad—perhaps a sister or daughter. She is resting her right elbow on the back of the couch and with her right hand appears to be clasping the corner of her himation, rendered in faint relief. Behind her on a low step stands a diminutive servant-girl clad in a chiton. She is holding an indistinct object, perhaps a cup, in her hands. With the possible exception of this servant-figure, who may be wearing a 'bun', the women have their hair looped up at the back of the head apart from a few strands that escape at the nape of the neck. Beneath the relief there is crudely cut the inscription:

Ἀριστέας
Ζωσίμου.
Aristeas, son of Zosimos.

The hair-styles of Aristeas and his wife and daughter seem to suggest a date in the middle years of the third century A.D. The letter-forms of the inscription concur in favouring a third-century dating.

C. middle years of the third century A.D.

Clarke, *Marbles* 11 f. no. 13; Idem, *Travels* 4° III (=II. 2) 372, 8° VI 76 f.; *CIG* II 2262; *AA* 1864 172; Michaelis, *Anc. Marbles* 251 no. 24; Chapman, *Handbook* (2nd ed.) 46; *JdI* XXII (1907) 127 no. 3; *JHS* LXII (1942) 14 no. III. *b*.

(I) CRIMEAN GRAVE-RELIEFS

136 Grave-stele of a woman PLATE 45

Transferred from the old University Library. Presented to the University by Professor E. D. Clarke. From the ancient Phanagoria, near the Cimmerian Bosporus. Inv.: GR.22.1865.

P.H. 0·422 m. Foraminiferous greyish-white limestone. Top broken away. Underside recut in modern times. Face of relief badly chipped. Back worn smooth by subsequent use. Modern clamp-hole in upper surface.

The sunken relief-panel shows a lady, not improbably the deceased, seated on a throne and with her feet resting on a footstool. She appears to be wearing a chiton and, over it, a himation; the latter garment seems to have been carried up over the back of her head as a veil and to be clasped near its outer edge in her raised left hand. Instead of the usual slave with a kalathos or pyxis, she appears to have a free-born young girl in attendance on her—perhaps a half-grown daughter. The girl stands before her, similarly clad in a chiton and a himation. Her arms, in the enveloping veil of the himation, seem to repeat the gesture of the mother. The workmanship of the relief is rather summary. The sides of the stele have simply been dressed with the point.

For the type cf. G. von Kierseritzky and C. Watzinger, *Griechische Grabreliefs aus Südrussland* 28 f. no. 157 f., especially 35 no. 201, pl. 14; for the pose, cf. also **135** above. Better-preserved examples from the same general area that have been dated by letter-forms suggest that the present stele is assignable to the first century B.C. or the first century A.D.

C. first century B.C.–first century A.D.

Clarke, *Marbles* 4 no. 5; Idem, *Travels* 4° I 404 n. 1, 8° II 82 n. 1; Köhler, *Mémoire sur les îles* 258; Michaelis, *Anc. Marbles* 251 no. 25; Chapman, *Handbook* (2nd ed.) 45; G. von Kierseritzky and C. Watzinger, *Griechische Grabreliefs aus Südrussland* 34 no. 190.

137 Part of a multiple grave-stele to Timotheos and other members of the same family PLATE 45

Transferred from the old University Library. Presented to the University by Professor E. D. Clarke. From the ancient Phanagoria, near the Cimmerian Bosporus. Inv.: GR.24.1865.

P.H. 0·547 m., depth c. 0·22 m. max. Moderately fine-grained whitish marble (as **138***), with a yellowish-brown patina. Only the bottom part of the stele is preserved, terminating below in a broad tang for insertion in a socketed plinth. Broken away above. Chipped at the edges, lower corners and on the reliefs. Mounted on a modern base. Modern clamp-hole in top.*

The stele shows a distinct taper from bottom to top and this is echoed by the sunken panels of relief which are narrower towards the top in the same way as those of **63**, **64** and **135**. Of the relief of Timotheos on one side of the stele, little survives save the legs and tail of a horse and the feet of a human figure standing by its head. Underneath is cut the inscription:

Τειμόθεος Δάσειος χαῖρε.
Τειμόθε[ο]ς, ὁ πάτρας ὅσιος φώς, παῖς δὲ Δάσειος,
τρῖς δεκά⟨δ⟩ας ἐτέων τερματίσας ἔθανες·
ἆ τάλαν, οἰκτείρω σε πολυκλαύστωι ἐπὶ τύμβωι·
⟨ν⟩ῦν δὲ συνηρώων χῶρον ἔχοις φθίμενος.

Timotheos, son of Daseis, farewell.
Timotheos, the upright man of your land, son of Daseis, after completing thrice ten years you died. Poor man, I pity you by your much bewept tomb. Now, in death, may you occupy the place of your fellow heroized ones.

In line 2 it is also possible to read Πάτρας, as equivalent to the κώμη Πατραεύς near Phanagoria, mentioned in Strabo 494. The inscription reads δεκάτας for δεκάδας in line 3 and HYN for νῦν in line 5. The συνηρώων of line 5 seem best interpreted as the other heroized dead of the same family buried in the same plot under the same joint memorial, as will be seen from the further discussion of the monument below.

On the other side of the stele a relief-panel is preserved almost intact, but the name of the deceased is lost. The centre of the relief is occupied by a representation of a horse, apparently scaled down somewhat in size as against the adjoining human figures. By its head stands its rider, seemingly clad in Scythian 'trousers', jacket and short cloak. By the tail of the horse stands a much-effaced female figure, probably dressed in a chiton and himation and apparently holding a square object, perhaps a casket. The background of the relief has only been roughly trimmed with the point. The badly chipped relief-figures were better finished, but the work was, none the less, rather summary. Of the inscription cut above the relief, only the end survives:

- - - - - - - - - -
- - [χ]αῖρε.
................, *farewell.*

The middle part of this stele, going immediately above the section in Cambridge, may be preserved in a fragment in the Archaeological Museum in Feodosiya; see Kierseritzky and Watzinger, *op. cit.* 62 no. 357, 106 no. 609, pl. 42.[1] It is of the same size and material and shows the same, otherwise unparalleled, feature of having reliefs on both sides. If this interpretation is correct, it is possible to complete the relief of Timotheos as showing the deceased mounted on horseback and attended by a boy or groom. The Daseis commemorated in the domestic scene immediately above could well be Timotheos' father of the same name. The reliefs on the other side of the stele were set rather lower and had their inscriptions cut above them, instead of underneath. The next relief, as revealed by the Feodosiya fragment, shows a man and a woman standing frontally. The inscription is not preserved and all the upper part of this portion of stele remaining in Russia is broken away. The monument is thus probably revealed as a multiple grave-stele celebrating at least four different members of the same family and, not improbably, more. For such multiple monuments see *op. cit.* nos. 624, 691, 703, etc.; but the Cambridge-Feodosiya memorial, if rightly interpreted, is by far the most elaborate of its kind. All of the reliefs and inscriptions would seem to have been cut within a relatively short time of each other and to be all datable to about the first century A.D. The memorials to Timotheos and his nameless kinsman, as preserved on the Cambridge fragment, may well have been the last additions to the stele.

C. first century A.D.

Clarke, *Marbles* 4 f. no. 6; Idem, *Travels* 4° I 404 n. 1, 435 n. 2, 8° II 82 n. 1, 120 n. 2; H. J. Rose, *Inscriptiones Graecae Vetustissimae* 417; *Classical Journal* XXX 147, XLVI 377; *CIG* II 2127 (where further early bibliography); G. Kaibel, *Epigrammata Graeca e Lapidibus Conlecta* 539; A. Michaelis, *Anc. Marbles* 251 no. 27; *Anthologia Palatina* (ed. of 1890) III 148 no. 351; V. V. Latyshev, *Inscriptiones Antiquae Orae Septentrionalis Ponti Euxini* II 200 no. 383; Chapman, *Handbook* (2nd ed.) 60; A. Ashik, *Bosporanisches Reich* II 61 no. 7; Извѣстія Арх. Комм. X (1904) 94 f., with fig., XIV (1905) 136; G. von Kieseritzky and C. Watzinger, *Griechische Grabreliefs aus Südrussland* 107 no. 612; E. H. Minns, *Scythians and Greeks* 627 n. 3, 660 no. 67, fig. 349; *JHS* LXII (1942) 15 no. V. 1; W. Peek, *Griechische Vers-Inschriften* 439 no. 1477.

138 Grave-stele showing a woman and children (?) PLATE 45

Transferred from the old University Library. Presented to the University by Professor E. D. Clarke. From the ancient Phanagoria, near the Cimmerian Bosporus. Inv.: GR.23.1865.

P.H. c. 0·695 m., depth c. 0·22 m. max. Moderately fine-grained whitish marble of the same type as **137.** *Apparently broken surfaces at top and bottom, the top bearing traces of a subsequent cup-shaped hollow. The original point-dressed back and sides have been rubbed smooth by subsequent wear. Surface of relief badly chipped and its framing broken away at the edges.*

The stele is tall and narrow. The sunken panel of relief represents a lady sitting on a throne set upon a

[1] Photographs and details of the suspected join have been sent to the relevant museum authorities in the Soviet Union, but, up to the time of writing, it has not been possible to arrange with them for the matter to be resolved by the use of casts.

low platform and with her feet resting on a footstool. She is probably wearing a chiton and a himation and in a pose resembling that met with on **136** (*q.v.*). For the plain legs of the throne cf. Kierseritzky and Watzinger, *op. cit.* 44 no. 251, pl. 17; for the way that it is set on a low dais cf. *ibid.* 106 no. 609, pl. 42. Beside the mother's feet stands a small draped figure, now almost entirely obliterated, but apparently representing a child. A second child, this time clearly a boy, appears on a kind of raised plinth in front of the mother's head. This device of placing the figures of children on raised base-lines or plinths is a common feature of the Bosporan grave-reliefs, as witness *op. cit.* 38 no. 214, pl. 14, 46 no. 263, pl. 18, 47 nos. 269, 271, pls. 17, 19. It may not derive so much from Hellenistic representations of statues on reliefs as from crude local attempts to show perspective. Certainly it seems clear that live children, not statues, are represented and, in a case such as the present, the aim is probably to give prominence to a tiny figure. The date, in so far as it is possible to assess the style at all, is probably of about the first century A.D.

C. first century A.D.

Clarke, *Marbles* 4 no. 4; Idem, *Travels* 4° I 404 n. 1, 8° II 82 n. 1; Köhler, *Mémoire sur les îles* 258; Michaelis, *Anc. Marbles* 251 no. 26; Chapman, *Handbook* (2nd ed.) 50; G. von Kierseritzky and C. Watzinger, *Griechische Grabreliefs aus Südrussland* 43 no. 250.

(J) PALMYRENE GRAVE-RELIEFS

The inscriptions are shown transcribed into Hebrew characters, but with the conventions usual in classical epigraphy. The authors are indebted to Dr D. Diringer for checking the readings and for many valuable suggestions.[1]

139 Grave-relief showing a mother and child PLATE 46

Purchased. Reputedly from Palmyra. Inv.: GR.9.1888.

P.H. 0·57 m., H. of relief 0·162 m. max. Hard, greyish-white limestone with patches of yellow incrustation. Relief-ground broken away to both sides of the head, taking with it almost all of the inscription. Head of child missing. Damaged at feet of child, right arm and brow of mother. Nose of mother restored in plaster. Bottom of slab recut level in modern times. Traces of red on brooch.

The top of the mother's head originally extended *c.* 0·09 m. above the top of the relief-ground. The back of the slab is unworked, its original edges point-dressed. The mother has her head turned somewhat to her left. She is dressed after the Palmyrene fashion in an under- and an over-chiton. The latter garment is fastened with a large, round clasp in front of her left shoulder. Her hair is parted above the middle of the brow and brushed up at the sides over her ears. A single lock hangs down on to her right shoulder, but otherwise, over the crown and back of the head, the hair seems to be bound up into a kind of sakkos. She is wearing her cloak as a veil over her shoulders and over the back of her head. Ear-rings with pendants are set in her ears. With her hand she is baring her left breast for the diminutive child held in her left arm. The child is clad in a short, sleeved chiton and grasps a bunch of grapes in the left hand. Of the inscription above the mother's left shoulder, only the end of the last line survives:

- - - - - - - - - -
- - - - - - - - - -
חב[ל] - - - - -
..........*Alas!*

In his *Studier over Palmyrensk Skulptur* Ingholt has related this relief to his no. PS 44, *op. cit.* pl. 13. 4, which is dated to A.D. 169. For the soft facial treatment and classicizing character one may also compare his nos. PS 42–3, dated to A.D. 154 and 161 respectively. This would seem to argue a date in about the third quarter of the second century A.D., but it is to be observed that the type seems to continue, with negligible modification, until much later; e.g. compare *op. cit.* no. PS 53, pl. 16. 2, dated to A.D. 240–1.

C. third quarter of the second century A.D., or possibly later.

Chapman, *Handbook* (2nd ed.) 39; H. Ingholt, *Studier over Palmyrensk Skulptur* 137 no. 411.

[1] Where the proper names are quoted in the text in English characters, they are given in their unvocalized form. This may make them somewhat difficult to pronounce, but has seemed the wisest course to follow in an unspecialized publication such as this, because of the many uncertainties obtaining in the matter of their vocalization.

140 Usurped grave-relief of a woman

PLATE 46

Purchased. Reputedly from Palmyra. Inv.: GR.8.1888.

P.H. 0·485 m., H. of relief 0·116 m. max. Hard, somewhat foraminiferous, greyish-white limestone with a little yellowish incrustation. Broken away at the bottom and along the upper part of the right edge. Nose restored in plaster. Chipped at eyes and fingers. The following details of jewellery had been removed by recutting, apparently already in antiquity; a jewelled frontlet over the brow, bracelets around both wrists and two strings of beads about the neck and a cord-like chain carrying an oval, locket-shaped amulet. The original inscription above the woman's right shoulder has also been effaced, probably at the same time, and replaced by a few crudely scratched signs.

The relief shows the bust of a woman dressed in much the same fashion as the mother on **139** (*q.v.*), but rendered in a somewhat harsher style. Again, the main garments are an under- and an over-chiton, similarly fastened, and a cloak worn as a veil over the back of the head and the shoulders. Here, however, like Tmụr on **141**, the woman clasps the edge of her veil with one hand whilst, with the other, she holds a corner of the garment below her breast. Beneath the sakkos confining her hair she originally wore a jewelled frontlet over her brow, but this has been removed in the recutting, along with several other items of jewellery listed above. Others have been left intact, namely her ear-rings, the clasp of her over-chiton, a tight, choker-like necklet with a single pendant, and two rings on the little finger of her left hand. Of the original Palmyrene inscription above the lady's right shoulder, only the fifth (?) and last line has survived the recutting sufficiently to be still legible:

- - - - -
- - - - -
- - - - -
- - - - -
חבל

..............*Alas!*

The second inscription cut over the top of it may best be judged from Plate 46. Because of the many uncertainties obtaining, no transcription will here be attempted. It is presumably this inscription that Ingholt has described as a forgery, although it seems possibly to be ancient work in a crude running hand, most probably naming the lady for whom the relief had been usurped and divested of its jewellery. If this inference is correct, the new owner would seem to have been a much poorer person! The period may have been that of Palmyra's final decline. Usurpation may have been commoner than is supposed on Palmyrene reliefs, but is usually hard to detect because of the rough tooling of the background.

Ingholt has related this relief to his nos. PS 43 and PS 46, *op. cit.* pls. 13. 3, 14. 2, dated respectively to A.D. 161 and A.D. 184. It is thus most plausibly to be assigned to the second half of the second century A.D.

C. second half of the second century A.D.

Chapman, *Handbook* (2nd ed.) 39; H. Ingholt, *Studier over Palmyrensk Skulptur* 141 no. 441.

141 Grave-relief of a man, shown with his wife and sons

PLATE 46

Purchased. Reputedly from Palmyra. Inv.: GR.6.1888.

H. 0·537 m., H. of relief 0·09 m. max. Greyish-white limestone with a faint golden patina and heavily encrusted with lime deposit. Of the relief-slab itself both bottom corners, the right edge and the left-hand part of the top edge are broken away; also chipped away are the left hand of the deceased and the cup it was holding. Restored in limestone is a section of the background of the relief between the head of the deceased and that of his nearest son. The nose of the wife, Tmụr, is restored in plaster. There is a repair at the left knee of the figure of the deceased. The preserved part of the left edge shows signs of having originally been rebated to fit in a slot.

The back of the relief-slab is unworked; its lower edge is dressed level with the claw-chisel. The relief itself shows the dead man banqueting in the presence of his family—a common type of representation at Palmyra, where it is occasionally employed in elaborate grave-triclinia. Ultimately it is derived from the funerary-banquet scenes on Greek hero-reliefs such as **36**, **61**, **63** f. The couch itself, if it was indicated at all, would have been carved on the block immediately below, as on *Syria* XVIII (1937) pl. 4. Here the deceased is shown reclining on a cushion and a mattress spread upon it. The mattress is embroidered with flowers set in the lozenge-shaped interstices between crossing bands. The dead man is wrapped about in a himation worn over loose trousers and a short, richly embroidered, long-sleeved chiton bound with a narrow belt. His shoes, too, are finely adorned. In his left hand he held a hemispherical cup in front of him. His beard and hair are rendered in shallow relief. His eyes, like those of the other figures on the relief, have drilled pupils and outlined irises. Only a very little survives of the inscription above his right shoulder which originally gave his name and particulars:

- - - - - [צ[לם
- - - - - - - בר
- - - - - - סרבָ

Portrait of....., son of.......SRB (?)....

His two sons, Uhbi and Mlk'l, are shown standing behind. Their hair is lanker than their father's and they appear to be dressed after the Greek fashion in chiton and himation. The inscriptions between their heads read as follows:

צל⟨מ⟩ והבי
ברה
צלמ מלכאל
ברה

Portrait of Uhbi, his son. Portrait of Mlk'l, his son.

ברה appears to have been written for the more usual בנה. The name Uhbi may be of Arabic derivation; Mlk'l is an ordinary Semitic name, attested in Hebrew. Tmur, the widow of the deceased, is shown by his feet, seated on a high cushion. Like the lady on the usurped relief, **140**, she is dressed in an under- and an over-chiton, as well as in a himation worn over the back of her head as a veil and clasped at its edges in both her hands. Again the hair is bound up in the same kind of sakkos. She has a similar ornamented frontlet over her brow and similar ear-rings in her ears. She also wears a pearl necklace around her neck and has the usual elaborate clasp fastening her over-chiton. Above her left shoulder is cut the inscription:

צלמת תמור
ברת והברת
אתתה

Portrait of Tmur, daughter of Uhbrt, his wife.

The name Tmur may be a variant of Tamar. Uhbrt might be from the same root as Uhbi above.

On the type of elaborate embroideries shown on this relief see *Syria* XVIII (1937) 4 f. The treatment of the head of the deceased finds its best-dated parallels in the late second century A.D., e.g. Ingholt, *op. cit.* no. PS 19, pl. 6. 2, dated to A.D. 189. The fashion in which the widow is shown also seems of about this period, as may be seen from a comparison with **140**, although a date into the early third century A.D. is perhaps not entirely to be excluded.

C. late second, or possibly early third, centuries A.D.

Chapman, *Handbook* (2nd ed.) 39; *Berytus* II (1935) 70, pl. 31. 3; L. Budde, *Die Entstehung des antiken Repräsentationsbildes* 13, pl. 32.

142 Grave-relief of Zn' PLATE 46

Purchased. Reputedly from Palmyra. Inv.: GR.7.1888.

H. 0·5 m., H. of relief 0·165 m. max. Hard greyish-white limestone. The point-dressed edges of the slab have been chipped away at the upper part of the right side and at various points at the bottom. The back of the slab is unworked.

The relief shows a frontal bust of the dead man, Zn', clad in a sleeved chiton and a himation. The top of his head does not rise above the upper edge of the relief-ground. The irises of his eyes are incised, but the pupils are only marked by a very faintly scratched outline, perhaps used as a guide in painting. The way that the texture of the short beard is suggested by pitting the surface may derive from a device found on Roman portraits of the third century A.D. The following inscription is somewhat clumsily cut on the unevenly trimmed background of the relief above the deceased's left shoulder:

זנא בר
ידעבלָ
חבל

Zn', son of Id'bl. Alas!

The name, Zn', seems to be a foreign one of Graeco-Roman origin, possibly Zeno; Id'bl, on the other hand, is a good Semitic name.

This relief may be compared with Ingholt, *op. cit.* no. PS 21, pl. 6. 4, and no. PS 28, pl. 9. 3, dated respectively to A.D. 204 and 246–7. It is probably itself to be assigned to the early–mid third century A.D.

C. early–mid third century A.D.

Chapman, *Handbook* (2nd ed.) 39; L. Budde, *Die Entstehung des antiken Repräsentationsbildes* 13, pl. 31.

(K) A GRAVE-ALTAR AND A FUNERARY STELE FROM ITALY

143 Grave-altar to Titus Statilius Hermes

PLATE 48

Presented by Dr J. Disney. Probably acquired in Italy. Inv.: GR.60.1850.

H. 0·77 m., D. 0·288 m. max. Luna marble. The altar appears to have been re-used in modern times as a kind of base. An almost vertical hole, 0·04 m. in diameter, has been bored right through it with a heavy steel drill and may have been intended, in conjunction with a cup-shaped hollow in the top, to carry a swivel-mount. Subsequently, a heavy iron rod of slightly larger diameter has been bedded in the upper part of this hole. To judge from a circular recutting of the top of the altar, this seems to have served to hold in position a round object such as a marble grave-vase. In addition to the reworking already mentioned, parts of the upper surface of the altar seem to have been retrimmed with the point.

The base and the back of the altar have rusticated surfaces. The main relief zone at the sides and in front is bounded above and below by heavy mouldings. On the two front corners are carved heads of Ammon and, on the back corners, rams' heads. These last are appropriate as the animal sacred to the god Ammon. All four protomai have garlands tied to their horns with the aid of fillets whose ends are shown fluttering free. The garlands at the sides are of laurel, that in front of an assortment of fruit, leaves and pine-cones. Underneath the protomai birds are shown pecking at the ends of the fillets; at the front corners are eagles, at the back swans with their necks arched gracefully backwards. On the sides of the altar above the garlands are figured richly ornamented libation vases, an oinochoe on the left side, a phiale on the right. On the front, between the inscribed panel and the garland, is a vigorous small relief of a lion attacking a wild ass. Beneath the garland two small birds are fighting over a butterfly. The crowning of the monument is decorated with an antithetical pattern of acanthus leaves and rosettes, terminating at the sides in volutes with large flowers set in their 'eyes'. The inscription on the panel in front reads as follows:

DiIs · manibus
sacrum
T(ito) · Statilio · Hermeti.
Statilia · Philaenis
fecit · coniugi
suo · carissimo
et · bene
merito · de · se.

Sacred to the deified dead, Titus Statilius Hermes. Statilia Philaenis made it for her husband who was very dear and kind to her.

Grave-altars with this general type of decoration were already established by the middle years of the first century A.D., as witness that of Marcus Licinius Crassus Frugi from the Tomb of the Pisones, now in the Museo Nazionale Romano; see W. Altmann, *Die römischen Grabaltäre der Kaiserzeit* 37 f. no. 1. But this seems distinctly earlier than the Cambridge altar, which has more in common with late-first-century-A.D. examples in the Uffizi: G. A. Mansuelli, *Galleria degli Uffizi, le sculture* I 212 f., nos. 218–19. It may, on the other hand, seem typologically earlier than early-second-century-A.D. altars such as Mansuelli, *op. cit.* 216 f. no. 224, G. Lippold, *Kat. vaticanischen Museums* III. 2. 387 f. no. 22, pl. 167, but its execution is not necessarily of earlier date, as may be seen by comparing the sides of the last example cited with those of the Cambridge altar. Although such features as the outlined irises and drilled pupils of the protomai are soundly attested on monuments of this kind before the end of the first century A.D., the transversely striated brows of the heads of Ammon may strike a genuinely late note.

C. late first–early second centuries A.D.

Memoirs of Thos. Hollis, Esq. II pl. at end; J. Disney sr., *Cat. Hyde* 4, appendix 18 no. 12, with pl.; J. Disney jr., *Museum Disneianum* 127 f., pls. 57–8; Marsden, *Cat. Disney Coll.* 85 no. 43; Michaelis, *Anc. Marbles* 266 no. 91; Chapman, *Handbook* (2nd ed.) 50; *CIL* VI 26766.

144 Grave-stele of Pompeia Margaris

PLATE 44

Presented by Dr J. Disney. Found in the mid-eighteenth century in the Villa del Cinque outside the Porta Pinciana, Rome. Inv.: GR.54.1850.

H. 0·625 m. Luna marble. Sawn surfaces at bottom and at back, the latter certainly ancient. To judge from a broken surface at the back and the treatment of the rusticated edges, the right side had a somewhat deeper return, now broken away, of about the same thickness as the main part of the stele, making the monument originally rather

L-shaped in plan. The stele may thus have been set, e.g., against an external corner of a grave-building. Right acroterion partly broken away. Minor chips missing elsewhere. Modern dowel-holes in underside. Pierced modern metal bar set in top.

The sunken relief-panel shows the dead woman, Pompeia Margaris, clad in a stola or tunica and a cloak, reclining, as in sleep, on a low sofa. Beneath the couch appears a footstool or casket, seen at a three-quarter angle. The dead woman's back is supported by cushions and her right hand still limply clasps a pomegranate as symbolic of her translation to the other world. Her pet dog is shown trying in vain to waken her. Over the brow the woman's hair is arranged in three rows of tight spiral curls. The rest of her hair, apart from small escaping locks at the nape of the neck, is carried back to a twice-coiled plait at the back of the head. The stele is crowned with a pediment and lateral acroteria. The acroteria are decorated with half-palmettes whilst, in the pediment, there is carved a laurel garland tied with a ribbon. In a large, rectangular, profiled recess beneath the relief-panel there is cut the following inscription:

D(iis) · m(anibus)
Pompeiae
Margaridi
fidelissimae.
Felicio
coniugi · suae
b(ene) · m(erenti)
posuit.

To the deified dead, the right faithful Pompeia Margaris. Felicio set it up to his kind wife.

On the name, Margaris, cf. Bechtel and Fick, *Die griechischen Personennamen* 330. Scenes of this kind, with the dead shown reclining as if in sleep on a couch, are a common motif on Roman grave-reliefs, as witness, e.g., Altmann, *op. cit.* 168 no. 215, 192 f. nos. 258 f. For the present theme showing the dead woman on a couch with a pomegranate in her hand and her pet dog beside her cf. *CIL* VI 2330. The hair-style of the deceased dates the Cambridge stele to later Flavian or Trajanic times.

C. late first–early second centuries A.D.

Novelle fiorentine 1752 723; *Memoirs of Thos. Hollis, Esq.* II pl. at end; J. Disney sr., *Cat. Hyde* 8, appendix 17 no. 11, with pl.; J. Disney jr., *Museum Disneianum* 111 f., pl. 50; *AZ* V (1847) 160; Marsden, *Cat. Disney Coll.* 87 no. 77; Michaelis, *Anc. Marbles* 265 no. 85; Chapman, *Handbook* (2nd ed.) 53; *CIL* VI 24550; F. Cumont, *Le symbolisme funéraire des Romains* 398 n. 1; W. Altmann, *Die römischen Grabaltäre der Kaiserzeit* 191 f. no. 257; *AJA* LXIII (1959) 142.

(L) CINERARIA FROM ITALY

145 Cinerarium of Aelia Postumia and her husband PLATES 48–49

Presented by Dr J. Disney. Acquired in Italy. Inv.: GR.56.1850.

H. without lid 0·46 m. Luna marble. Lid missing. All four upper corners of the cinerarium itself broken away at the point where iron dowels originally secured the lid in position. Minor chips missing elsewhere.

The cinerarium rests on low feet at the corners. All four of its sides carry rich decoration in relief. This is framed at the top and bottom edges by a Lesbian kymation. Towards the top of each corner there is shown a boukranion, or ox-skull, its brow and horns bound about with fillets whose ends are fluttering in the wind. From these hang garlands heavy with fruit, flowers, leaves, grain, pine-cones and seed. Above the garlands on the front and back a small bird is to be seen, apparently darting at the end of one of the fillets. On the sides their place is taken by Gorgoneia. Below the garlands there are pairs of antithetically placed small birds on all four sides. Those in front are fighting over a lizard; those at the back appear to be drinking from a small pot set on the ground. One of the birds on the left side has a worm which is clearly occupying the attention of his companion, whilst the pair on the right side hold a moth and a seedpod (?) in their beaks. The inscription on the front of the cinerarium seems best interpreted as follows:

(Diis manibus *name of husband.*)
Aeli(a) · Postumia · uerna · fecit
si<b>i {t} ⟦a⟧ et
con<iu>gi carissimo
conquo · uIxit · an(nis) · xxiii · b(ene) · m(erenti).

(*To the deified dead,...* [name of husband].) *Aelia Postumia, born a slave, made it for herself and her very dear husband with whose kind self she lived twenty-three years.*

The authors are indebted to Mr A. G. Woodhead for the suggestion, followed here, that the name of the dead man was actually inscribed on the missing lid of the cinerarium. The first letter of *Aeli*(*a*) and the last of *uerna* seem to be cut over former erasures and there are several other possible ancient corrections of this type which cannot with certainty be identified because of the uneven character of the lettering. For *sibi* the inscription reads *siui*—at least, this seems a more reasonable interpretation than to follow the *CIL* in regarding this line as an otherwise unknown dative of an otherwise unknown proper name.[1] There follows a superfluous *t*, a completely erased *a* and then *et* in ligature. The inscription seems originally to have had *coniugi* spelt correctly, but one of the numerous ancient erasures has modified this to *conuigi*. *Con* for *cum* is not uncommon on inscriptions of this type and date. This is a truly magnificent monument to be set up by one born a slave and Aelia Postumia's reference to her humble origin is probably made not without pride. Nevertheless, it is probably against this background that the many errors of the inscription are best to be understood. It seems likely that the lady may have been barely literate and may have insisted over-strictly on the cutting of an inscription of her own preparing!

This fine, large cinerarium goes very closely with two from the Tomb of the Platorini and is quite probably from the same workshop; cf. Altmann, *op. cit.* 46, figs. 36–7. Its date thus probably falls still in the second quarter of the first century A.D. Early features are the generous proportions, the form of the garlands, the quality and character of the cutting and the absence of an inscription-plate. It is also of social significance as an interesting instance of the process, beginning at this time, whereby the cinerarium, hitherto confined to the family tombs of the rich and noble, was adapted to the use of freed slaves and the like. For a later form of the boukranion-and-garland motif cf. **160** below; for its Hellenistic antecedents cf. **71** and **72** above.

C. second quarter of the first century A.D.

Memoirs of Thos. Hollis, Esq. II pl. at end; J. Disney sr., *Cat. Hyde* appendix 12 no. 6, with pl.; J. Disney jr., *Museum Disneianum* 119 f., pls. 54, 54*a*; Marsden, *Cat. Disney Coll.* 83 no. 1; Michaelis, *Anc. Marbles* 265 no. 87; Chapman, *Handbook* (2nd ed.) 38; *CIL* VI 10951.

146 Cinerarium of Julia Anthis and Tiberius Claudius Hermias PLATE 47

Presented by Dr J. Disney. Acquired in Italy. Inv.: GR.57*a*.1850.

H. without lid 0·255 m. Luna marble. Original lid missing; in earlier publications it has been shown with the lid from another cinerarium, **147** *below. Very slightly chipped at the edges.*

The inscribed panel is framed with entwined acanthus foliage and rosette-like flowers, their convolutions developing symmetrically from a central cluster of leaves beneath the inscription. In a corresponding position above the middle of the inscribed panel a bird is shown attacking a small snake. The excessively deep control-drillings for the decoration themselves form a pattern, but tend rather to disrupt the effect of the design as a whole. The inscription reads as follows:

Ti(berius) · Claudius · Hermias
fecit · Iuliae · Anthidi,
coniugi · suae
carissimae, · et
sibi. · Vixit · ann(is) · xxxvi.

Tiberius Claudius Hermias made it for Julia Anthis, his very dear wife, and himself. She lived thirty-six years.

Recessed relief-panels on both sides of the cinerarium show branches of laurel with very fleshy leaves. On each side two small birds may be seen pecking at the berries.

The ornament of the face and sides of this cinerarium is of a type that comes to the fore in the Claudian period, but continues popular throughout Neronian and Flavian times. The present example, as already implied by Altmann (*op. cit.* 124), does not fall early in this development. On the other hand, the plump rosettes are probably to be dated before later Flavian times.

C. third quarter of the first century A.D. or slightly later.

Memoirs of Thos. Hollis, Esq. II, pl. at end; J. Disney sr., *Cat. Hyde* 9, appendix 14 no. 8, with pl.; J. Disney jr., *Museum Disneianum* 121 f., pl. 55; Marsden, *Cat. Disney Coll.* 86 no. 51; Michaelis, *Anc. Marbles* 265 no. 88; Chapman, *Handbook* (2nd ed.) 54; *CIL* VI 15111; W. Altmann, *Die römischen Grabaltäre der Kaiserzeit* 134.

147 Lid of a cinerarium PLATE 47

Presented by Dr J. Disney. Acquired in Italy. Inv.: GR.57*b*.1850.

H. (lid only) 0·103 m. Luna marble. Only the lid is preserved. In earlier publications this is regarded as part of **146** *above, to which it clearly does not belong by reason*

[1] Without emending the text it is perfectly possible to read this line, in its present form, as '*siuit et*'. However, it seems much more probable that something more closely approximating to an established formula is really intended.

alike of its different size and decoration. Acroteria slightly chipped. Small clamp-holes for fastening in sides.

The lid is in the form of a gabled roof covered with scale-shaped tiles. In front the pediment is decorated with an oak garland tied with a ribbon. To either side it is flanked by acroteria with deeply cut half-palmettes. At the sides of the lid, however, the edges of the roof and the faces of the acroteria above are carved in representation of ashlar masonry. This probably simply continues the decoration of the sides of the lower member of the cinerarium and suggests that very probably this was of a type in the form of a naïskos; cf. Altmann, *op. cit.* 136 f. For its appearance when complete cf. A. Sadurska, *Inscriptions latines et monuments funéraires romains au Musée National de Varsovie* 46 f. no. 8, pl. 13. For the treatment of the front of the lid cf. **144** above. The date is probably likewise in the late first or earlier second centuries A.D.

C. late first–earlier second centuries A.D.

Bibliography as for **146**.

148 Cinerarium of Marcus Flavius Hyla

PLATE 47

Transferred from the Museum of Archaeology and Ethnology, Cambridge. Provenance unknown. Inv.: GR.52.1952.

H. 0·291 m. Luna marble, with the surface somewhat worn and pitted. Repaired at a break through the right-hand part of the cist. Bottom edge of right side recut. There has been a very little cleaning, e.g. on the eyes of one of the Ammon-protomai.

At the upper part of the front corners of the cist are carved heads of the god Ammon, their horns bound with fillets. A rich garland of fruit, flowers and pine-cones is shown hanging from these across the front of the cinerarium. A swan with spread wings appears in the space between the garland and the inscribed panel. To either side below the garland are figured hawks which are shown pecking at the fillets fluttering from the Ammon-protomai. On the base beneath them and in the middle there are incised minute tabulae. The following inscription is somewhat unevenly cut on a profiled rectangular panel above the garland:

M(arcus) · Flauius · Hyla
hic · situs · est.
Marcus Flavius Hyla is laid here.

Both of the sides are decorated with an enormous central rosette flanked by four smaller flowers in the corners. The lid is in the form of a gabled roof of scale-shaped tiles with foliate volutes at the sides. A second pair of volutes occupy the centre of the pediment. In all cases the volutes have rosettes set in their 'eyes' and palmettes in their inner angles. A twist-pattern runs along the front of the lid under the pediment.

This cinerarium belongs to a well-defined group with very similar decoration in front and, at the sides, either large rosettes or palmettes. The inscriptions of many also show a similar careless lettering. A typical example is that in the Capitoline Museum in Rome: *CIL* VI 17702, H. Stuart Jones, *Cat. Museo Capitolino* 55 no. 9, pl. 11, D. Mustilli, *Museo Mussolini* 44 no. 27, pl. 30. On the evidence of type and garland-form they seem clearly later than the middle of the first century A.D. Apart from this, an example in the British Museum helps to fix their chronology more closely; see *CIL* X 582, A. H. Smith, *BMC Sculpture* III 350 no. 2362. This was set up by an Imperial freedman of the Julio-Claudian dynasty, Tiberius Claudius Inopus, for his wife who died at the early age of thirty. Under these circumstances, a date for this cinerarium in the second half of the first century A.D. seems almost certain and this is probably also applicable to the group as a whole.

Second half of the first century A.D.

149 Cinerarium of Gnaeus Caesius Atticus

PLATE 47

Presented by Dr J. Disney. Found at Rome in a columbarium inside the Valerian Wall at the start of the Via Appia and Via Latina. Inv.: GR.58.1850.

H. without lid 0·24 m., depth 0·263 m. Luna marble. Tip of the nose of one of the Ammon-protomai broken away; minor chips missing elsewhere. Lid lost. Surface harshly cleaned.

At the upper part of both front corners of the cinerarium are carved heads of the god, Ammon, with their horns bound with fillets from which a heavy garland is shown hung across the front of the cinerarium. This is probably intended as of laurel, despite the somewhat serrated edges of the leaves. Two small birds are shown pecking at its berries from below; two more are to be seen fighting above it. The lower part of each of the front corners of the cinerarium is occupied by the figure of a large water-bird with spread wings and neck arched backwards as it pecks at the hanging end of one of the fillets. To judge from similar representations on monuments of this kind such as **143** above, it seems almost certain that swans are intended. The leaves of the garland have been extensively undercut with the drill. The heads of Ammon seem to have had the pupils of the eyes faintly indicated; one protome actually has the pupil of one eye drilled, but this may be due to recutting in the modern cleaning. The following inscription is carved on a profiled panel above the garland:

Cn(aeo) · Caesio
Attico.
Iulia · Cypare
coniug(i) · cariss(imo).

To Gnaeus Caesius Atticus. Julia Cypare (made it) for her very dear husband.

The proportions of this cinerarium and the general arrangement of its decoration are still much the same as those of the group considered under **148** above and it is probably of about the same date, although the execution seems less sure and may be slightly later. Also the decoration of the sides is much more summary and, apart from completing the corner-figures of swans and Ammon-heads with fillets, is confined to incised diagonal lines.

Second half of the first century A.D. or slightly later.

Memoirs of Thos. Hollis, Esq. II pl. at end; J. Disney sr., *Cat. Hyde* appendix 13 no. 7; J. Disney jr., *Museum Disneianum* 123 f., pl. 56 no. 7; Marsden, *Cat. Disney Coll.* 84 no. 36; Michaelis, *Anc. Marbles* 266 no. 89; Chapman, *Handbook* (2nd ed.) 54; *CIL* VI 13968; W. Altmann, *Die römischen Grabaltäre der Kaiserzeit* 99.

150 Cinerary urn PLATE 50

Presented by Dr J. Disney. Probably acquired in Italy. Inv.: GR.52*a*.1850.

Diam. c. 0·27 m. Luna marble. Lid missing. Slightly chipped. Formerly illustrated with the lid of doubtful authenticity, **192** *below, which does not fit it. Surface somewhat encrusted.*

The genuineness of this uninscribed urn has long been doubted, but, so far as can be determined, without justification. It is of a type well attested in the first century A.D., as witness the example from the Tomb of the Platorini, Altmann, *op. cit.* 46, fig. 33. Also comparable is G. Lippold, *Kat. vaticanischen Museums* III. 2. 378 f. no. 10, pl. 163. Much closer in shape and, in fact, of identical proportions is an urn in the Palazzo Doria in Rome.

C. first century A.D.

Memoirs of Thos. Hollis, Esq. II pl. at end; J. Disney sr., *Cat. Hyde* 4, appendix 23 no. 17; J. Disney jr., *Museum Disneianum* 113 f., pl. 51; Marsden, *Cat. Disney Coll.* 85 no. 47; Michaelis, *Anc. Marbles* 265 no. 83; Chapman, *Handbook* (2nd ed.) 53.

151 Cinerarium of Quintus Calidius Pothus and Valeria Maxima PLATE 50

Presented by Dr J. Disney. Probably acquired in Italy. Inv.: GR.59*a*.1850.

H. without lid 0·226 m. Luna marble. Lid missing. The top has been recut in modern times to fit the lid from another cinerarium of distinctly smaller dimensions, **152** *below. Minor chips missing.*

Each of the front corners of the cinerarium is occupied by a massive tripod-lebes with lion-claw feet and with palmettes at the top of the legs. A large, round, sacred stone draped with knotted woollen fillets is set in the top of each cauldron. A garland of fruit, flowers and pine-cones hangs down under the inscribed panel from two large nails to either side of it. Four small birds are pecking at the fruit, two from above and two from below. The top of the relief and the edges of the inscribed panel are framed with a twist-pattern. The inscription reads as follows:

DiIs manibus
Q(uinti) Calidi · Pothi. · Valeria
Ias · coniugi bene meren(t)i
et · Valeriae Maximae · f(iliae)
Calidius · Eleuth(e)r(us) · l(ibertus) · fecer(unt).

To the deified spirit of Quintus Calidius Pothus. Made by Valeria Ias for her kind husband and by Calidius Eleutherus, a freedman, for Valeria Maxima, their daughter.

The name, *Pothi*, has Greek authority and so need not be an abbreviation for *Pothini*; for *Valeria* the *CIL*, without justification, reads *Vallria*; for *Ias* Michaelis suggests *Ias(o)*. The name of Calidius Eleutherus' patron is not given, but numerous freedmen of a Quintus Calidius are attested epigraphically.

Cineraria of this type are not uncommon, but there is little reliable evidence for dating them. The scheme of decoration recalls **149**, but the squatter and narrower proportions seem later. The garland-type is more evolved than that of **148**, but not necessarily as late as that of **153**. The cauldrons with sacred stones are probably meant to symbolize the Delphic tripod and omphalos, which are similarly shown as supports for statues of Apollo, e.g. J. P. J. Brants, *Description of the Ancient Sculpture of the Museum of Archaeology of Leiden* no. 12, pl. 7.

C. late first or first half of the second centuries A.D.

Memoirs of Thos. Hollis, Esq. II pl. at end; J. Disney sr., *Cat. Hyde* 10, appendix 19 no. 13, with pl.; J. Disney jr., *Museum Disneianum* 124 f., pl. 56 no. 13; Marsden, *Cat. Disney Coll.* 85 no. 48; Michaelis, *Anc. Marbles* 266 no. 90; Chapman, *Handbook* (2nd ed.) 53;

CIL VI 14066; W. Altmann, *Die römischen Grabaltäre der Kaiserzeit* 121 no. 124.

152 Lid from a cinerarium PLATE 47

Presented by Dr J. Disney. Probably acquired in Italy. Inv.: GR.59*b*.1850.

H. (lid only) 0·062 m. Luna marble. Only the lid is preserved. Both rear corners broken away. Chipped elsewhere. Root-marks on underside. In modern times used as a lid for the larger cinerarium, **151**.

The lid is in the shape of a roof with scale-shaped tiles and with foliate volute-balusters at the sides. The front of the pediment is decorated with an acanthus-leaf motif, with a Lesbian kymation above and with a 'ribbon-twist' below. Rosettes are set in the 'eyes' of the volutes. Once again, a close dating is difficult, although the long, narrow shape of the lid suggests that it belonged to a cinerarium of much the same proportions as **151** and, not improbably, of about the same period.

C. late first or first half of the second centuries A.D.

Bibliography, in the main, as for **151**.

153 Cinerarium of Marcus Ulpius Fortunatus PLATE 51

Presented by Dr J. Disney. Acquired in Italy. Inv.: GR.55.1850.

H. 0·693 m. Luna marble with traces of a brown patina. The lid was attached by clamps at the sides and a small part of the rim of the cist has been broken away on the right side when these were forced open.

This cinerarium has adopted the tall, narrow shape usual for grave-altars. Heads of the god Ammon are shown towards the top of the front corners of the cist. Their horns are bound with fillets from which an oak garland hangs low across the front of the cinerarium. A winged Gorgoneion occupies the space above the garland under the inscribed panel. Towards the bottom of the front corners of the cist there are carved masks wearing Phrygian caps. The inscription on the front of the cinerarium reads as follows:

D(iis) · m(anibus)
M(arco) · Vlpio
Aug(usti) · lib(erto)
Fortunato.
Philetus · pater
et · Vlpia · Plusias
coniugi · b(ene) · m(erenti) · f(ecerunt).

To the deified dead, Marcus Ulpius Fortunatus, Imperial freedman. Made by his father, Philetus, and by Ulpia Plusias for her kind husband.

The inscribed panel is surrounded with a Lesbian kymation and an incised ivy pattern. The same ivy pattern also extends along the top and bottom edges of the cist. The lid is in the form of a steeply-pitched, gabled roof. The front edges of the pediment are decorated with an ivy pattern of the kind met with on the cist. Its centre is occupied by the figures of two dolphins twined about a trident and holding shells in their mouths. It is flanked to either side by lateral acroteria in the form of half-palmettes. The top of the lid and the back of lid and cist have rusticated surfaces. The running-drill has been extensively used on this cinerarium, e.g. in the cutting of the oak garland. The various heads show outlined irises. The pupils of the eyes of the Gorgoneion and dolphins have been drilled, but in the case of the Ammon-protomai and the masks the drilling is confined to the eye on the front side of the monument, giving these heads a curious winking appearance.

The deceased is apparently a freedman of the Emperor, Trajan, and, as a consequence, this monument cannot be earlier in date than that Emperor's reign. It thus plainly refutes the erroneous theory that grave-monuments of this kind with Ammon-protomai had ceased to be made before the end of the reign of Domitian; cf. *Revue des études latines* XXVI (1948) 32 f. Indeed, a comparison with work of the turn from the first to the second centuries A.D. (see under **143**) suggests that this cinerarium is distinctly later. The form of the masks in Phrygian caps recalls the corner-masks of sarcophagi from the time of Hadrian on. Also, the Gorgoneion closely resembles her sisters on garland-sarcophagi of about the same period (cf. **156**). On the other hand, the circumstance that the dead man's father survived him would seem to dissuade too late a dating.

First half of the second century A.D.

Memoirs of Thos. Hollis, Esq., II pl. at end; J. Disney sr., *Cat. Hyde* 5, appendix II no. 5, with pl.; J. Disney jr., *Museum Disneianum* 117 f., pl. 53; Marsden, *Cat. Disney Coll.* 85 no. 44; Michaelis, *Anc. Marbles* 265 no. 86; Chapman, *Handbook* (2nd ed.) 48; *CIL* VI 29203.

154 Cinerarium of Marcus Aurelius PLATE 50

Presented by Dr J. Disney. Found in Rome near the Tomb of Caecilia Metella; the alleged provenance from Baiae, cited in *Novelle fiorentine* and followed by Mommsen, is false. Inv.: GR.51.1850.

H. without lid 0·249 m. Luna marble. Lid missing.

Surface slightly chipped. Two clamp-holes in wall for attachment of lid.

The cist of this cinerarium is carved from two pieces of marble, the bottom being cut separately and inserted inside the wall. The round, flat-bottomed shape, tapering towards the top, is of a type commonly met with amongst cinerary urns of pottery. Here, however, an important difference is introduced by the presence of incised lines giving the wall the effect of ashlar masonry, as if of a tower. On the front of the cinerarium this decoration is interrupted by the inscription-panel. Originally this was confined to the upper half of the wall, but, before the inscription was cut, it was extended to the full height of the cinerarium. The inscription reads:

D(iis) · m(anibus)
M(arco) · Aur(elio) · M(arci) · f(ilio) ·
Aelia · Gall(ica)
Vi<m>inacio. ·
Mil(es) · coh(ortis) · iv · pr(aetoriae), ·
uixs(it) · ann(is) · xlv, ·
mil(itauit) · ann(is) · xiiii. ·
Aurelia · Nice ·
marito · suo
b(ene) · m(erenti) · posuit. ·

To the deified dead, Marcus Aurelius, son of Marcus, of the tribe Aelia Gallica, from Viminacium. A soldier of the fourth praetorian cohort, he lived forty-five years and served fourteen. Aurelia Nice set it up for her kind husband.

For *Viminacio* the inscription reads *Viuinacio*; almost certainly Viminacium in Moesia is meant.

The employment of the tribal name, *Aelia Gallica*, probably indicates a date after the organization of the municipality of Viminacium by Hadrian. A round cinerarium in the Vatican, likewise with decoration in the form of ashlar masonry, seems assignable to the early third century A.D.; cf. G. Lippold, *Kat. vaticanischen Museums* III. 2. 224 no. 92, pl. 104. But this approximates in shape to the type of **155** and seems distinctly later in date than the present urn which is probably still of the second century A.D.

C. mid-late second century A.D.

Novelle fiorentine 1752 270; *Memoirs of Thos. Hollis, Esq.* II pl. at end; J. Disney sr., *Cat. Hyde* appendix 8 no. 2, with pl.; J. Disney jr., *Museum Disneianum* 109 f., pl. 49; Marsden, *Cat. Disney Coll.* 85 no. 40; T. Mommsen, *Inscr. reg. Neapol.* 6813; Michaelis, *Anc. Marbles* 264 no. 82; *CIL* VI 2525; Chapman, *Handbook* (2nd ed.) 53; Vermeule in *Transactions of the American Philosophical Society*, New Series 50, part 5 (1960) 25 no. 344, 70, fig. 81.

155 Cinerarium of Titus Flavius Verus

PLATE 50

Presented by Dr J. Disney. From Pozzuoli, the ancient Puteoli. Inv.: GR. 50. 1850.

H. without lid 0·256 m. Luna marble. Lid missing. Surface slightly chipped. Three small holes in wall for clamps to attach the lid.

Above a heavy base-moulding the wall of this circular cinerarium is decorated with well-carved, undulating fluting. The inscription is cut on a richly profiled tabula ansata. It shows cursive elements in its letter-forms and reads as follows:

D(iis) m(anibus)
T(ito) F̣l(auio) Vero Aug(ustae) ·
lib(erto) · tab(ulario) · rat(ionis) ·
aquarior(um). · Co<n>-
iugi bene m<e>-
renti Octa-
uia Thetis f(ecit). ·

To the deified dead, Titus Flavius Verus, Imperial freedman and keeper of the accounts of the guild of water-carriers. Octavia Thetis made it for her kind husband.

The inscription reads *coiugi* for *coniugi*; it also has *mfrenti* for *merenti*, but it is noteworthy that *e* and *f* are almost indistinguishable at other points as well.

This kind of cinerarium combines the undulating fluting typical of the *sarcophagi bacellati* (cf. **163**) with an inscription-plate in the form of a tabula ansata. On the analogy of the related sarcophagus-types it seems unlikely that it could date before the early third century A.D. A lower limit in the mid third century A.D. is suggested by the general eclipse of the practice of cremation by about that date. The most likely identification of Titus Flavius Verus' Imperial patron, as consistent with this dating, is Flavia Titiana, daughter of Titus Flavius Sulpicianus and wife of Pertinax who was Emperor in A.D. 193. During her husband's short reign she adopted the title of Augusta and may well have liberated slaves to mark his accession. As Titus Flavius Verus seems to have served the guild of water-carriers for a considerable period after obtaining his freedom, his death would probably fall in the period in the earlier part of the third century A.D. indicated by the type of the cinerarium. Amongst other examples of urns of this type one may cite:

Museo Capitolino 4503: H. Stuart Jones, *Cat. Museo Capitolino* 97 no. 18, pl. 33;

Lateran 10590: *CIL* VI 17163;

Vatican: G. Lippold, *Kat. vaticanischen Museums* III. 2. 336 f. no. 77, pl. 147;

Warsaw: A. Sadurska, *Inscriptions latines et monu-*

ments funéraires romains au Musée National de Varsovie 50 f. no. 9, pl. 14.

First half of the third century A.D.

Novelle fiorentine 1755 415; Cimaglia, *Antiquit. venust.* (1757) 195; *Memoirs of Thos. Hollis, Esq.* II pl. at end; J. Disney sr., *Cat. Hyde* 5, appendix 10 no. 4, with pl.; J. Disney jr., *Museum Disneianum* 107 f.,pl. 48; Marsden, *Cat. Disney Coll.* 85 no. 42; T. Mommsen, *Inscr. reg. Neapol.* 2889; J. C. von Orelli, revised by W. Henzen, *Inscriptionum Latinarum selectarum collectio* 6570; Michaelis, *Anc. Marbles* 264 no. 81; *CIL* vi 1743 (with addendum on p. 971); H. Dessau, *Inscriptiones Latinae Selectae* i 1608; *CIL* x 33731; Chapman, *Handbook* (2nd ed.) 54.

(M) SARCOPHAGI OF GREEK TYPE

156 Gorgoneion, probably from a garland-sarcophagus PLATE 51

Presented by Dr J. Disney. Acquired in Italy (?). Inv.: GR.43.1850.

P.H. 0·249 m. Pentelic marble. Broken in modern times from the wall of a sarcophagus. Modern dowel-hole in underside. Possible traces of stucco on surface.

The Gorgon-head has long hair parted over the centre of the brow and a pair of snakes knotted under the chin. The relief has never been completely finished and the tooling is clearly visible. The evidence is mainly of the use of the flat chisel in long, shallow strokes parallel with the surface, although the gouge is also to be detected about the eyes and in the hair. The preliminary working of the eyelids and the hollow of the lips is also of interest. A small part of the inner surface of the sarcophagus is preserved at the back. It has been evenly dressed with the point.

Gorgoneia of this kind are commonly met with on garland-sarcophagi, the type being especially frequent in Asia Minor.[1] To judge from its material, however, the present fragment seems more likely to be from an Attic sarcophagus, although the presence of stucco also raises the possibility of an Alexandrian origin. For sarcophagi of this type from Alexandria see G. Maspero, *Le Musée Égyptien* III (1915) 16 n. 1, pls. 18–19, A. Adriani, *Repertorio d'arte dell'Egitto greco-romano*, ser. A, I 22 f. nos. 3 f., pls. 3 f. An unfinished piece such as this cannot be dated with any precision, but the relief is distinctly shallow and the cutting, so far as it has been completed, restrained.

C. second century A.D.

J. Disney sr., *Cat. Hyde* 3 no. 36; J. Disney jr., *MS Cat.* 180; Marsden, *Cat. Disney Coll.* 86 no. 56; Michaelis, *Anc. Marbles* 261 no. 74; Chapman, *Handbook* (2nd ed.) 39.

157 Fragment from the rim of an Attic sarcophagus PLATE 52

Bequeathed by the Rev. T. Worsley. Provenance unknown. Inv.: GR.1*d*.1885.

P.H. 0·224 m. Pentelic marble. Broken away below and at both sides. Chipped at the outer surface and at the projecting rim at the top of the inner edge, serving to hold the lid of the sarcophagus in position.

The fragment is from the top of the cist of an Attic sarcophagus and has its upper surface shaped to receive the lid. The preserved decoration of the outer surface is purely architectural in character. At the top is carved a meander pattern with double and single rosettes. Beneath this comes a row of egg-and-dart, followed by an elongated bead-and-reel motif. The lowermost preserved unit of all is a plain raised band.

The choice and arrangement of the decorative motifs derive from much older prototypes such as the Alexander Sarcophagus in Istanbul. But the elongated bead-and-reel and the deep, wide form of the 'eggs' of the ovolo are of a kind which, in Italy at least, tends to date from Hadrianic times on; cf. *BSR* XXI (1953) 118 f. This type of decoration seems to be confined to Kallipolitis' earliest classes of Attic sarcophagi; see V. G. Kallipolitis, Χρονολογικὴ κατάταξις τῶν Ἀττικῶν σαρκοφάγων τῆς Ῥωμαϊκῆς ἐποχῆς 65 f. A good example is the sarcophagus of Metilia Torquata in Naples, although on this the Ionic has been replaced by a Lesbian kymation; see Robert, *Die antiken Sarkophagreliefs* II 29 f. no. 22, pl. 10; *Museo Nazionale di Napoli, le raccolte archeologiche* 15, fig. 47; Kallipolitis, *op. cit.* 15 no. 11.

C. second–third quarters of the second century A.D.

Chapman, *Handbook* (2nd ed.) 47.

[1] Cf. G. Mendel, *Cat. Constantinople* III 394 f. nos. 1158 f.; *JHS* LIII (1933) 202; Arif M. Mansel and Aşkıdil Akarca, *Perge'de Kazılar ve Araştırmalar* pls. 5, 6, 15–17.

158 Lid of an Attic sarcophagus PLATE 51

Presented by Vice-Admiral T. A. B. Spratt. From Arvi in southern Crete. Inv.: GR. 1.1853.

L. 2·24 m., W. 0·952 m., H. (lid only) 0·433 m. Pentelic marble with heavy fault-lines running longitudinally. At the left end broken away at the top of the pediment and at both lateral acroteria; at the right end chipped at the right lateral acroterion and damaged at the edges of the pediment; at two points this damage appears at one time to have been made good by marble restorations which have since been removed.

The lid is in the form of a gabled roof covered with leaf-shaped tiles and resting on a plain kymation-member below. The tiles are much more deeply carved on one side and this has been taken as corresponding with the original front side of the coffin. Lateral acroteria are set at the four corners. These have plain, curving surfaces, possibly intended to carry painted decoration. The right end of the lid has never been completely finished and still retains its lifting-boss. The pediment at this end is occupied by the relief of a garland bound with a ribbon. This, too, is unfinished and has simply been roughed out with the gouge and chisel. On the other hand, the relief in the pediment at the left end of the lid has been fully finished. It shows a lebes flanked by an antithetical pair of crouching panthers. Their raised fore-paws are in very shallow relief and have partly had to be incised on the background.

As a rule, lids of this type with a plain kymation are associated with the earlier Attic sarcophagi of Imperial date; cf. Kallipolitis, *op. cit.* 35 f. The relief of the panthers also seems early; cf. the similar groups in the pediments of the sarcophagus of the second quarter of the second century A.D., **161** below.[1]

C. second–third quarters of the second century A.D.

Chapman, *Handbook* (2nd ed.) 36; A. Giuliano, *Il commercio dei sarcofagi attici* 53 no. 310.

159 Relief fragment, probably from an Attic Amazonomachy-sarcophagus

PLATE 51

Purchased. Provenance unknown. Inv.: GR.95 *c*.1906.

Greatest dimension 0·199 m. Pentelic marble. Only head, neck and a small part of the right arm preserved. Nose chipped. Broken away from a relief-ground at the back.

This fragment probably formed part of the relief decoration of a large sarcophagus. It consists of a soft-featured head, probably that of a woman, with curling hair and clad in a Phrygian cap, together with much of the neck and a part of an outflung right arm against the side of the head. The right side of the head has only been roughed out and was clearly not meant to be directly visible. Accordingly, it seems most probable that the fragment is from the figure of a dying Amazon lying sprawled on her right side and outflung right arm at the bottom of a battle scene on an Attic sarcophagus. The right side of the head would not then have been visible because of the proximity of the base. The side-flaps of the Phrygian cap are represented in the raised position, fastened together at the top. The cap and the curls of the hair show extensive use made of the running-drill. A small wisp of hair is also shown hanging down against the left cheek. The pupils of the eyes are not drilled, although it is not clear whether this is due to the unfinished state of one side of the head or reveals an attempt to show the glaze of death. The preliminary working of the lips recalls that met with on **156**. Venus-rings are indicated on the neck.

Closest in style to the Cambridge head seems a fragmentary Amazonomachy-sarcophagus in the Fogg Museum in Harvard; see *Harvard Studies in Classical Philology* XLVII (1936) 216 f.; R. Redlich, *Die Amazonensarkophage des 2. und 3. Jahrhunderts n. Chr.* 49 f., pl. 3; Kallipolitis, *op. cit.* 24 no. 118. This has been dated by Kallipolitis to the end of the second or early third centuries A.D. It has not been possible to verify at first hand whether the Cambridge fragment could be from the same sarcophagus. It seems to show a somewhat harsher use of the running-drill, but this it is impossible to judge from photographs only. Certainly, it seems to come from a sarcophagus of similar style and probably of about the same date.

C. end of second–early third centuries A.D.

AJA LXIII (1959) 143 no. 15.

[1] Cf. also the rather similar pair of lions on the back of an Attic sarcophagus in Athens of Kallipolitis' Early Group: Robert, *Die antiken Sarkophagreliefs* III. 2. pl. 70, no. 216*c*.

(N) SARCOPHAGI OF ITALIAN TYPE

160 Child's sarcophagus with griffins and sacred emblems PLATE 52

Presented by Lord Carmichael. Provenance unknown. Inv.: GR.7.1920.

L. 1·237 m., H. 0·48 m., W. 0·435 m. Luna marble. Restored in marble are the whole of the rear lateral acroterion on the right end and the upper half of its counterpart on the left end. Holes for two clamps at each end for securing the lid. Surface slightly weatherworn. The sarcophagus has been photographed on four modern lion's-claw feet.

In the middle of the front of the cist is carved a female figure terminating below in a cluster of acanthus leaves. She holds a basket of apples and grapes on her head and is flanked by an antithetical pair of winged griffins. These twine their tails through those of a further pair facing in the other direction. These outermost griffins are grouped antithetically with others carved on the ends of the cist and flank leaf-encrusted baetyls rising out of clusters of acanthus leaves at the front corners of the sarcophagus. The griffins have the pupils of their eyes boldly drilled in a manner met with on grave-altars. At the rear corners of the cist are shown upright burning torches. The lid is in the form of a gabled roof with a raised frieze along the front edge, perhaps deriving from the relief sima—the usual type of lid on early Italian sarcophagi. The frieze is decorated with boukrania from which hang fluttering fillets and garlands successively of oak, laurel, grain and flowers. Above the garlands are carved ritual implements associated with religious practices: an aspergillum, a phiale, an oinochoe and a lituus. The aspergillum is used for sprinkling sacred water; the phiale and oinochoe are, of course, the usual vessels employed in pouring libations; and the lituus is the emblem of the college of augurs. The pediments at the ends are decorated with laurel garlands tied with ribbons. They are flanked by lateral acroteria. The decoration of the front acroteria simply completes the corner-boukrania of the frieze just described; the ill-preserved rear acroteria may have been carved with leaves or half-palmettes. The back surface of the lid is point-dressed, that of the cist sawn.

The decoration of this sarcophagus is rich in religious symbolism, as witness the ritual implements, sacred baetyls, torches, etc. It is also important by reason of its probable early date. The garlands and ritual paraphernalia of the frieze on the lid relate it closely to the so-called Priest's Sarcophagus in the Vatican, W. Amelung, *Kat. vaticanischen Museums* I 256 no. 126, pl. 26; this has been dated to the first quarter of the second century A.D. because of the resemblance between its griffins and those on a frieze-fragment from Trajan's Forum in the Lateran; see J. M. C. Toynbee, *The Hadrianic School* 216, pl. 49. 1. The Cambridge sarcophagus is not so finely carved, but the way that it employs boukrania, instead of Erotes, to support the garlands recalls the usage of a yet earlier period; cf. G. Rodenwaldt, *Der Sarkophag Caffarelli* (83rd *berliner Winckelmannsprogramm*) passim. For the ritual implements one may also compare the frieze, H. Stuart Jones, *Cat. Museo Capitolino* 261 no. 100, 262 f. no. 104, pl. 61.

The griffins on the Cambridge sarcophagus are of the same breed as those from the Basilica Ulpia in Trajan's Forum; see *JdI* LI (1936) 76 f., figs. 5–6. Some details such as the less curving tips of their wings and their striding posture are also to be compared with the lion-griffins on the Priest's Sarcophagus discussed above. Certainly they seem to be distinctly earlier than the lion-griffins with similarly intertwined tails on a sarcophagus in Baltimore; this has been compared with the frieze of the Faustina Temple in the Roman Forum and dated accordingly in the later second quarter of the second century A.D.: see K. Lehmann-Hartleben and E. C. Olsen, *Dionysiac Sarcophagi in Baltimore* 17 f., 44 f., 63 f., figs. 16–18, where theories as to the significance of the religious symbolism will also be found advanced.

C. first quarter of the second century A.D.

AJA LXI (1957) 242 n. 154, LXIII (1959) 143 no. 19.

161 Sarcophagus showing the triumphal return of Dionysos from the East PLATES 53–55

Presented by Admiral Sir Pulteney Malcolm. From Arvi on the south coast of Crete. Inv.: GR.1.1835.

L. (as restored) 2·216 m., H. 0·697 m., W. 0·67 m. Luna marble. Assembled from many fragments and mounted on a modern plinth at the bottom. The missing parts of the walls and lid have been supplied in the form of flat areas of plaster but no attempt has anywhere been made to restore the damaged parts of the relief decoration. To strengthen the restoration cist and lid have been joined together with plaster. Originally the lid was attached by two small iron clamps at each end. An attempt will now be made to list the principal damage to the relief decoration, beginning with the front of the cist. Of the spotted pantheress or leopardess heading the procession, the fore-legs are missing, also parts of the hind-paws and much of the rim of the krater underneath her. Of the young satyr with a wineskin coming behind, both knees and the left foot are broken away. Nothing survives of the satyr (?) in shallow relief behind him save for the lower part of the legs. The elephant has been chipped at the surface, but is otherwise intact; the left hand of its mahout is missing, as also the right fore-arm of the flute-playing maenad seated on its back; this last figure also has the back of the head and the right part of the double flute broken away. The satyr with a child on his shoulders following the elephant has lost his tail, right calf and thigh, left arm and parts of the panther-skin and thyrsos it held. The group of a Seilenos supported by a maenad and a satyr has suffered damage at the lower part of the chiton of the Seilenos and at the head and right calf of the maenad; the lower part of the right leg of the satyr is missing. The dancing figure of Pan has lost much of the upper part of the left leg, as well as the lower edge of his skin cloak. The male centaur of the pair drawing Dionysos' chariot has both his right legs missing and, in addition, the end of the drinking-horn in his right hand. The chariot has part of the rim and one spoke of the wheel broken away; the surface in this vicinity has been much corroded by moisture and the detail is indistinct as a consequence. Part of the shaft of Dionysos' thyrsos is missing. The relief of Pan and Erotes at the left end of the cist has been much corroded by moisture, but is otherwise intact. That at the right end showing two satyrs with the child Dionysos has been damaged by a transverse break across the edge of the head and the right upper arm of the older satyr and through the legs of his younger companion. Of the frieze along the front edge of the lid showing a symposium of satyrs and maenads the following elements are missing; the right foot of the maenad, eighth figure from the left, everything save the top of the head of the satyr behind her, tenth from the left, and the lower part of the body and much of the face of his companion, eleventh from the left. Chipped are the cup held by the maenad, twelfth from the left, and the hands of the satyr beside her, thirteenth from the left. The left end of the lid has been chipped at the top of the pediment. At the right end part of the cap of the rear corner-mask has been broken away and the edges of the pediment have been chipped, particularly below, where they were in contact with the clamps fastening the lid. The two front corner-masks are also slightly chipped.

The main scene on the front of the cist shows the return of the god Dionysos in triumph from the Orient. At each end it is framed by trees, to the right an elm entwined with a grape-vine, to the left a laurel, largely concealed behind the maenad with a tympanon. In a sense, these two trees belong more truly to the scenes at the ends of the cist to which they provide a transition. The procession is also wending its way past scattered pine-trees, two of which are to be seen in the background. It is headed by a spotted pantheress or leopardess, bounding over an over-turned krater and looking back at the young satyr behind her. This youthful figure has slewed round in his course in his efforts to adjust the load of a bulging wineskin on his left shoulder. He wears a pine garland in his hair and has a panther-skin draped over his left arm. Another satyr seems to have been following very closely behind him, but most of this figure, in very low relief, is now lost.

Next comes a richly caparisoned African elephant guided, with an instrument suspiciously resembling a pedum, by a young, skin-clad satyr astride his neck.[1] In common with the other figures on the elephant's back, he is shown on a greatly reduced scale. He seems to be in conversation with a maenad reclining on the beast's shoulders. She is clad in a chiton and himation and has an ivy garland in her hair. She brandishes a thyrsos in her right hand and steadies the massive kantharos in her left hand by resting it on top of a lidded basket. A young satyr beside her, also holding a kantharos, grasps at the head of her thyrsos. On the haunches of the elephant squats a further maenad similarly clad, but ungarlanded, and blowing a double pipe. In the wake of the elephant walks a satyr carrying a satyr-child on his shoulders and holding a thyrsos and a panther-skin in his left arm. The child has the build of those appearing in the frieze on the front of the lid and, like them, is as yet devoid of a tail. Especially striking is the treatment of the back-muscles of the satyr carrying him.

Behind comes a group of four figures which dominates the centre of the relief: a drunken Seilenos supported by a satyr and a maenad and watched by a further satyr. The Seilenos has swerved back in his tracks. His gaze seems to be directed into the distance, probably at the god in his chariot. He wears an ivy garland on his head, holds a second in his left hand and appears to be clad in a long-sleeved chiton and a short cloak. A heavy krater overturned on the ground may have fallen from his outstretched right hand. The maenad supporting his left arm is likewise garlanded with ivy. She wears a fluttering chiton and

[1] On the more usual form of the goad, the modern ankus, see Sir John Beazley, *Etruscan Vase-Painting* 213 f.

a cloak bound round her waist. The satyr supporting the right armpit of the Seilenos wears a skin loin-cloth; his back affords a further fine study of muscle-texture. His companion in the background is garlanded with pine. Next comes the god Pan, a skin cloak flung over his left shoulder, dancing with a tambourine in front of Dionysos' chariot. A beribboned pedum lies on the ground behind him.

The god's chariot is drawn by a pair of centaurs, the one male and the other female. The male centaur has a garland of ivy on his silen-like head and a panther-skin draped over his left arm with which he is clasping his partner. A redundant satyr's tail protrudes from the lower edge of the human part of his back. He is gazing back at the god in the chariot as, with his raised right hand, he pours a libation from a drinking-horn. His companion holds a pine branch in her right arm and a kantharos with her left which is placed round the centaur's neck. Her hair is bound with a fillet. The rear part of her body is indicated only in very shallow relief. The chariot itself is richly adorned with reliefs. On the front panel, flanked by two columns with spiral fluting and Corinthian capitals, Eros appears to be shown teasing the god Pan. Pan has his arms bound behind him and his tormentor seems to be pulling his hair and beard. On the side of the chariot are shown a naked child grasping a beribboned thyrsos, a young satyr holding a torch, and a crouching panther. The hub of the wheel is carved in the shape of a lion's head. The god Dionysos stands in the chariot. He has an ivy garland in his hair and wears an animal skin knotted at his left shoulder. In his left hand he grasps a thyrsos bound with ribbons. In contrast to the vigorous activity of the other figures of the frieze, the god gives an impression of studied serenity. This is heightened by the subservient animality of the crouching satyr supporting his right side. This figure has a long necklet of flowers and wears a garland of pine in his hair. Behind the chariot dances a maenad with a tympanon, or tambourine. She is naked save for a cloak over her left arm. The carefully balanced composition of the whole relief is remarkable. It may be tabulated thus:

Maenad and tambourine. Satyr and wineskin.
Chariot group. Elephant group.
Pan. Satyr and child.
Seilenos group.

Both ends of the cist are fully decorated.[1] The relief is slightly shallower than in front, but no less careful. In both cases the scene is framed by a tree to either side and a drape hanging from them serves as a background. At the left end the trees are a much-pruned pine and a laurel. Under them two Erotes are shown carrying the drunken god Pan. The wings of the left-hand Eros are not indicated, but it is probably to be inferred that they are concealed behind his back and furled. Pan is shown ithyphallic, but displays few other signs of activity. His goat's ears droop and he has a drunken smile on his lips and a faraway look in his eyes. This last effect is heightened by the way the pupils are barely indicated, whilst everywhere else they are boldly drilled.

At the right end, in a similar setting, are shown two satyrs holding torches, the one of them young and beardless and with a skin draped round his loins, the other older and naked apart from a chlamys over his left shoulder. Between them they are carrying a fruit-filled liknon, or winnowing-fan (cf. **128**), in which is seated a young child. Probably the god Dionysos himself is represented while yet an infant, although it is to be noted that the baby is rendered in much the same style as the satyr-children appearing elsewhere on the sarcophagus.

The lid of the sarcophagus is in the form of a gabled roof. Its front corners are decked with heads of youthful satyrs. That at the right end has little pouches of tissue under the ears like those met with on **83**. The rear corners of the lid carry masks on a much smaller scale wearing Phrygian caps. The pediments at both ends are occupied by reliefs showing a krater piled high with fruit and flanked by an antithetical pair of crouching panthers.

The front of the lid carries the usual raised panel of relief, in this case representing a banquet. Against a background of hanging drapes, satyrs and maenads recline on couches strewn with panther-skins. On the floor in front of them stand a variety of cups and ladles and a wine-krater. The frieze divides itself into scenes. In the left-hand one, two satyrs listen rapturously to a maenad playing on the lyre. By way of reward one of them offers her his garland. The next scene falls into two units. On the one side a satyr drinks a toast to the maenad beside him whilst a satyr-child eats grapes on the floor in front of them. Next to them an elderly satyr is being offered a garland and grapes by his maenad companion. He seems more concerned at his empty cup and nods imperiously to an old serving-woman who comes tottering up with another. The left part of the next

[1] The photographs of the ends of the sarcophagus have had to be taken from impressions because of the inaccessible position in which the monument is at present displayed. It is hoped that it will be possible to show it to better advantage with improved display facilities in the near future.

scene is missing. The first two figures were satyrs. The maenad beside them is being addressed by the satyr on the next couch. By a strange contortion he also has a child balanced on his knees and clasped by the maenad on his other side. In the case of this satyr of divided attentions it seems uncertain how far the artist really intended a misshapen, back-to-front creature and how far he has simply combined elements from two different figures in his repertoire without allowing for the resultant torsion of the back.

This monument, commonly known as the Pashley Sarcophagus from its original publication in Robert Pashley's *Travels in Crete*, ranks as one of the finest extant works of its kind. Although found in Crete, it seems reasonably certain from its style that it was produced at a workshop in Italy, most probably in Rome itself. Several other sarcophagi of Italian type have individual figures or groups that are almost identical and may have been carved in the same workshop or in others closely related to it. Thus, to commence with the front of the cist, the dancing maenad with a tambourine recurs on a sarcophagus in the Museo Nazionale Romano: Lehmann-Hartleben and Olsen, *op. cit.* fig. 30, *centre*. Both she and the young satyr with the wineskin seem also to be found, in a somewhat modified form, on a sarcophagus in Copenhagen: F. Poulsen, *Kat. over antike Skulpturer* 527 no. 777*a*, *Billedtavler, Tillaeg* I 12. The pair of centaurs and the dancing figure of Pan have exact counterparts on a coffin in Munich: A. Furtwängler, *Illustrierter Kat. der Glyptothek* 16 no. 223, pl. 31; Idem, *Ein Hundert Tafeln* pls. 41–2. The scene at the left end of the cist with two Erotes carrying the drunken Pan recurs on two other sarcophagi of Italian type, British Museum 2298 and Naples 6677, as well as on one Greek example; see F. Matz, *Ein römisches Meisterwerk, der Jahreszeitensarkophag Badminton-New York* (*JdI Erg* XIX) 79, pl. 10*b*. One of these monuments seems to have influenced artists such as Giovanni Andrea Podestà and A. Veneziano; cf. A. von Salis, *Antike und Renaissance* 118, 120 f., pl. 27*d*. The group at the other end of two satyrs carrying the child, Dionysos, in a liknon is also to be found on a sarcophagus in Naples: E. Gerhard, *Antike Bildwerke* pl. 111. 3; Roux, *Mus. secr.* pl. 27. It is probably this monument, formerly in the Farnese Collection, that is copied in an engraving by Marcantonio Raimondi; cf. A. Bartsch, *Le peintre graveur* XIV 186 no. 230. The significance of the scene has been discussed by Miss Harrison in *JHS* XXIII (1903) 292 f.[1] The banqueting satyrs and maenads along the front of the lid also recur elsewhere, although somewhat differently arranged, e.g. Turin: S. Reinach, *Répertoire des reliefs* III 423. 5; Paris: F. Cumont, *Le symbolisme funéraire des Romains* pl. 32, *Musée du Louvre, Cat. sommaire des marbres antiques* 116 no. 475, pl. 53; Baltimore: Lehmann-Hartleben and Olsen, *op. cit.* 11 f., fig. 2. A further example has just been found in excavations carried out by the British School at Rome on an early Papal church site at Santa Cornelia.

It will thus be seen that a great many of the figures on the Cambridge sarcophagus do not want for exact parallels. A number of other monuments also show general resemblances to it without suggesting any specific relationship like that observed with those listed above. Broadly comparable in this way is a sarcophagus in the Lateran, J. M. C. Toynbee, *The Hadrianic School* pl. 40. 1. Similarly, for the reliefs on the front of the lid one may compare Gerhard, *op. cit.* pl. 108. 2; for the centaurs on the front of the cist, *Bull. Comm. Arch. Communale di Roma* LX (1933) 200 f., pl. C; for the group of the drunken Seilenos, Lehmann-Hartleben and Olsen, *op. cit.* fig. 2, Reinach, *op. cit.* III 69. 6; and for the piping maenad on the elephant, Toynbee, *op. cit.* pl. 39. 3. The elephant himself is much as on later Dionysiac triumph-sarcophagi, e.g. the fragment, H. Stuart Jones, *Cat. Palazzo dei Conservatori* 92 f. no. 28*b*, pl. 35. The relief on the front of Dionysos' chariot showing Eros teasing Pan seems closest to that carved on the syrinx of the group of Pan and Daphnis, or Olympos, Naples 6329, although the figures are reversed. Also comparable are a sarcophagus lid in Naples, Museo Nazionale 108440, and the Casali Sarcophagus in Copenhagen: Poulsen, *op. cit.* 528 f. no. 778, *Billedtavler* pl. 66. Similar scenes occur in wall-paintings, e.g. W. Helbig, *Wandgemälde* nos. 404, 406.

Even amongst sarcophagi showing identical elements of decoration it seems that the Cambridge example must take a very early place. This is borne out in general by the shallow depth of the relief and by the more cogent and meaningful composition. The studied grouping of the figures on the front of the cist has already been considered. Similar observations apply to the banqueters on the front of the lid. How important, for example, as giving meaning to a group, is the old serving-woman, in appearance rather like a terracotta grotesque! Yet this figure is omitted from the other known examples of this frieze. The execution of the Cambridge sarcophagus could

[1] Also comparable is a variety of Roman terracotta relief showing a satyr and a maenad carrying or swinging the child Dionysos in a liknon; cf. H. von Rohden, *Die antiken Terrakotten* IV. 1, *Architektonische römische Tonreliefs* 37 f., pl. 99.

well be still of Hadrianic date. In any case, it can hardly be very much later.

Second quarter of the second century A.D.

R. Pashley, *Travels in Crete* I 275 f., II 2 f., pl. facing 7, figs. on 18, 19; *Deutsche Kunstblätter* III (1852) 292 f.; *AA* 1864 171; *AZ* 1873 33; Michaelis, *Anc. Marbles* 252 f. no. 31; Chapman, *Handbook* (2nd ed.) 57 f.; *JHS* XXIII (1903) 296 fig. 4; S. Reinach, *Répertoire des reliefs* II 443. 1–3; K. Lehmann-Hartleben and E. C. Olsen, *Dionysiac Sarcophagi in Baltimore* 29 n. 57; *Handbook and Guide* (1960) 10; F. Matz, *Ein römisches Meisterwerk, der Jahreszeitensarkophag Badminton-New York* (*JdI Erg* XIX) 79.

162 Sarcophagus with scenes from the life of Achilles PLATE 56

Presented by Dr J. Disney. It had been acquired for the collection at the Hyde in 1761 by purchase from Mr Lloyd; previously in the palace of the Marchese Cavalieri in Rome. Inv.: GR.45.1850.

L. 1·67 m., H. 0·565 m., W. 0·495 m., H. of relief c. 0·06 m. Cist of Proconnesian marble, lid of Luna marble. Despite the difference in material, the clamp-holes at the ends show that lid and cist were actually used together and the distinctive style of the heads suggests that both are from the same workshop. The cist is preserved virtually intact. Missing are only the right thumb of the fleeing daughter of Lykomedes beside Odysseus, the tips of the fingers of the right hand of Diomedes and a small part of the top of the left end of the cist where the lid has been prised off. The lid has been assembled from three large joining fragments. Two small areas at the lower edge of the relief-panel in front and one at its top have been restored in marble. Minor chips are missing elsewhere. There are traces of root-marks on both members.

The main relief frieze on the front of the cist shows Achilles, brought up as a girl at the court of Lykomedes in Skyros, having his true nature revealed by the gift of weapons brought by the Achaean envoys from Troy. The scene divides itself into three units: in the centre Achilles, framed by startled daughters of Lykomedes, on the left a more placid group of the remainder of the royal family, on the right the Achaean legation in active entreaty.

At the sound of the war-trumpet Achilles has seized the shield and spear. He still wears a woman's peplos, whose open side reveals a muscular right leg that has already cast aside its shoe. A helmet lies on the ground before him, but his long hair is still bound up in a feminine sakkos. A himation, looped over his arms, flutters behind him. Before him kneels the princess Deidameia, entreating him to stay. To either side two more of Lykomedes' daughters flee in alarm, forming an agreeably symmetrical grouping, the one turning her front to the spectator, the other her back. The right-hand girl has just sprung up from a chair. To the left, behind Deidameia, a woman is shown seated on a stool. Possibly the queen herself is represented, flanked by three more of her daughters. At her feet is a ball, apparently of wool from her spinning. Behind stands Lykomedes, the king, resting his right hand on a low pillar or altar and watching the whole scene with a regal detachment. He wears a long, girdled, sleeved chiton—the stage-costume of a king—shoes, a cloak and, in his hair, the royal diadem.

The Achaean delegation to the right is headed by Odysseus, clad in a chlamys and pilos and with a sheathed sword in his left hand. Behind comes the herald in his girdled chiton, himation and high-laced sandals, blowing the long tuba with all his might. He is followed by Diomedes, also in a chlamys and carrying a sword. Both he and Odysseus have their right hands outstretched in gesticulation as they urge Achilles to come with them. The four right-hand figures are in much bolder relief than the remainder and small struts have been left to link their heads with the background. Others occur at the trumpet and the right thumb and elbow of Odysseus.

The ends of the sarcophagus are occupied with subsequent exploits of Achilles at Troy. At the left end is shown the death of Hector at Achilles' hands after their decisive single combat outside the walls of Troy. Hector sprawls on the ground, clad in full armour and still gripping his sword and shield. Achilles stands above him, ready to strike home. He is shown naked and armed with sword and shield. The relief at this end is quite unfinished and the figure of Achilles, in particular, has been little more than roughed out. Incised ashlar blocks in the background are intended to give a summary indication of the walls of Troy.

At the right end Achilles is seen killing Penthesileia, Queen of the Amazons. Again, Achilles is shown naked, apart from a helmet, and armed with a sword and shield. He has seized Penthesileia by the hair as he prepares to deliver the *coup de grâce*. This is the fateful moment, so beloved in ancient art, when love stirs in him for the woman he has just mortally wounded. The Amazon queen is sprawled in front of her rearing horse. She is clad in long boots and in a short chiton that leaves one breast bare. She still clutches her battle-axe and her Thracian shield, or pelta. This relief, too, has not been fully finished, although it has been carried further than that at the left end. The surface has been worked over with the rasp, but has received very little polishing. Nevertheless, Penthesileia's face is one of the most effective on the whole sarcophagus.

The lid has a raised panel of relief in front and masks at its front corners. It is otherwise completely flat and has quite abandoned the earlier form in the shape of a gabled roof. By far the finest features are the corner-masks. These take the form of masterly grinning heads of the god Pan, with long, drooping goats' ears and rams' horns. The centre of the relief-panel on the front of the lid is occupied by a thymiaterion. To each side of it there are pairs of rather full-bodied winged sphinxes grouped antithetically about lidded amphorae. These vessels very probably have a symbolic significance as cinerary urns. At both ends of the lid there are simple representations of thunderbolts in relief. The lid is slightly narrower than the cist but, as has already been seen, it clearly belongs to it. The underside of the cist is point-dressed, its back sawn; the top of the lid is rusticated.

The markedly individual style of the Cambridge sarcophagus cannot be closely paralleled and makes it difficult to date its execution with any precision. Iconographically, however, it seems assignable to the middle years of the second century A.D. or slightly later. The closest parallels for the central group of Achilles flanked by fleeing daughters of Lykomedes seem to be found on Attic sarcophagi which Kallipolitis has recently assigned to the time of Hadrian or Antoninus Pius; cf. Robert, *Die antiken Sarkophagreliefs* II 23 f. no. 20, 29 f. no. 22, pls. 6, 10; Kallipolitis, *op. cit.* 15 nos. 11 and 13. But the resemblance is of a general rather than a detailed kind. In many ways far closer is an Italian sarcophagus now lost and known only from Pozzo's drawing; see Robert, *op. cit.* II 44 f. no. 28, pl. 18. This provides tolerably close parallels for the figures of Achilles, Lykomedes, Deidameia, Odysseus and Diomedes, as well as echoing many elements in the composition. To judge from the handling of space and the employment of an architectural setting, this may be already of middle Antonine date. Although the reliefs on the Cambridge sarcophagus may seem earlier in design, they show one or two elements such as the vestigial chair between the fleeing daughter of Lykomedes and Odysseus that seem more meaningful on the other example. The scene showing Achilles and Penthesileia displays a faint kinship with some of the early Amazonomachy-sarcophagi; cf. Robert, *op. cit.* II 76 f., R. Redlich, *Die Amazonensarkophage des 2. und 3. Jahrhunderts n. Chr.* 5 f. The probable date for the Cambridge sarcophagus thus inferred on typological grounds would seem to fall in the middle–third quarter of the second century A.D. The flat form of the lid seems quite consistent with this, as a monument such as the Leukippidai sarcophagus in Baltimore shows the transition to this type already quite advanced in early Antonine times; see Lehmann-Hartleben and Olsen, *op. cit.* 64, figs. 11, 14–15. The heavy-featured heads and the thick folds of the drapery do not seem necessarily to indicate that the actual execution was any later, although, like the sagging bellies of the sphinxes, they are difficult to parallel. They are lacking on the unpolished figure of Penthesileia, which may suggest that they are the price paid for the pronounced ganosis of the front of the sarcophagus. A measure of the uncertainty obtaining on such matters may be gathered from the case of the Pentheus sarcophagus from St Peter's, showing somewhat similar drapery; originally assigned to the time of Commodus, it has now been proposed by Matz to redate it in early Antonine times; see J. M. C. Toynbee and J. Ward Perkins, *The Shrine of St Peter* 89, pl. 22; E. Kirschbaum, *The Tombs of St Peter and St Paul* pl. 9*b*; Matz, *op. cit.* 152 no. 1.

C. middle–third quarter of the second century A.D.

Memoirs of Thos. Hollis, Esq. I 129; *Memoirs of T. Brand-Hollis*, preface 5–6; J. Disney sr., *Cat. Hyde* 5 f., with pl.; J. Disney jr., *Museum Disneianum* 89 f., pls. 42, 42*a*; *AZ* v (1847) 159; *GGA* 1849 459; Marsden, *Cat. Disney Coll.* 85 no. 41; Michaelis, *Anc. Marbles* 262 no. 76; *Wiener Vorgeblätter* ser. C pl. 9, nos. 3–4; J. Graeven, *Tres Picturae Pompeianae* in *Geneathlicon Gottingense* 1888 124 n. 8; Robert, *Die antiken Sarkophagreliefs* II 43 f. no. 27, pl. 18; Chapman, *Handbook* (2nd ed.) 40 f.; S. Reinach, *Répertoire des reliefs* II 442. 1–3.

163 Dionysiac sarcophagus — PLATE 57

Presented by Dr J. Disney. Found in Rome in about 1740 at the Vigna Capponi, a little beyond S. Andrea della Via Flaminia. Purchased for the collection at the Hyde from W. Lloyd in 1761. Inv.: GR.46.1850.

L. 2·15 m., H. (without lid) 0·595 m., W. 0·64 m. Proconnesian marble, showing patches of brown incrustation. Lid missing. Broken away is the top of the pedum held in the right arm of the satyr in the left panel. Minor chips missing elsewhere. Two clamp-holes in the back of the cist and two at each end (one of them still containing lead) served for the attachment of the lid.

The front of the sarcophagus is divided into three areas of relief separated by two large panels of the undulating fluting characteristic of the *sarcophagi bacellati* (cf. **155**). These panels are framed by a moulding in the form of a plain kymation.

Each group of figures in relief stands on a kind of statue-base with mouldings at its top and bottom. In addition, the central group is framed by Corinthian pilasters carrying a low arch with half-palmettes set in the pendentives. In the centre Dionysos is shown, leaning on a satyr to his left as he pours a libation from a kantharos over a ram's head set on a tall, pillar-like altar. On his right he is watched by the goat-headed and goat-legged god, Pan. Dionysos has his hair wreathed in ivy. A further long garland of fruit and flowers hangs down from his left shoulder. He is otherwise naked apart from a cloak and his tall skin boots. Over his left arm the satyr carries a panther-skin at which a snake is darting from a round basket on the ground in front of him—doubtless the *cista mystica* of the Dionysiac cult. A panther between Dionysos' legs has one forepaw resting on the basket, the other on a pedum, or throwing-stick, lying on the ground.

The right-hand relief shows a dancing maenad with cymbals. She wears a girdled peplos with an overfold. This is fastened only at her left shoulder, leaving her right breast bare; it is also open at the side, revealing her left leg. A short mantle, fastened at the girdle around her waist, flutters up over her head. For the motif, cf. **131**.

In the corresponding position at the left there is carved a youthful satyr draped in a panther-skin and with a baby, not improbably the infant Dionysos himself, perched on his shoulder and clutching at his cheek and hair. The satyr holds a pedum in each hand. His face wears an exquisite expression of suffering and, like that of the satyr in the central relief, is decked with an incipient beard and moustache. At his feet are the heads of a ram and a goat and, between his legs and with its forepaws on the ram's head, a panther.

At the left end of the cist there is a summary shallow relief of a round shield over crossed spears. The right end, back, underside and interior are point-dressed. The front surface is finely polished, especially over the flesh areas and drapery of the reliefs. The heads show the use of the drill in the corners and pupils of the eyes, the corners of the mouth and the dimple on the chin. The running-drill has been extensively employed in the hair, etc.

The following sarcophagi seem akin to that in Cambridge:

(1) Vatican Museum: W. Amelung, *Kat. vaticanischen Museums* II 278 f. no. 99, pl. 25.

(2) Palazzo dei Conservatori: H. Stuart Jones *Cat. Palazzo dei Conservatori* 132 no. 8*a*, pl. 45.

(3) Villa Medici: M. Cagiano de Azevedo, *Le antichità della Villa Medici* 88 no. 134, pl. 39, where further examples listed.

(4) St Peter's: J. M. C. Toynbee and J. Ward Perkins, *The Shrine of St Peter* 89 f., pls. 24–7; Matz, *op. cit.* pl. 25*b*.

(5) St Peter's: Toynbee and Ward Perkins, *op. cit.* 56, 90, pl. 28.

Cagiano de Azevedo has suggested a date in the first quarter of the third century A.D. for (1)–(3), on the basis of a marriage scene dated by contemporary hair-styles which displays the same architectural framing for the central panel as these and the Cambridge sarcophagus; cf. *AA* 1933 447 f., figs. 26–7. (4)–(5) have a slightly more elaborate architectural setting in this position. (4) has been dated to the time of Alexander Severus by the portrait-heads on its lid. It may be doubted whether any of the others could be much earlier, although the central group on the Cambridge sarcophagus does seem to have earlier antecedents, e.g. Amelung, *op. cit.* II 313 f. no. 102λ, pl. 24.

C. later first–earlier second quarters of the third century A.D.

Memoirs of Thos. Hollis, Esq. I 129; *Memoirs of T. Brand-Hollis*, preface 4; J. Disney sr., *Cat. Hyde* I f. no. 2, with pl.; J. Disney jr., *Museum Disneianum* 85 f., pl. 41; *AZ* v (1847) 159; *GGA* 1849 458 f.; Marsden, *Cat. Disney Coll.* 85 no. 46; *AA* 1864 171; Michaelis, *Anc. Marbles* 263 no. 77; Chapman, *Handbook* (2nd ed.) 41; K. Lehmann-Hartleben and E. C. Olsen, *Dionysiac Sarcophagi in Baltimore* 22 n. 32.

164 Mask of Helios from a sarcophagus lid

PLATE 57

Presented by Dr J. Disney. Probably acquired in Italy. Inv.: GR.48.1850.

P.H. 0·274 m. Proconnesian marble. Chipped away at the top. Broken away at the left side and at the bottom of the back surface where it was attached respectively to the front relief-frieze and to the flat lid. Surface somewhat chipped and rubbed; shows traces of modern paint. Two modern dowel-holes in underside.

The fragment preserves the protome from the right front corner of a sarcophagus lid. It is in the form of a youthful head of the Sun-god with rich, waving hair and wearing a rayed crown. The surface of the flesh is well polished. The irises of the eyes are outlined and the pupils are marked by a semicircular drilling. The running-drill has been extensively and somewhat harshly used in the hair. The mask has a maximum depth of only 0·072 m. and its rear surface is saw-cut. The general character of the protome and the treatment of the hair and eyes suggest that it is from a sarcophagus of the later third or possibly even the beginning of the fourth centuries A.D. Cf. the Palazzo Corsetti fragment, A. Rumpf, *Die antiken Sarkophagreliefs* VI 289, pl. 60.

C. later half of third–beginning of fourth centuries A.D.

J. Disney sr., *Cat. Hyde* 8 no. 40; J. Disney jr., *MS Cat.* 142; Marsden, *Cat. Disney Coll.* 86 no. 55; Michaelis, *Anc. Marbles* 264 no. 79; Chapman, *Handbook* (2nd ed.) 56.

(O) EARLY MEDIEVAL

165 Crude relief of two lions (?)

PLATE 57

Provenance unknown. Inv.: GR.S.6.

P.H. c. 0·32 m. Compact, creamish-white limestone. Broken away above, below and at both sides. Head and tip of the tail of the right-hand beast missing. Modern clamp-hole in top.

The front of the block has been trimmed or worn smooth, but nevertheless shows an irregularly curving surface. On it is carved in outline an antithetical pair of rampant beasts. To judge from the form of the tails, most probably lions are intended, in which case the 'collars' about their necks may be meant to indicate the ruff of the mane. The creatures have one forepaw raised to each other's snout, the legs meeting at the elbow and forming a symmetrical pattern. Their other forepaws are lowered and placed one on top of the other. This is far too crude a piece of folk-art for any stylistic criteria to be applicable. The material could be an Egyptian limestone. The back surface is unworked or broken away.

Coptic (?).

VIII

ARCHITECTURAL PIECES, FURNITURE, ETC.

(A) ARCHITECTURAL MEMBERS

Note that reliefs, etc., fulfilling an architectural role have already been dealt with in the preceding chapters.

166 Antefix from the Parthenon PLATE 58

Presented by Professor Sir Charles Walston. Exact provenance not recorded. Inv.: GR.3.1885.

P.H. 0·339 m. Pentelic marble. Bottom part broken away, including the length of cover-tile at the back and the outer edges of the volutes in front. The palmette chipped away at the top and at one edge. The surface is somewhat worn and bruised.

The fragment preserves a large part of an antefix of approximately triangular section, as viewed in plan, with its outer face decorated with finely carved volute-and-palmette ornament. The palmette has a plastically indicated centre-line.

F. Brommer's identification of the fragment as from an antefix of the Parthenon seems fully justified by a close comparison of the size and decoration with other known examples from that building, e.g. A. Furtwängler and P. Wolters, *Beschreibung der Glyptothek, München* (1910) 158 no. 195; A. H. Smith, *Sculptures of the Parthenon* 70 figs. 132–3; *AA* 1936 317 f., figs. 1–5; *Die Antike* XVI (1940) 72 f. For the position of the antefixes on the temple cf. W. Hege and G. Rodenwaldt, *Die Akropolis* pl. 22; on their number and location in relation to the roof-tiles see *Hesperia Suppl.* VIII 259 f., pl. 26.

Third quarter of the fifth century B.C.

Chapman, *Handbook* (2nd ed.) 37; *Die Antike* XVI (1940) 73 fig. 9; *Hesperia Suppl.* VIII 266 n. 13; *AJA* LXIII (1959) 143 no. 5.

167 Fragment of moulding from the Erechtheion (?) PLATE 59

Presented by Sir John and Lady Sandys. Found on the Acropolis, Athens, in 1852, in the immediate vicinity of the Erechtheion. Inv.: GR.6.1919.

P.H. 0·105 m. Pentelic marble. Small part of the top surface preserved; broken away at the sides, bottom and back.

The fragment preserves a small part of an upper surface and a decorated face of an architectural block. Reading from the top downwards, the decoration consists of a plain Lesbian kymation, followed by a plain Egyptian-tongue moulding, respectively 0·019 m. and 0·028 m. in height. These are succeeded by a deeply and beautifully carved ovolo, 0·043 m. high, followed by a bead-and-reel ornament, *c.* 0·015 m. high, now largely broken away.

The quality and style of the cutting suggest that this is indeed, as it has long been believed, a fragment from the original decoration of the Erechtheion. So far as one may judge by eye without being able to measure the members *in situ*, it appears to be from the inner crowning of the architrave of the north porch of that building. This inner surface is not shown in sufficient detail on the published drawings of the temple to establish the identification beyond all shadow of doubt, but the present combination of decorative elements does not seem to recur elsewhere. For another fragment from the Erechtheion see **26** above.

Late fifth century B.C.

168 Miniature Ionic capital PLATE 58

Presented by Dr G. F. Rogers. From Girgenti, the ancient Akragas. Inv.: GR.5.1934.

H. 0·04 m., W. 0·09 m. max. Granular yellowish limestone. One corner completely broken away. This may have occurred in the withdrawal of whatever object was originally secured in the vertical hole through the middle of the capital, but the broken surfaces have since been rubbed smooth. Top of abacus abraded. Surface chipped at several points. Traces of a white wash over the outer faces of the capital, with the edges of the volutes picked out in red. Faint traces of red also on the outlines of the egg-and-dart ornament of the echinus.

This tiny capital is beautifully and carefully executed. Its purpose is uncertain. An irregularly shaped vertical hole seems to have passed through its centre and one possible interpretation is that this may have served to receive the tang of a votive statuette of bronze or silver; in that case the tang might also have been used to attach the capital to a miniature column underneath. The capital had a pair of volutes on each of its four vertical faces.

As this little work must be seen as a product of the local Sicilian tradition and not that of Greece proper, it is not easily dated with any precision. The great height of the canalis between the volutes is of a kind met with on Tarentine grave-monuments for the most part usually assigned to the second half of the fourth and early third centuries B.C. although some may be later; cf. H. Klumbach, *Tarentiner Grabkunst* 36 nos. 208 f., 80 f., pl. 27, and, more especially, Q. Quagliati, *Il Museo Nazionale di Taranto* 70. But the convex canalis of the Cambridge capital suggests a rather earlier date and relates it to an example from Locri in the Museo Nazionale, Naples, which is associated with a necking of a kind met with on the columns of the Erechtheion; see J. Durm, *Baukunst der Griechen* (3rd ed.) I 309 fig. 286; also comparable are some of the fragments, *Atti e Memorie della Società Magna Grecia* n.s. IV (1961) 75 f. For the four 'front faces' cf. Durm, *op. cit.* 317 fig. 295.

C. earlier fourth century B.C.

169 Corinthian pilaster-capital PLATE 58

Presented by Dr J. Disney. Reputedly from the Pantanella, Hadrian's Villa, Tivoli; sent by T. Hollis to T. Brand in July 1761. Inv.: GR.82.1850.

H. (without tenon) 0·592 m. Luna marble. Tip of central acanthus leaf restored. Those of many of the others broken away. Surface chipped elsewhere. Capital sawn away at back. Modern iron dowels in top. Modern (?) dowel-holes in underside. At the back of the top surface there is preserved a projecting tenon, 0·011 m. high, from the original attachment to the member above.

The alleged provenance gains some support from the existence of not-dissimilar free-standing capitals from the Nymphaeum at Hadrian's Villa, e.g. P. Gusman, *La villa impériale de Tibur (Villa Hadriana)* 238 fig. 355; *MemAmAc Rome* XI (1933) 123 pl. 11. 4; G. Lippold, *Kat. vaticanischen Museums* III. 1. 2, pl. 2. Also comparable are D. Mustilli, *Il Museo Mussolini* 173 no. 40, pl. 118; *NdSc* 1951 83 fig. 5; etc. But the drill-work on the Cambridge capital seems harsher and such details as the nicking of the edges of the central spines of the leaves suggest that it may be slightly later. These features are much more closely to be paralleled on the pilaster-capitals of the internal order of the Pantheon in Rome, which would seem to date from the rebuilding in the time of Hadrian or anyway not to be very much later. They are in any case well attested towards the middle of the century on the capitals of the Faustina Temple in the Forum.

C. second quarter–middle of the second century A.D.

J. Disney sr., *Cat. Hyde* 49 f.; J. Disney jr., *MS Cat.* 250; Marsden, *Cat. Disney Coll.* 87 no. 72 or 88 no. 83; Chapman, *Handbook* (2nd ed.) 58.

170 Corinthian pilaster-capital PLATE 58

Presented by Dr J. Disney. Provenance as for **169**. Inv.: GR.83.1850.

H. (without tenon) 0·592 m. Luna marble. Description as for **169**. *A modern restoration of the tip of the central acanthus leaf has been removed. Modern graffito, reading 'HY', written upside-down on the face of the abacus.*

Identical with **169** above, *q.v.*

C. second quarter–middle of the second century A.D.

Bibliography as for **169**.

171 Fragment from a small pilaster-capital PLATE 59

Bequeathed by Major R. G. Gayer-Anderson. From Egypt. Inv.: E.GA.3555.1943.

P.H. 0·069 m.; estimated width of capital when intact 0·159 m. Luna marble. The fragment is from the top left corner of an incrustation-capital. Broken away to right and below. Preserved surfaces include parts of the top, showing anathyrosis, the smooth-dressed back, and the left edge. Chipped, especially at the volute and at the top of the head of the satyr which originally projected above the main upper surface of the capital. There is a groove, 0·007 m. wide, behind the left edge, apparently to accommodate a thin facing-slab of marble.

The fragment preserves part of a miniature acanthus capital from a pilaster, doubtless serving as interior-wall or furniture decoration. In the middle of the upper part of the capital, above the main acanthus leaves, there is carved a satyr's head, its beard terminating below and to the side in leaves of acanthus. From these spring the corner volutes. The form of this decorative fantasy, no less than the kind of marble used, suggests Italian work. The control-drillings are still clearly visible.

The head of a satyr with a beard of acanthus leaves seems clearly related to the protomai of Dionysos with a beard of the same type. These are a common feature of Roman decorative art in Italy in Imperial times. In date they seem mainly to span the second century A.D. and it is to this period that the Cambridge fragment is probably to be assigned.

C. second century A.D.

172 Fluted acanthus-capital PLATE 59

Bequeathed by the Rev. T. Worsley. Provenance unknown. Inv.: GR.1*c*.1885.

H. 0·378 m., lower diam. 0·3 m. Proconnesian (?) marble. Of the lower part of the capital all of one side is broken away. Two of the four corners of the abacus are missing, the others chipped.

This piece shows an interesting blend of the acanthus capital with a fluted variety, possibly related to the palm capital but in practice employed as an alternative to the lotus capital. The abacus is of Corinthian type, with flowers in the middle of the sides. Only the upper part of the calyx is fluted. Below, there is a single row of acanthus leaves springing from an ovolo at the bottom of the capital. The top surface shows anathyrosis and a shallow, round sinking in the middle. Near it is a mason's mark in the form of a split-bar 'A'—almost certainly a Greek letter. The outer surfaces of the capital are unpolished and left in the flat-chisel and gouge stage. The acanthus leaves have been elaborately undercut with the drill, with small strengthening struts left where needed.

On the capital-type involved see *JRS* XXXVIII (1948) 66 f. More commonly found is the related Greek lotus-and-acanthus variety, as on the Tower of the Winds in Athens, J. Stuart and N. Revett, *Antiquities of Athens* I 19, pl. 7. But this variant type with fluting instead of the lotus leaves is also well attested, principally in Asia Minor, e.g. H. Stiller, *Altertümer von Pergamon* V. 2. 42, pl. 12. 3; *JRS* XXXVIII (1948) 68, fig. 11. 5. The form of the ovolo will hardly allow of a date before the second century A.D. for the Cambridge capital. On the other hand, the conservative-looking acanthus leaves seem unlikely to be very much later than the second century.

C. second century A.D., or slightly later.

Chapman, *Handbook* (2nd ed.) 70.

173 Antefix PLATE 59

Presented by Professor Sir Charles Walston. Provenance unknown. Inv.: GR.4.1885.

P.H. 0·251 m. Proconnesian (?) marble. Bottom edge broken away; length of cover-tile broken away from back. Surface chipped and pitted by weather and appears to show traces of faint calcination, presumably from fire.

The fragment preserves a large part of an antefix of roughly semi-circular section, as viewed in plan, and with its back rough-hewn with the point. Its vertical front face is decorated with an acanthus-and-palmette motif in relief. This is broadly modelled on Greek forms of the fourth century B.C., but readily betrays the Imperial date of its execution. It may be compared with examples of Imperial times from Italy, e.g. W. Amelung, *Kat. vaticanischen Museums* I 627 no. 481, 628 nos. 485, 487, pl. 66. The tightly coiled tips of the palmette probably favour a date in the second–third centuries A.D.; cf. the palmettes in the pendentives over the central relief on the third-century-A.D. sarcophagus, **163** above.

C. second–third centuries A.D.

Chapman, *Handbook* (2nd ed.) 37; *AJA* LXIII (1959) 143 no. 5.

174 Column shaft PLATE 59

Transferred from the old University Library. Presented to the University by Professor E. D. Clarke. From Egypt. Inv.: GR.29.1865.

H. 1·05 m., max. lower diam. 0·274 m. Porphyry.

This piece consists of a small, unfluted, porphyry column. Despite its highly polished surface, the shaping is somewhat imprecise and the shaft at many points is not exactly circular in section. The top and bottom are roughly dressed with the point, probably to provide a surface that will 'key' into mortar. The shape and finish suggest a date in late antiquity or early medieval times. The form is also singularly well adapted to Clarke's use of it as a dummy cannon in the bow of his boat!

Probably late Roman or early medieval.

Clarke, *Marbles* 3 f. no. 3; Idem, *Travels* 4° III (=II. 2) 47, 8° V 70 f.; Chapman, *Handbook* (2nd ed.) 59.

175 Two fragments from the framing of a Coptic arch PLATE 59

No record as to circumstances of acquisition. From Egypt. Inv.: E.SS.41.

Total depth 0·27 m., W. of acanthus moulding without framing 0·136 m. Compact white Egyptian limestone. Both fragments have part of their back surface preserved, showing traces of adhering mortar, and part of the inner edge of the arch; the outer edge is broken away. The smaller fragment has a transverse dressed surface, representing a junction in the masonry of the arch.

The edges of the moulding on both fragments

show a distinct curve, revealing that both are from the inner frame of an arch, possibly over a door or porch, but quite probably simply over a wall-niche. The full identity of size and decoration indicates that both are from the same archway. Their moulding is framed by two stepped plain bands on the inner edge and by a heavier plain band on the outer. Their sharply-cut, formalized pattern of acanthus leaves is of a kind that seems to emerge in the mid fifth century A.D., on Kitzinger's analysis, and to continue popular in this type of architectural position in the sixth century A.D. and even later; see *Archaeologia* LXXXVII (1937) 186 f., especially the example, 192, pl. 70. 4, from Ahnas.

Coptic work of about the mid fifth–sixth centuries A.D. or slightly later.

176 Coptic pilaster-capital PLATE 59

Presented by Sir W. M. Flinders Petrie. From Egypt. Inv.: E.1.1890.

H. 0·252 m., W. of pilaster originally set underneath 0·19 m. Compact white Egyptian limestone. Broken away at the back. Sawn away in modern times at both sides, the damaged upper parts of the sides of the capital itself being also cut back at the same time. Original upper and lower surfaces of the block preserved with their marking-out lines. Traces of white plaster over the surface.

This piece consists of part of a wall-block carrying an acanthus pilaster-capital in shallow relief. The capital seems to have lacked a profiled abacus, but still unmistakably shows its derivation from the Corinthian order as may be seen from a comparison with **169** and **170**. The flower still survives at the top, although the volutes have been replaced by extremely attenuated acanthus leaves. The leaves themselves have been reduced to two slightly overlapping ranges and are well on the way to being schematized into a single plane; on this progressive formalization see *Bulletin de la Société d'Archéologie Copte* X (1944) 107, on the form shown by the Cambridge capital, *ibid.* fig. 6. The sharply cut leaves of this example seem in general later than those of the Ahnas capitals assigned by Kitzinger to the mid–late fifth century A.D.; see *Archaeologia* LXXXVII (1937) 187 f. The leaf-type may be rather compared with R. Engelbach and others, *Riqqeh and Memphis* VI 34, pl. 62. 55. On the other hand, the broader stage of evolution shown by the Cambridge capital is already attested at Ahnas, as witness J. Strzygowski, *Cat. Cairo, Koptische Kunst* 73 no. 7347, fig. 100.

Coptic work of about the sixth century A.D.

Chapman, *Handbook* (2nd ed.) 66.

177 Coptic pilaster-capital PLATE 59

Presented by Sir W. M. Flinders Petrie. From Egypt. Inv.: E.2.1890.

H. 0·245 m., W. of pilaster originally set underneath 0·215 m. Compact white Egyptian limestone with patches of yellowish-brown incrustation. Broken away at sides and back. Original top and bottom surfaces of the block preserved, with marking-out lines. The carved surface of the pilaster-capital is badly chipped, particularly towards the top and bottom. Faint traces of white plaster in angles and crevices.

This example, too, consists of part of a wall-block carrying a pilaster-capital in shallow relief. It is not identical in size or decoration with **176**, but so similar in style and execution as to suggest that both may be from the same building. On its dating see under **176**.

Coptic work of about the sixth century A.D.

Chapman, *Handbook* (2nd ed.) 66.

178 Fragment from the framing of a medieval arch PLATE 59

Presented by Dr J. Disney. Acquired in Naples about 1755. Inv.: GR.62.1850.

Maximum dimension 0·355 m. Proconnesian marble. Broken away at both ends, where it has been trimmed level in modern times. The other edges have also been recut to disguise the curve of the arch. The back surface is entirely recut and has been carved with the relief-bust of a man.

The fragment is from the framing of quite a large arch. It is decorated with a pattern of intertwined vines and bunches of grapes, in which the treatment of the leaf and its springing also suggests the influence of medieval derivatives of acanthus motifs. A very close parallel for the decoration is afforded by a twelfth-century-A.D. well-head in Venice, although the carving of the leaf on the Cambridge fragment seems as though it may suggest a slightly earlier date.

Despite a skilfully applied false patina, the relief on the back seems undeniably a later addition. The garlanded bust was variously identified by its former owners as Augustus and Julius Caesar. It may be usefully compared with an eighteenth-century gem-portrait of Caesar by A. Pichler; see G. Lippold, *Gemmen und Kameen des Altertums und der Neuzeit* 186, pl. 158. 6. Cf. also the Renaissance and later relief portraits, **207** f. below.

Italian work of the eleventh–twelfth centuries A.D. with a later relief on its back.

J. Disney sr., *Cat. Hyde* 49 no. 56; J. Disney jr. *Museum Disneianum* 67, pls. 32, 32*a*; *AZ* V (1847) 158; Marsden, *Cat. Disney Coll.* 86 no. 58; *AA* 1866 301; Michaelis, *Anc. Marbles* 266 no. 93; Chapman, *Handbook* (2nd ed.) 41; *AJA* LXIII (1959) 142.

(B) FRAGMENTS FROM THE PLASTER DECORATION OF INTERIOR WALLS

179 Silen's head, probably from a console PLATE 60

Presented by the Egypt Exploration Fund. From Naukratis. Inv.: GR.61.1887.

P.H. at the angle at which it was originally mounted 0·165 m. Coarse white plaster containing a little grog. Broken away at the back where it was formerly attached to the wall. Most of the acanthus decoration broken away at the bottom and, doubtless, originally also to both sides of the head. Part of the top surface preserved, showing the impression of the wood-planking of the ceiling. Traces of brownish pigment on eyes, eyebrows, nostrils, beard and edge of garland.

The fragment preserves the head of a silen inclined forward through an angle of about 45° and part of an approximately vertical surface below decorated with acanthus leaves. It appears to have been mounted in the angle between wall and ceiling. The silen is shown wearing a garland with a central medallion, executed after a fashion met with on Egyptian plaster mummy-portraits of Imperial date.

Of the vast quantities of such Alexandrian stucco wall-decoration that once existed, a little, such as the present fragment, is sufficiently well preserved to give some idea of its original high quality; cf. also R. Pagenstecher, *Ausgrabungen in Alexandria (Expedition Ernst von Sieglin)* I. A. 97 no. 5, pl. 42; C. S. Ponger, *Kat. der griechischen und römischen Skulptur im Allard Pierson Museum zu Amsterdam (Allard Pierson Stichting Bydragen* XI) 88 f., especially no. 182, pls. 38–9. These are difficult to date with reference to plaster modelling in Italy and elsewhere and are probably rather to be seen against the background of the Egyptian employment of stucco for elements that would elsewhere probably be executed in marble. The present example seems to have formed part of a human-headed console of a kind met with in marble in Imperial Roman times, e.g. Arif Müfid Mansel, Emin Bosch and Jale İnan, *Side 1947* pls. 14–15, figs. 14–16.

Egyptian work, probably of Imperial date.

180 Bull's head PLATE 60

Presented by the Egypt Exploration Fund. From Naukratis. Inv.: GR.60.1887.

P.H. c. 0·14 m. Coarse white plaster containing a little grog. Broken away at the back. Tip of right horn and almost all of left missing, as also both ears. Traces of a smoother, white-plaster surface-coating. Remains of a brownish pigment on the eyes.

The fragment preserves the head of a bull, probably forming part of the decoration of a wall. There are traces of fillets or ribbons bound round both its horns and probably the fragment formed part of a bull's-head-and-garland motif such as that met with on **71** and **72** above. In Egypt, as in most of the eastern provinces, this form of decoration is by no means confined to the Hellenistic period but persists throughout Imperial times. The present fragment is identical in material and pigmentation with **179** above. Also, such stylistic details as are comparable (e.g. the rendering of the eyes) seem closely similar. It thus seems quite likely that both pieces are of the same date and may well have formed part of the same system of decoration.

Egyptian work, probably of Imperial date.

(C) FURNITURE, ETC.

181 Leg from a table PLATE 61

Presented by Dr J. Disney. Probably acquired in Italy. Inv.: GR.72*a*.1850.

H. as restored 0·746 m. Laconian rosso antico. *Assembled from fragments. Restored in red marble are the ankle of the lion's leg, a part of the leg a little below the acanthus leaves, the tip of the front leaf itself, the left ear of the lion's head and his upper jaw and nostrils, and the table-support rising above the head, together with the flat panel it carries. Also restored are the black inlaid eyes of the lion. Minor restorations have been made in plaster. The paw seems to have been extensively recut and may not originally have belonged to this leg. Modern dowel-holes in the back for attachment to an iron support since removed.*

Thomas Hollis had this leg restored and mounted by Wilton some time after the middle of the eighteenth century. By way of a base he employed the portion of a candelabrum, **182** below. The much-restored leg itself was probably one of three supporting a small round table of the kind to be seen on the somewhat later relief, **135** above. It is in the form of the paw and leg of a lion, terminating above in acanthus foliage from which emerge the head and neck of a lion bearing the table-support.

Almost identical table-legs, but of Luna marble, are displayed in Naples as being from Pompeii, e.g. Museo Nazionale 6823, 110031. They are not quite so slender at, and just below, the 'knee', but otherwise reveal the same proportions, the same rather narrow kind of head and the characteristic 'ruffs' of mane to either side of the jaws and above the brow. The Cambridge leg may well be later, but probably not very much so.

C. first century A.D. or slightly later.

J. Disney sr., *Cat. Hyde* 4, 5 no. 26; J. Disney jr., *Museum Disneianum* 228, pl. 94 *right*; Marsden, *Cat. Disney Coll.* 84 no. 37; Chapman, *Handbook* (2nd ed.) 47.

182 Base of a candelabrum (?) PLATE 60

Presented by Dr J. Disney. Inv.: GR.72*b*.1850.

H. 0·125 m. Luna marble. Assembled from two joining fragments. Missing are parts of the upper and lower edges (formerly restored) and, on two sides, the coiled outermost tips of the half-palmettes under the upright buds. Minor chips broken away elsewhere. Restored in marble is part of the upper rim above one of the lion-claw feet. Minor restorations have been made in plaster. The vertical edge of the plinth has been recut save under one of the lion-claw feet. In addition to the ancient dowel-hole, c. 0·035 m. in diameter, passing vertically through the middle, there are traces of a modern dowel-hole to one side of it from Wilton's employment of the piece as a base for the table-leg, **181** *above. The surface has been chipped and worn and shows traces of root-marks.*

The function of this delicately ornamented, decorative member cannot be determined with complete certainty. Probably it carried a small candelabrum. Its upper surface has a large socket in the shape of a regular hexagon, *c.* 0·095 m. on a side, apparently intended to receive an upright, six-sided member which was anchored in position by a central dowel. But, as the dowel-hole passes right through the bottom of the present block, it remains possible that this did not function alone as the base but may have been secured to a further member underneath. The vertical edge around the bottom of the preserved part has been extensively recut, probably to conceal minor damage, although what traces there are of the original surface suggest that its shape has not been very drastically modified. The decoration has been very finely carved. Lion-claw feet have been set at three of the corners of the six-sided base. From these half-palmettes radiate to either side, being arranged symmetrically with their outer coiled tips supporting buds carved in relief at the other three corners. The decoration has something of the same spirit as that of the couch-legs, **183** below, and is probably of about the same date.

Carved in Italy, probably in about the early–mid second century A.D.

Bibliography as for **181** above, although it is not specifically mentioned.

183 Various couch-legs of similar type and decoration PLATE 61

Purchased. Formerly in the Hope Collection. Inv.: GR.14.1917, GR.15.1917, GR.16.1917, GR.17.1917.

All are of Luna marble. Their individual descriptions follow:

a *H. 0·917 m. Assembled from two joining fragments. Surface partly cleaned.*

b *H. as restored 0·887 m., P.H. of ancient part 0·725 m. Assembled from fragments. Bottom part restored in marble, including almost all of the lower rosette and part of the right edge of the lowermost palmette.*

c *P.H. of ancient part 0·39 m. Only the bottom half is preserved. It has been harshly cleaned. The middle part of the central volute-member has been restored in marble. The upper half of the leg has been supplied by an ancient fragment of the same type but with somewhat different decoration,* **e** *below. This is in a differently veined marble and of a different thickness (only 0·044 m. as against 0·051 m.).*

d *H. 0·92 m. Assembled from four fragments, the second from the top being extensively cleaned and having part of its rosette restored in plaster. The top right corner has been trimmed for a restoration now lost.*

e *P.H. of ancient part 0·413 m. Only the upper half preserved. Employed by the modern restorer to supply the upper part of* **c** *above, to which it does not appear to belong. Surface cleaned. Part of floral decoration restored in plaster.*

a *and* **b** *have their back surfaces dressed smooth, with a hook-shaped dowel-hole behind at about the level of their upper rosettes, apparently to take a light metal strut coming up obliquely from below. They also have two and three dowel-holes respectively in their top surface.* **c**, **d** *and*

e *have sawn rear surfaces.* **d** *and* **e** *each have a single dowel-hole for attachment in their top surface.* **c** *and* **d** *both show a slight projection under their rusticated feet.*

These legs are of a traditional type that had been current since archaic Greek times. By Imperial Roman times when they were carved they had tended to assume an old-fashioned or hieratic character. Accordingly, A. B. Cook sought to identify them as the legs of a throne for a divinity. However, the absence of suitable attachments for horizontal members seems rather to weigh against their being from a chair or throne. Also, it is to be observed that their decoration tends to divide them into pairs of which the one member is on a slightly larger scale than the other, viz. **a** and **b**, **c** and **d**, **e** remaining for the present isolated although clearly of the same general group. This variation in height probably indicates that the legs are from couches, the taller being set at the head, the shorter at the foot. Even so, the far from secure arrangements for their attachment by tiny dowels make it doubtful if they ever functioned as weight-carrying legs for practical couches. There is further to be considered the distinct possibility that, although there seem to be preserved parts of no fewer than five legs in the same style, no more than two of them may have belonged to any one couch. This circumstance may well suggest that these pieces may have served as the non-functional front legs of dummy couches in a tomb. Such couches are well attested in Greek graves, e.g. L. Heuzey and H. Daumet, *Mission archéologique de Macédoine* 261 f., pls. 16, 20, 21, G. M. A. Richter, *Ancient Furniture* figs. 157, 167, 168, 177. The same practice is also occasionally to be found in Roman tombs of Imperial date, with couch-legs of the present type actually employed, e.g. F. Fremersdorf, *Das Römergrab in Weiden bei Köln* fig. 8, pl. 4.

In harmony with their old-fashioned appearance, the decoration of these legs has been carried out in an austerely classicizing style. With the exception of **e**, all the legs have acanthus-framed palmettes above and below the central volute member, with rosettes at the tips of the palmettes; **e** shows an elaborate variation with leaves and flowers in a contemporary style and with the finer detail incised on the relief-ground. The character of the decoration makes it most likely that the legs date from about the first half of the second century A.D. Closely akin to them is a fragmentary example in Berlin, *Beschreibung der antiken Skulpturen* 429 f., nos. 1092*a–b*. This shows traces of paint and gilding—devices that may also have been employed on the Cambridge legs although no traces of them now survive.

C. early–mid second century A.D.

Sale Cat., Christie, 23rd–24th July, 1917 32 no. 205; A. B. Cook, *Zeus* II. I. 760 n. 2, fig. 703; G. M. A. Richter, *Ancient Furniture* 121, fig. 286; *Bull. Inst. Arch. Bulg.* XIII (1939) 279, fig. 313; *AJA* LXIII (1959) 142 no. 2.

184 Part of a table-support (?) PLATE 60

Presented by Dr J. Disney. Probably acquired in Italy. Inv.: GR.71.1850.

H. 0·915 m. Polished black basalt. Restored in basalt or black marble are all the back half of the lion's leg, the back of his mane, his upper jaw and nostrils and one corner of the support on top of his head. The rear part of this support is broken away. Adapted, apparently after the main restorations had been made, to some kind of hydraulic installation coming down from above and issuing from the lion's jaws. Some at least of the restorations were made by Wilton in the eighteenth century; this is the same man that worked on **181** *and* **182**.

This piece consists of an extremely massive lion's leg, merging above into the head of a lion which carries the spreading member on which the table rested. The very heavy proportions and the circumstance that the back surface is either broken away or restored make it probable that this piece was not originally a free-standing table-leg like **181**, but constituted rather the decoration of one end of a broad, solid support of the kind used under large, rectangular tables. There seems a good likelihood that the original part is of Imperial date. If so, the lunate drilled pupils and the extensive employment of the running-drill in the mane probably indicate that it should be assigned to about the second–third centuries A.D.

C. second–third centuries A.D.

J. Disney sr., *Cat. Hyde* 4 no. 20; J. Disney jr., *Museum Disneianum* 227 f., pl. 94 *left*; Marsden, *Cat. Disney Coll.* 85 no. 49; Chapman, *Handbook* (2nd ed.) 50.

185 Sundial PLATE 60

Purchased. From Egypt. Inv.: GR.100.1906 (formerly E.7.1906).

H. 0·468 m. White Egyptian limestone. Rear part of left segment broken away. Surface chipped. The two metal pointers missing from their oblique dowel-holes at the top outer corners of the dials.

This is an example of the variety of time-piece in which the usual dial of a quarter of a hollow sphere is itself divided into two equal parts set side by side, so that there are separate dials for morning and afternoon. Both segments have their curving inner surface marked with six hour-lines and with roughly concentric curves for the range of shadow-length. The dials rest on a pentagonal support, terminating in front in a crude and highly schematic lion's paw and at the back in a plane surface decorated with vertical fluting.

For a discussion of ancient sundials see *RE* s.v. *horologium*; on their construction see Vitruvius ix. 7. 1 f., on their different types, Idem ix. 8. 1. For a more elaborate example of the present variety cf. *IG* XII. 5. 645. This has been equated, though probably wrongly, with the *pharetra*, or quiver-type, of Vitruvius. If shape is any guide to nomenclature it seems much more plausibly to be identified as his *pelecinum*, or dove-tail-type, which was invented by Patrokles. The Cambridge sundial appears to be a creation of Imperial times. The highly schematic form of its lion's paw might seem to favour a late Imperial date. But such ineptitudes are not confined to the decoration and the instrument seems in general of poor and careless workmanship. Dr D. J. de S. Price, who has examined it closely, reports that it is incapable of functioning as an accurate timepiece and that its dials and calibrations have been cut by crude, rule-of-thumb methods and without making proper calculations. A fuller publication of the object will be made in Dr Price's forthcoming *Corpus of Ancient Sundials.*

Egyptian work of Imperial date.

IX

SCULPTURES OF UNCERTAIN DATE OR AUTHENTICITY

186 Statuette of a goddess or female votary

PLATE 61

Purchased (Marlay addition no. 18). Reputedly from the harbour town of Knossos in Crete. Inv.: GR. 1. 1926.

H. 0·22 m. Fine-grained marble of a creamish-grey colour with extensive veins of a deep reddish brown. Broken away are the front part of the top of the head-dress, much of the right breast and the right hand clasping it. The statuette has been carved from two pieces of marble jointed at the waist where a tapering round peg, between 0·0095 and 0·011 m. in diameter fits loosely into a square hole in the lower member which measures c. 0·011 m. on a side. Both halves are assembled from fragments, with missing areas supplied in tinted plaster. The upper part has been repaired across both arms and at breaks through the head, face and head-dress. The lower half has been assembled from some four or five fragments, with more extensive plaster restoration in the missing areas between them. The underside of the statuette has an irregularly cut dowel-hole for attachment c. 0·019 m. in diameter. The surface shows signs of exposure to moisture.

She is shown standing with her head bent slightly forward and her eyes downcast and with both hands lightly clasping, or anyway touching, her bare breasts. A young and earnest face is framed by long, waving hair. This is parted over the centre of the brow and apparently confined in front by a kind of net. Behind the ears it hangs down freely on to her shoulders and back. She wears a tall head-dress in three sections; these are each in the shape of a truncated cone and would seem to be quite differently contrived from the spiral turban of the faience snake-goddess from the 'Temple Repository' at Knossos; see Sir Arthur Evans, *Palace of Minos* I, colour frontispiece. The bottom of each section is shown adorned with beads or pearls in front, but these are not carved in detail at the back. Her dress is discussed at length in A. J. B. Wace, *A Cretan Statuette in the Fitzwilliam Museum* 9 f. It appears to consist of three pieces, a bodice, a long skirt and a kind of apron. The bodice is short-sleeved and tight-fitting and may have been 'boned' under the breasts which it leaves bare after the Minoan fashion. It seems to have been fastened in front in the middle. The skirt is long and bell-shaped, rounded in front and slightly V-shaped in plan at the back. It has several rows of horizontal tucks or cording near its upper and lower edges, according to Professor Wace's interpretation of the incised lines at these points. Between these there are attached four pleated flounces, horizontal in front but dropping down somewhat over the V-shaped back. The apron fits tightly over the skirt at the waist and hangs down low over the loins in front and at the back. It is decorated with an incised checker-board pattern surrounded by a guilloche. The figure's breasts are full and heavy, but her wrists and preserved left hand are excessively tiny. Because of the jointing at the waist, the tight girdle about the statuette's middle is, in fact, awkwardly carved in two halves which do not properly match. The joint at this point is also most insecure and lacks a runnel for pouring metal. The suggestions so far advanced (Wace, *op. cit.* 3 f.) as to how the two halves were originally fastened together seem unconvincing and the analogies drawn with the procedure for joining the hand-made and wheel-made parts of certain Minoan terracotta statuettes seem hardly apposite.

On the basis of her costume, this figure has been assigned to a position slightly later than the faience statuettes from the 'Temple Repository' at Knossos (Evans, *op. cit.* I frontispiece and 501 f.; T. Bossert, *Art of Ancient Crete* figs. 289–90) and dated accordingly near the beginning of the Late Minoan I period in the sixteenth century B.C. But, although endorsed by some of the leading authorities in the field, the statuette's authenticity has been widely doubted on a number of counts. Indeed, still-prevalent gossip names its modern author and describes the circumstances of its production, although rumours of this kind are no longer able to be verified. A few other such stone statuettes are known whose genuineness seems beyond dispute (e.g. Evans, *op. cit.* III 426 f., figs. 292–3; J. Boardman, *The Cretan Collection in Oxford* 66, fig. 26*a*, pl. 23), but it has been felt that the poor quality of the marble of the Fitzwilliam figure makes it an unlikely medium for so elaborate a work and its pronounced veining renders it an unsuitable ground for polychromy. It has also been considered that the statuette simply recombines elements known from other works such as the faience figures without contributing significant new features of dress, etc. Nilsson has declared that the pose, with the hands clasping the breasts, is un-Minoan in character. Equally suspect have been the relaxed stance and the sensitive quality of the face. To arrive at a proper assessment of the situation it seems desirable to consider first the statuette's surface condition and technique and then its stylistic affinities.

The surface of the figure has certainly been subject to considerable moisture which has caused the red veins in the material to swell. Dr C. L. Forbes of the Sedgwick Museum of Geology has expressed the view that, in a comparatively dry soil, it might take centuries to bring about this condition, but that it could be induced in a vastly shorter period by continuous soaking. This exposure to moisture has blurred the detail of the surface and so makes it difficult to pronounce on the tools used. Casson has claimed to have detected the employment of a steel gouge on the flounces of the skirt, but a recent microscopic examination has failed to produce proper confirmation of this. Indeed, some of the narrower grooves still show traces of abrasion. The drilling of the guilloche around the apron seems to conform to Bronze Age practice and the cutting of the checker-board appears to have been done with an abrasive or else with a file, since the artist was unable to control the length of the incision made. The delicately curving surfaces of the face, on the other hand, seem to suggest the use of a hard cutting edge such as a steel flat-chisel, but the waterworn condition here, too, precludes any definite pronouncement. It is, in any case, to be noted that the obvious devices of the modern forger such as the application of a false patina and the use of acid are not to be detected.

The resemblance shown to it by a small group of forged marble figures does little to invalidate the position of the Fitzwilliam statuette. For these see Evans, *op. cit.* IV. 1. 35 f., 193 f., figs. 21, 149–51, suppl. pls. 44, 47. A further example by the same hand is stored in the basement of the Museum of Classical Archaeology in Cambridge. It seems to have been bought as a forgery in Greece in 1928 and its box carries the label: 'PITZOY ψευδομινωϊκή. A direct comparison with the Fitzwilliam statuette has left no doubt that it is the work of a clumsy and unintelligent modern imitator of vastly inferior artistic ability. These figures are of a larger scale than the Fitzwilliam example and in a different marble. They seem to show evidence of modern tooling, a false patina and deliberate pitting with acid.

As remarked long ago by Sir Arthur Evans, the closest stylistic affinities shown by the Fitzwilliam figure are rather to a group of gold and ivory statuettes. These comprise the Boston goddess (*AJA* XIX (1915) 237 f., pls. 10–16; Evans, *op. cit.* III 438 f., figs. 304–5, 307, 317), the Toronto girl (Evans, *op. cit.* IV. 1. 28 f., figs. 14–16, pl. 27) and possibly the 'boy-god' (Evans, *op. cit.* III 442 f., figs. 309, 314, 316). Of these, the Boston goddess may be in a different position from the remainder in that it became known earlier and shows more of the inner tension and sense of movement appropriate to Minoan art. But it seems, none the less, difficult to separate it stylistically or technically from the other items. Indeed, it is simply the close relationship existing between these works that tends to render them suspect as a group. Their heads are in essentially the same rather 'modern' style, they are in a similar fragmentary condition and their surfaces give a superficially convincing appearance of antiquity.[1] Probably all that can be said at present is that it seems quite possible that they may be extremely skilful modern forgeries but that this does not yet admit of final proof.

C. sixteenth century B.C., *if genuine.*

The Times 6 February 1926; *Illustrated London News* 13 February 1926; *Cambridge Ancient History*, Plates I, frontispiece, p. xv; A. J. B. Wace, *A Cretan Statuette in the Fitzwilliam Museum, a Study in Minoan Costume* 3 f., pls. 1–5; *JHS* XLVII (1927) 299 f.; *Philologische Wochenschrift* 1928 1158 f.; *Orientalische Literaturzeitung* 1928 353 f.; *Classical Review* XLIII (1929) 18; Sir Arthur Evans, *The Palace of Minos at Knossos* II. 1. 235 f., fig. 133, IV. 1. 32 f., fig. 17*a–b*; S. Casson, *The Technique of Early Greek Sculpture* 3, 5 f.; J. Chittenden and C. Seltman, *Greek Art* (*Burlington House Exhibition, 1946*) 24 no. 26, pl. 6; M. P. Nilsson, *The Minoan-Mycenaean Religion* (2nd ed.) 296 n. 27, 313 n. 20; *Handbook and Guide* (1960) 8, 57, pl. 1; *Concise Encyclopaedia of World History* (*Hutchin-*

[1] The gossip concerning the modern authorship of the Fitzwilliam statuette tends to assign these works to the same hand. If it is to be trusted, then they are also immune from conviction by carbon dating, since their ivory is reputed to have been purloined from a Minoan deposit of unworked tusks excavated at Knossos. Also comparable is the statuette, Evans, *op. cit.* IV. 2. 468 f., figs. 394–8, 401, suppl. pl. 53; the relationship of other chryselephantine figures, such as *AJA* XLVI (1942) 254 f., pls. 15–16, is less clear.

son) 44, with colour text-fig.; J. Boardman, *The Cretan Collection in Oxford, the Dictaean Cave and Iron Age Crete* 66 n. 1; *The Observer* 24 September 1961 35, with fig.

187 Head of a goddess or girl, from a statuette PLATE 62

Bequeathed by C. S. Ricketts and C. H. Shannon. Provenance unknown. Inv.: GR. 102. 1937.

P.H. 0·086 m. Foraminiferous, white volcanic ash of an extremely light, coke-like texture. Broken away at the base of the neck. Surface lightly chipped and worn, particularly about the left ear, and showing a brownish surface discoloration.

The face is rather full, with a mouth that goes up at the corners and obliquely set eyes. There are disc-shaped ear-rings in the ears and a stephane or 'beaked' fillet in the hair, completely encircling the head. The hair is long and combed so that it radiates out from a point towards the back of the crown of the head. It is gathered into six loops over the brow. Behind, the main hair-mass extends down at the back of the neck, but a single tress appears to hang down in front of each ear.

The genuineness of this little head is seriously in doubt on the evidence of such features as the long locks of hair hanging down in front of the ears, the modelling of the cheeks and the form of the head-band or stephane. The head shows a general resemblance to Sicilian and Locrian terracottas of the end of the archaic period and of early classical date, e.g. R. Kekule von Stradonitz, *Die antiken Terrakotten* II, *Die Terrakotten von Sicilien* pls. 1, 5; *Ausonia* III (1908) 192 f., figs. 44–5; R. A. Higgins, *BMC Terracottas* I 326 no. 1202, 329 no. 1211, pl. 165. Whensoever it was executed, it would seem to have been modelled on work from this area.

After the style of South Italian or Sicilian work of the late first–early second quarters of the fifth century B.C., *but showing inconsistencies.*

188 Bearded head of a god (?), from a statuette PLATE 62

Bequeathed by C. S. Ricketts and C. H. Shannon. Provenance unknown. Inv.: GR. 101. 1937.

P.H. 0·137 m. Foraminiferous white volcanic ash of the same kind as employed for **187**. *It shows a brown patina. Broken away at the neck and at the tip of the nose. Surface chipped and worn, especially at the edges of the hair and beard.*

The wavy hair is combed so that it radiates from a point at the crown of the head. It is held in place with a head-band of round section which has no knot or hanging ends. Over the brow the hair is rendered as two superimposed rows of tightly coiled spiral curls; at the back of the neck it is turned under in a roll. The ends of the moustache are curled and the rest of the beard is rendered as three rows of stylized hook-shaped curls. The eyes with their up-tilted outer corners and curving outlines are perhaps faintly reminiscent of those of **187** above. The lips are slightly parted and a sense of age is conveyed by the sagging planes of the cheeks. The distinct asymmetry of the face and beard suggests that the head was carved to be seen from its left side at a three-quarter angle.

Once again the closest stylistic affinities are with South Italian and Sicilian work of the end of the archaic period and of early classical times, amongst which one may in particular cite the head of Zeus on a metope from Temple E at Selinus, probably dating to *c.* 470 B.C.; see G. M. A. Richter, *Sculpture and Sculptors of the Greeks* fig. 187, H. Kähler, *Das griechische Metopenbild* fig. 59. But Professor B. Ashmole, who has kindly scrutinized this head and **187** above on behalf of the Museum, has pointed out that its execution cannot possibly be so early. Such features as the developed modelling of the cheeks, the absence of any indication of teeth in the open mouth and the form of the head-band would seem to mark it rather as a skilful copy, although whether of a much later date in antiquity or of modern times it is more difficult to state with absolute certainty. But, in the absence of other more closely comparable material, such affinities as it may seem to show with **187** tell rather against its genuineness.

After the style of the later first–second quarters of the fifth century B.C., *but of much later execution.*

189 Miniature herm PLATE 62

Bequeathed by C. S. Ricketts and C. H. Shannon. Provenance unknown. Inv.: GR. 103. 1937.

P.H. 0·155 m. White limestone. Broken away at the bottom. Chipped at the edges of the shaft and at the projecting slabs at the shoulders. Repaired across the lower part of the shaft. Nose restored in plaster. Round holes 0·007 m. in diameter drilled through sides of shaft above and below shoulder-slabs; vertical dowel-hole of same size in underside. Surface somewhat encrusted.

The two holes through the sides would suggest that the herm is to be interpreted as a miniature version of the kind of railing-support figure met with in **96**. The shaft is ithyphallic and broadens towards the top where it has the chest indicated plastically. It carries the head of a youth with an archaic smile on his lips and with long hair hanging down his back.

This is crimped up high over the brow and apparently fastened with a fillet whose ends hang down on to the shoulders, not, however, as one might expect, from the nape of the neck, but from behind the ears like shoulder-locks. The eyes, ears, ends of the fillet and hair over the brow and crown of the head are rendered in sharp and rather minute detail.

This little herm purports to be an archaistic work of about early Imperial date, but its style seems as unconvincing as its function seems improbable.

Ostensibly archaistic work of about early Imperial date, but probably a modern forgery.

190 Cinerarium of Marcus Flavius Priscus

PLATE 62

Transferred from the Museum of Archaeology and Ethnology, Cambridge. Provenance unknown. Inv.: GR. 53. 1952.

H. 0·388 m. Luna marble. Slightly chipped. The surface of the lid has been somewhat corroded by moisture. The cist shows root marks, but these are soluble in water and seem to contain dye.

Towards the top of the front corners of the cist are carved protomai of the god Ammon, with fillets bound round their front horns but not about those at the sides. From the fillets hangs a rich garland of fruit and flowers. Above it, just under the inscribed panel, there is carved a small portrait bust framed in a shell and flanked by crudely finished swans with their necks arched backwards. The portrait head has long hair parted over the centre of the brow and carried round towards the back of the head. It seems difficult not to interpret it as the head of a woman. Underneath the garland are shown two small birds pecking at the flowers. The lower parts of the front corners of the cinerarium are occupied by crouching winged sphinxes, their bodies rendered as if divided at the angle so that they each present two side views. On both sides of the cist there is a crude low relief showing a centaur holding a basket of fruit from which he is passing a bunch of grapes to an Eros seated on his rump. The centaurs have satyr's ears and a redundant set of genitals in front. The inscription is cut on a rectangular panel framed with a Lesbian kymation. It reads as follows:

DiIs Manibus
M(arci) · Flaui · M(arci) · f(ili)
PrIsci.
Vix(it) · a(nnis) · xviii.

To the deified spirit of Marcus Flavius Priscus, son of Marcus. He lived eighteen years.

The lid is in the form of a roof covered with leaf-shaped tiles, flanked by leaf-covered, roll-shaped members at the sides with rosettes carved at their ends. In the pediment are shown a pair of small birds apparently pecking at berries.

The front of this cinerarium may be compared with **148** above and it is, in fact, even closer to others which may belong to the same group, e.g. G. Lippold, *Kat. vaticanischen Museums* III. 2. 259 no. 37, pl. 126. Its presumptive date would thus seem to fall in the second half of the first century A.D. The reliefs of centaurs and Erotes, also, seem a barbarous version of a theme popular in the first century A.D., as witness the grave-altar of Amemptus in the Louvre, Mrs A. Strong, *Roman Sculpture from Augustus to Constantine* pl. 25. The front of the cist has not been fully finished and much of it has been left at the flat-chisel and gouge stage. It is possible that many of the peculiarities of the decoration might be attributed to an unskilled or provincial hand. But there are some anomalies that are much more difficult to account for. Thus one would expect the portrait bust not to be carved until the inscription was cut. Yet the bust carries the head of a woman and the inscription describes the deceased as a young man of eighteen. Also the physical structure of the centaurs seems almost inconceivable in the first century A.D. The root marks which might seem to confirm the genuineness of the cist tend, by their form, rather to increase the doubt as to its authenticity.

C. second half of the first century A.D., if genuine.

191 Cinerary urn, ostensibly of Lucius Sentius Coccetus

PLATE 62

Presented by Dr J. Disney. Acquired in Italy. Reputedly found near the Tomb of Caecilia Metella on the Via Appia. Seen and described by Amati while in the hands of Vescovali. Inv.: GR. 53. 1850.

H. 0·523 m., diam. 0·295 m. Luna marble. Surface chipped, e.g. at the nose of one of the protomai. Lid assembled from fragments, with small areas restored in marble. Parts of the surface of the urn are heavily corroded, possibly by acid. Apparent traces of root marks. The inscription has been picked out in colour.

The urn is of the type already discussed under **150** above. For handles it has protomai showing the heads of young satyrs. Their faces are markedly full-cheeked and reveal an element of individuality, as if child-portraits are intended in the guise of young satyrs. The hair over their brows is crimped up high after the fashion of an adult hair-style of the later first century A.D.; cf. **108** above. The inscribed panel is framed by a plain kymation and a twist-pattern, with incised ivy ornament to either side. The inscription reads:

L(uci) Senti L(uci) l(iberti)
Cocceti.
V(ixit) · a(nnis) · i · m(ensibus) · vi.
Nolite dolere parentes;
hoc faciundum ⟨f⟩uit.

Of Lucius Sentius Coccetus, freed slave of Lucius. He lived one year and six months. Parents, do not grieve; this had to be.

In the last line it reads *euit* for *fuit*. It is transparently a modern copy of a known ancient inscription, *CIL* VI 26203. On the rim of the urn, above the inscribed panel, there is incised a tiny triangle. The lid is of conical shape with a large knob at the top.

As has been seen, the inscription on this urn is a recognized forgery. A close examination of the surface of the marble does not bear out the contention of the *CIL* that this is incised over an erased ancient inscription. It seems more likely that the whole urn may be a modern creation. The satyr-head-portraits fail to carry conviction, in particular in the matter of their hair-style and the shape of their ears. Whatever their date, however, they are an ingenious and delightful invention. Apart from this, the general type of the urn, with protomai for handles, seems soundly attested, e.g. D. Mustilli, *Il Museo Mussolini* 44 no. 26, pl. 26. The restored lid, which fits quite well, may possibly be authentic quite independently of the urn.

C. later first century A.D., *if genuine.*

Amati, Vatican MS 9747 f. 25 I; J. Disney jr., *Museum Disneianum* 115 f., pl. 52; Marsden, *Cat. Disney Coll.* 85 no. 45; Michaelis, *Anc. Marbles* 265 no. 84; *CIL* VI under 26203; Chapman, *Handbook* (2nd ed.) 53.

192 Lid of a cinerary urn, inscribed as of Accia Tullia — PLATE 62

Presented by Dr J. Disney. Probably acquired in Italy. Inv.: GR. 52*b*. 1850.

P.H. of lid 0·175 m. Luna marble. Missing are the urn and the tall finial of the lid. The vertical support behind the inscribed panel is socketed to receive the latter, fashioned from a separate piece of marble and possibly taking the form of a baetyl-like erection. However, there is little clear evidence that it was in fact ever fitted. The surface is chipped at a few points and somewhat corroded by moisture (or possibly acid). This lid has previously been published on the urn, **150** *above, which it does not fit.*

The lid is bounded with a twist-pattern at the rim and decorated with acanthus-like leaves twining about seed-heads and rosette-like flowers. Under the inscribed panel two tiny birds are shown pecking at the seed. The panel itself is framed with a twist-pattern and, on three sides, with a leaf-kymation of Roman type. The cutting at the corners suggests that this might also originally have extended along the lower edge and have been removed to allow room for the inscription. On its upper and outer edges the panel is decorated with an incised ivy pattern. At the back it is supported by a kind of column of acanthus leaves, with the decoration of the lid extending up to either side. The inscription itself reads:

Haue. Acciae
P(ubli) · f(iliae) · Tulliae
SOL · TI · B · F

Farewell. To Accia Tullia, daughter of Publius....
(The remainder unintelligible.)

As already recognized by Michaelis, this inscription appears to be a modern forgery. Certainly, its last line seems to be meaningless. This does not automatically dismiss the lid as a whole as a modern forgery, although it creates a strong likelihood that this is the case. In the present instance the condition of the surface of the inscribed panel might be interpreted as consistent with the erasure of an ancient inscription in order to receive the modern one. If, on the other hand, the lid is a forgery, then its sculptor showed a remarkable grasp of, and sensitivity for, Roman decorative art of the later first and first half of the second centuries A.D. For the ornament one may compare the baetyl in Padua, K. Lehmann-Hartleben and E. C. Olsen, *Dionysiac Sarcophagi in Baltimore* fig. 35.

C. later first–first half of second centuries A.D., *if genuine.*

Memoirs of Thos. Hollis, Esq. II pl. at end; J. Disney sr., *Cat. Hyde* 4, appendix 23 no. 17, with pl.; J. Disney jr., *Museum Disneianum* 113 f., pl. 51; Marsden, *Cat. Disney Coll.* 85 no. 47; Michaelis, *Anc. Marbles* 265 no. 83; Chapman, *Handbook* (2nd ed.) 53.

193 Head of a man — PLATE 61

Purchased. From Eskişehir, near the ancient Dorylaion in Phrygia. Inv.: GR. 71. 1906.

P.H. 0·176 m. Moderately coarse-grained greyish-white Asia Minor marble. Broken away at the neck. Traces of modern cleaning or minor recutting around the edges of the hair, garland, nose, eyes, mouth and underside of chin.

The fragment appears to preserve a beardless male head of a highly unusual style. The hair is not shown in detail save around its lower edge, where small curls seem to be indicated. Just above these there is a projecting mass which, in its present somewhat recut condition at least, seems to represent a kind of garland. The highly stylized features might seem to indicate either an archaic or a medieval date. Such crude local stone sculptures of archaic date as are extant from Phrygia seem to be of a rather different character, e.g. *AM* XXII (1897) 25 f., pl. 2; *Dergisi* VIII. 1 pl. 2; *Anatolia* IV pls. 37–40. The garland may suggest affinities with Phrygian grave-busts of later Imperial times, but the face is vastly more stylized in character than any to be found on these. It must, in fact, be admitted that for the present and in the absence of any known adequate parallels this head has to be regarded as undatable. See also p. 128.

Medieval (?).

AJA LXIII (1959) 143 no. 17.

X

RENAISSANCE AND LATER SCULPTURE FORMERLY CONSIDERED ANCIENT

Any full-scale publication of these sculptures would lie as far beyond the scope of the present volume as it is beyond the competence of its authors to accomplish. As a consequence, nothing more will here be attempted than a brief list quoting the relevant bibliography and giving extremely tentative short descriptions. It is hoped that, for all its probable shortcomings, this will do something to remove past confusions and misconceptions.

(A) SCULPTURES IN THE ROUND

194 Statuette of the Virgin and Child, or Charity

Presented by Dr J. Disney. Provenance unknown. Inv.: GR. 3. 1850.

P.H. 0·476 m. Veined alabaster. Broken away are the head, left fore-arm, right hand and both feet of the female figure, the head, left arm and all the lower part of the body of the child. An iron pin in a knot of drapery at the breast of the standing figure may have provided secondary support for an attribute held in her missing right hand. The surface is chipped and much corroded by water.

The fragment preserves the greater part of a heavily draped female figure with a veil over the back of the head, standing with her right leg slightly flexed and holding a child in the crook of her left arm. The good workmanship led Michaelis sadly astray about both material and date. Professor J. W. Pope-Hennessy, who has kindly examined the statuette on behalf of the Museum, reports that it is of Flemish origin and probably dates from the first quarter of the sixteenth century A.D.

Flemish work of about the first quarter of the sixteenth century A.D.

J. Disney jr., *MS Cat.* 128; Idem, *Museum Disneianum* 55, pl. 27; *AZ* v (1847) 158; *GGA* 1849 447, 449; Marsden, *Cat. Disney Coll.* 84 no. 34; Michaelis, *Anc. Marbles* 256 no. 34; Chapman, *Handbook* (2nd ed.) 45.

195 Eros standing beside a greave (?)—support-figure to a larger statuette or group

No record of acquisition or provenance. From the Disney Collection? Inv.: GR. S. 7.

P.H. 0·181 m. Alabaster. Broken away at bottom and one side. Left hand and leg of Eros missing. In poor condition with the surface badly chipped and eroded by water.

The fragment seems to preserve the standing figure of Eros with a somewhat protuberant belly, moderately long hair and exaggerated Venus-rings at the neck. He is naked save for a thin wisp of drapery held across the body and his furled wings seem to be somewhat cursorily indicated at the back. To his right there appears to be an empty greave standing upright over which a mass of drapery is being tumbled by one of the figures of the main group. Possibly the fragment formed the support to a group of Ares and Aphrodite. The bad surface condition precludes any stylistic judgment.

Possibly Western European (Flemish or German?) work of the sixteenth century A.D. or slightly later.

196 Head of a Dacian

Presented by Dr J. Disney. Acquired in Italy (?) in the mid eighteenth century. Inv.: GR. 12. 1850.

H. 0·296 m. Veined alabaster. Intact apart from a broken area at the bottom of the back of the neck. Surface condition fresh.

The sculpture consists of the head and neck of a Dacian wearing a Phrygian cap. He has a short beard and moustache and a Trajanic hair-style. The workmanship is excellent, but the sculptor has been so thoroughly imbued with his Roman originals of the time of Trajan that it is difficult to assess the date of execution. A very similar modern head of a Dacian is now in Boston; it is carved in porphyry; see R. Delbrueck, *Antike Porphyrwerke* pl. 54.

Of Renaissance–eighteenth-century-A.D. date (perhaps most plausibly early eighteenth century?).

J. Disney sr., *Cat. Hyde* 2 no. 10; J. Disney jr., *Museum Disneianum* 9, pl. 5; *AZ* v (1847) 157; *GGA* 1849 446; Marsden, *Cat. Disney Coll.* 84 no. 13; Michaelis, *Anc. Marbles* 257 no. 43; Chapman, *Handbook* (2nd ed.) 52.

197 Restoration of the head of Pan for an ancient group of Pan and Daphnis

Presented by Dr J. Disney. 'From the Palazzo Farnese.' Acquired by T. Hollis in 1752. Inv.: GR.29.1850.

H. c. 0·34 m. Carrara marble. Left horn repaired. Neck irregularly cut, dowelled and plastered to fit a broken ancient surface.

The head of the god was turned sharply to the left and conforms to the ancient type appropriate to the figure of Pan in the third-century-B.C. group of Pan and Daphnis (or Olympos) as known from numerous copies of Imperial date; for a list of the ancient replicas see W. H. Roscher, *Lexikon der griechischen und römischen Mythologie* III 1453 f. The relevance, if any, of this restoration to the famous group of this type from the Palazzo Farnese, now in the Museo Nazionale in Naples, rests somewhat obscure; for the Naples group see the plate, B. Maiuri, *Il Museo Nazionale di Napoli* 35. Its present restorations by Carlo Albacini are of somewhat later execution. Hollis's ascription of the head to Michelangelo seems unduly optimistic. It is a dry work that follows the prescribed type closely and gives little clue as to the date at which it was carved.

Italian work of Renaissance to eighteenth-century-A.D. date (perhaps most plausibly early eighteenth century?).

Memoirs of Thos. Hollis, Esq. II 821; J. Disney sr., *Cat. Hyde* 2 no. 31 (where it has been confused with **200** below); J. Disney jr., *MS Cat.* 66; Marsden, *Cat. Disney Coll.* 84 no. 33; Michaelis, *Anc. Marbles* 260 no. 60; Chapman, *Handbook* (2nd ed.) 37.

198 Head, probably for the restoration of an ancient copy of Doidalsas' Aphrodite

No record of acquisition or provenance. Possibly from the Disney Collection? Inv.: GR.S.8.

H. c. 0·219 m. Carrara marble. Dowelled and fitted at the neck to match an ancient broken surface. This fitted surface has since been partly recut to provide a level base at the neck.

The distinctive angle of neck and head make it a reasonably sound inference that this restoration was intended to fit an ancient statue of the general type of Doidalsas' crouching Aphrodite; on Doidalsas' statue and its copies see R. Lullies, *Die kauernde Aphrodite* passim. The restorer has only loosely approximated to the ancient type. The hair is bound in two knots, one at the crown and the other at the back of the head. The small and delicate mouth and eyes, the over-full cheeks and the weak chin all suggest work of the sixteenth–eighteenth centuries.

C. sixteenth–eighteenth centuries A.D.

199 Head of Athena

Presented by Dr J. Disney. Probably acquired in Italy in the mid eighteenth century A.D. Inv.: GR.8.1850.

H. 0·475 m. Carrara marble. Only the front half of the head is shown, as if in relief. The patina of the flattish, point-dressed rear surface suggests that the head may have been cut from an ancient block. Apparently trimmed with the point around the edge of the neck.

The sculpture shows the head and neck of Athena on a scale distinctly larger than life-size. She wears a helmet of truncated and misinterpreted Corinthian form in the raised position on the back of her head. Her hair is parted in the middle and, above the ears, brushed out over the sides of the helmet. Locks hang down on to her shoulders to either side. Her eyes have incised irises and pupils. The head is the product of tolerable workmanship in a classicizing style, but executed without proper understanding of the subject.

Italian work of Renaissance–eighteenth-century-A.D. date.

Memoirs of Thos. Hollis, Esq. II 821; J. Disney sr., *Cat. Hyde* 4 f. no. 6; J. Disney jr., *MS Cat.* 36; Marsden, *Cat. Disney Coll.* 83 no. 7; Michaelis, *Anc. Marbles* 257 no. 39 (where confused with J. Disney jr., *Museum Disneianum* I, pl. I); *JHS* XIX (1899) I f., fig. I; Chapman, *Handbook* (2nd ed.) 57 (where also confused with *Museum Disneianum* I, pl. I).

200 Herm of Pan

Presented by Dr J. Disney. Bought from W. Lloyd in 1761. Inv.: GR.21.1850.

H. 0·356 m. Carrara marble. Surface chipped and worn at many points. Restored, partly in plaster and partly in marble, at several points on the garland and at both horns. Square socket cut out in underside. Dowel-holes in sides for the projecting slabs at the shoulders of the herm.

The sculpture consists of the head and chest of Pan, shaped to form the upper part of a herm. The god has horns and pointed ears and is garlanded with ivy. The head has something of the character of sixteenth-century Italian bronze 'fauns' misrepresented in the guise of Pan, but it is so vigorous and consistent and rings so true in style as to suggest that the artist was inspired by an ancient work. Interestingly comparable is the *rosso antico* herm of Pan from the Meander Valley in Berlin (inv. 1723); see R. Kekule von Stradonitz and B. Schröder, *Die griechische Skulptur* (3rd ed.) 285; F. Winter, *Altertümer von Pergamon* VII. 2. 222 no. 259. Possibly a copy of this or some related work then extant and since lost may have provided the artist with his source of inspiration. The Berlin herm itself was not discovered until the nineteenth century.

Italian work of Renaissance–eighteenth-century-A.D. date.

J. Disney sr., *Cat. Hyde* 3 no. 7 (where confused with **197** above); J. Disney jr., *Museum Disneianum* 29, pl. 15; *AZ* v (1847) 158; Marsden, *Cat. Disney Coll.* 84 no. 31; Michaelis, *Anc. Marbles* 259 no. 52; Chapman, *Handbook* (2nd ed.) 52.

201 Garlanded head of Domitian (?)

Presented by Dr J. Disney. Apparently acquired in Italy in the mid eighteenth century. Inv.: GR.11.1850.

H. 0·365 m. Carrara marble. 'Broken away' at the base of the neck; deliberately cut 'broken' surface at the back of the head.

The artist has attempted, not very successfully, to produce an Imperial portrait-head wearing an oak garland. The piece was acquired by Hollis as representing the Emperor Domitian, and to judge from the weak attempt to imitate a Flavian hair-style and the characteristic rendering of mouth and brow such was indeed the artist's intention. On the ancient portraits of this emperor see under **108** above. The eyes have incised irises and pupils and there is clumsy drill-work on the hair and garland. The execution is somewhat poor, the detail rather fussy.

Italian work of about the eighteenth century A.D. (?).

Memoirs of Thos. Hollis, Esq. II 821; J. Disney sr., *Cat. Hyde* 2 no. 3; J. Disney jr., *Museum Disneianum* 7, pl. 4; *AZ* v (1847) 157; *GGA* 1849 446; Marsden, *Cat. Disney Coll.* 84 no. 20; Michaelis, *Anc. Marbles* 257 no. 42; Chapman, *Handbook* (2nd ed.) 40.

202 Statuette of Seilenos playing the flute

Presented by Dr J. Disney. Apparently acquired in Italy in the mid eighteenth century. Inv.: GR.4.1850.

H. 0·49 m. Carrara marble. 'Repaired' at neck, right wrist and left upper arm of silen and across the flute. Pseudo-restorations of the upper and lower parts of the flute and of the fingers of the silen's left hand now missing. Parts of the surface about his shoulders deliberately cut back and 'restored' in plaster. Bogus patina, particularly over the lower part of the group.

A silen, garlanded with ivy, is shown seated on a rock and playing the flute. He is naked apart from a tasselled cloak draped across the rock and his right thigh. A shaggy-coated sheep-dog gazes up at him from the ground at his side.

An Italian pseudo-antiquity of the eighteenth century A.D. (?).

J. Disney sr., *Cat. Hyde* 5 no. 25; J. Disney jr., *Museum Disneianum* 59, pl. 28; *AZ* v (1847) 158; *GGA* 1849 447, 459; Marsden, *Cat. Disney Coll.* 83 no. 5; Michaelis, *Anc. Marbles* 256 no. 35; Chapman, *Handbook* (2nd ed.) 52.

203 Bust of a young god, or a youth

Presented by Dr J. Disney. Bought in Leghorn in 1830. Reputedly discovered in Populonia in 1828. Inv.: GR.25.1850.

H. 0·418 m. Carrara marble. Tip of nose restored in marble by Sir Richard Westmacott.

The bust seems to be a free creation in the style of a Greek work of the later fourth century B.C. without being identifiably copied from any specific ancient statue-type. The head is slightly turned and inclined to the right. The surface rendering and the treatment of the eyes suggest a date no earlier than the later eighteenth century A.D.

Italian work of the late eighteenth–early nineteenth centuries A.D.

J. Disney jr., *Museum Disneianum* 39, pl. 20; *AZ* v (1847) 158; *GGA* 1849 447; Marsden, *Cat. Disney Coll.* 83 no. 11; Michaelis, *Anc. Marbles* 259 no. 56; Chapman, *Handbook* (2nd ed.) 57.

204 Bust of a young satyr

Presented by Dr J. Disney. Reputedly found in 1826 near the Church of Santa Agnese, two miles outside the Porta Pia, Rome, and given to Disney in 1827. Inv.: GR.24.1850.

H. 0·38 m. Carrara marble. Tip of nose restored in marble.

This piece consists of the bust of a young satyr with his head thrown back laughing. He has pointed ears and, on his brow, tiny horns. The bust is of the general shape of the upper part of a herm, but with its sides tapering excessively towards the bottom. This is a not very competent work, freely based on an ancient type, but not copying it exactly; cf. G. Lippold, *Kat. vaticanischen Museums* III. 2. 244 no. 18, pl. 109; *EA* 4387–8; G. Kaschnitz-Weinberg, *Sculture del Magazzino del Museo Vaticano* 85 no. 171, pl. 37.

Italian work of about the eighteenth–early nineteenth centuries A.D.

J. Disney jr., *Museum Disneianum* 37, pl. 19; *AZ* v (1847) 158; Marsden, *Cat. Disney Coll.* 83 no. 6; Michaelis, *Anc. Marbles* 259 no. 55; Chapman, *Handbook* (2nd ed.) 52.

205 Portrait-head of a man

Presented by Dr J. Disney. Reputedly 'discovered' in the vicinity of Florence where it was bought by Disney in November 1829. Inv.: GR.26.1850.

H. 0·277 m. Carrara marble. Dowelled at the neck for mounting on a bust, from which it has been removed since its publication by Disney.

The sculpture shows the vigorous head of a man in early middle age with furrowed brows, thick, curling hair and side-whiskers. Pozzi's description of this piece as being 'of the latest style', so naïvely misconstrued and quoted by Disney, is precisely true. It is in fact an outstandingly fine contemporary portrait of the 1820's. The surface shows faint traces of a pattern of control-drillings, suggesting that the marble version was executed from a model of clay or plaster.

Italian work of the earlier nineteenth century A.D.

J. Disney jr., *Museum Disneianum* 41, pl. 21; *AZ* v (1847) 158; Marsden, *Cat. Disney Coll.* 84 no. 17; Michaelis, *Anc. Marbles* 259 no. 57; Chapman, *Handbook* (2nd ed.) 40; *AJA* LXIII (1959) 142 (where apparently confused with **111** above; this head may also have been confused by Bernoulli, for which see under **110** above).

(B) RELIEFS

206 Medallion with a Gorgoneion in relief

Presented by Dr J. Disney. Acquired in Italy in the mid eighteenth century (?). Inv.: GR.61.1850.

H. 0·305 m., diam. 0·33 m. Gritty yellowish limestone. Chipped at several points. Traces of white plaster over the surface with, over this, remains of dark red on the background and the mouth of the Gorgon.

This piece shows a Gorgoneion carved in relief on a flat disc with its bottom cut level to provide a standing surface. The head has rather sparse snakes for hair, two of them being knotted under the chin. The mouth is open and deeply hollowed, the brow wrinkled. In general the work suggests a purely literary concept of a Gorgoneion rather than one derived from ancient art.

Work of Renaissance date (?).

Memoirs of Thos. Hollis, Esq. II 820; J. Disney sr., *Cat. Hyde* 9 no. 44; J. Disney jr., *Museum Disneianum* 65, pl. 31; Marsden, *Cat. Disney Coll.* 87 no. 71; Michaelis, *Anc. Marbles* 266 no. 92; Chapman, *Handbook* (2nd ed.) 56.

207 Medallion with a relief-portrait of the Emperor Nero

Presented by Dr J. Disney. Bought in Venice about 1752. Reputedly from Athens. Inv.: GR.63.1850.

Diam. 0·372 m. Carrara marble. Broken and repaired in recent times. Chipped at edges.

This piece consists of an oscillum-shaped, circular medallion with a shallow relief-portrait of the Emperor Nero. He is shown in profile, beardless and wearing the rayed crown of the Sun-god. The head has been closely copied from ancient coin-types, e.g. H. Mattingly, *BMC Coins of the Roman Empire* I pls. 43. 9–10, 44. 2–4, 47. 1, etc. A closely similar Renaissance medallion of the same emperor is to be found in the Capitoline Museum in Rome; see H. Stuart Jones, *Cat. Museo Capitolino* 145 no. 15*a*, pl. 37.

Italian work of the late fifteenth–sixteenth centuries A.D.

Memoirs of Thos. Hollis, Esq. II 820; J. Disney sr., *Cat. Hyde* 10 no. 52; J. Disney jr., *Museum Disneianum* 71, pl. 34; *AZ* v (1847) 158; *GGA* 1849 451, 452; Marsden, *Cat. Disney Coll.* 87 no. 69; Michaelis, *Anc. Marbles* 266 no. 94; Chapman, *Handbook* (2nd ed.) 56.

208 Relief-portrait, probably of Marcus Vipsanius Agrippa

Presented by Dr J. Disney. Apparently acquired in Italy in the mid eighteenth century. Inv.: GR.64.1850.

H. 0·365 m. Carrara marble. Slightly chipped at

edges. The relief-ground shows traces of dark paint, edged with gold.

The relief is carved on a panel, rectangular in shape at the bottom and rounded at the top. It shows the laurel-crowned bust of a man, seen in profile. This seems to have been acquired as a portrait of Agrippa and a comparison with coin-types suggests that such was probably the artist's intention; cf. Mattingly, *op. cit.* I pl. 26. 7–8, K. Lange, *Herrscherköpfe des Altertums* pl. 105.

Italian work of about the late fifteenth–sixteenth centuries A.D.

J. Disney jr., *MS Cat.* 178; Idem, *Museum Disneianum* 79, pl. 38; *AZ* v (1847) 159; Marsden, *Cat. Disney Coll.* 86 no. 65; Michaelis, *Anc. Marbles* 267 no. 95; Chapman, *Handbook* (2nd ed.) 41.

209 Relief-portrait, possibly of the Empress Faustina the Younger

Presented by Dr J. Disney. Acquired in the eighteenth century from the Mead Collection, possibly before the Mead sale as it is not identifiably listed in *Museum Meadianum*. Inv.: GR.68.1850.

P.H. 0·272 m. Carrara marble. Top part of the panel broken away. Slightly chipped elsewhere. Sawn surface at back, concave mouldings at edges.

The relief-plaque is rectangular in shape so far as it is preserved. It shows the bust of a woman seen in profile and with her lips slightly parted as if in speech. This relief seems to have been acquired as a portrait of Faustina. Faint resemblances do in fact exist between the head and coin-types of Faustina the Younger; cf. M. Wegner, *Die Herrscherbildnisse in antoninischer Zeit* pl. 63. But the artist has treated his subject with such freedom that it is doubtful if a certain identification is possible. On the ancient portraits of Faustina the Younger see under **116** above. The way that the mouth is shown open as if in speech is perhaps derived from the ancient device noted on **101a** and **102**. This relief is similar to **207** and **208**, but the cutting is somewhat harsher.

Italian work of about the late fifteenth–sixteenth centuries A.D.

J. Disney sr., *Cat. Hyde* 11 no. 108; J. Disney jr., *MS Cat.* 148; Marsden, *Cat. Disney Coll.* 86 no. 64; Michaelis, *Anc. Marbles* 267 no. 99; Chapman, *Handbook* (2nd ed.) 56.

210 Relief-portrait, possibly of the Emperor Hadrian

Presented by Dr J. Disney. Apparently acquired in Italy in the mid eighteenth century. Inv.: GR.67.1850.

H. as restored 0·281 m. Proconnesian marble. The upper part of the plaque has been restored in marble. The surface of the original part has a weather-worn appearance.

The rectangular plaque carries a relief showing the laurel-garlanded head of a man in profile. The old identification of this as a portrait of Philip of Macedon seems highly improbable. To judge from the distinctive curls over the brow, it appears much more likely that the artist really intended a profile portrait of the Emperor Hadrian, loosely based on coin-types such as Lange, *op. cit.* pl. 133. In that case the work is rather incompetent, with the ear greatly exaggerated in size and the chin somewhat weakened.

Italian work of about the sixteenth century A.D. (?).

J. Disney sr., *Cat. Hyde* 49 no. 57; J. Disney jr., *MS Cat.* 146; Idem, *Museum Disneianum* 83, pl. 40; Marsden, *Cat. Disney Coll.* 86 no. 57; Michaelis, *Anc. Marbles* 267 no. 98; Chapman, *Handbook* (2nd ed.) 56 (where wrongly given as Clarke Collection).

211 Cameo-like relief of a Julio-Claudian prince or emperor

Presented by Dr J. Disney. Apparently acquired in Italy in the mid eighteenth century. Inv.: GR.69.1850.

H. 0·169 m. Cut in cameo technique from a fine-grained, slightly translucent piece of white marble with a more opaque vein running through it at the back. Right edge deliberately broken away. Bottom part 'restored' in marble. Mounted on slate at the back. Bogus root-marks, etc., on the relief-ground. Laurel garland tinted.

The relief represents the naked upper part of the figure of a prince or emperor facing towards the right and wearing a laurel garland in his hair. The surface of the flesh has been highly polished to contrast with that of the relief-ground. The figure seems broadly based on ancient cameo portraits such as that in Vienna, A. Furtwängler, *Antike Gemmen* III fig. 163; cf. also the great cameo in Paris, *ibid.* I pl. 60.

Italian work of about the eighteenth century A.D. (?).

J. Disney sr., *Cat. Hyde* 49 no. 231; J. Disney jr., *MS Cat.* 172; Marsden, *Cat. Disney Coll.* 86 no. 60; Michaelis, *Anc. Marbles* 267 no. 100; Chapman, *Handbook* (2nd ed.) 56.

212 Relief panel showing Bacchic masks

Presented by Dr J. Disney. Apparently acquired in Italy in the mid eighteenth century. Inv.: GR.42.1850.

H. of relief panel 0·231 m., H. of frame 0·302 m. Relief panel of Carrara marble; frame partly of rosso antico *and partly of veined red marble. The relief is backed with slate. The two upper corners of the relief panel are 'restored' in marble; it is repaired at the lower right corner. Surface somewhat stained.*

The relief panel shows two masks resting on rocky ground and with a diminutive thyrsos behind them. The left mask, beardless and wearing both a fillet and an ivy garland, is probably to be interpreted as representing the youthful Dionysos rather than a maenad. That to the right portrays a Seilenos. The irises of the eyes are incised. This piece is clearly based on Roman decorative reliefs such as T. Schreiber, *Hellenistische Reliefbilder* pl. 100; in antiquity similar scenes also occur on oscilla (e.g. **127** above) and garland sarcophagi. The poor quality of the execution of the present example can almost be matched amongst Roman work, e.g. W. Amelung, *Kat. vaticanischen Museums* II 710 f. no. 440, pl. 79. However, its fussy detail and the modern character of both the heads reveal it as a creation of about eighteenth-century date. The relief is mounted in a frame of *rosso antico* and veined red marble.

Italian work of about the eighteenth century A.D. (?).

J. Disney sr., *Cat. Hyde* 10 no. 53; J. Disney jr., *MS Cat.* 152; Marsden, *Cat. Disney Coll.* 87 no. 68; Michaelis, *Anc. Marbles* 261 no. 73; Chapman, *Handbook* (2nd ed.) 41.

213 Relief with the bust of a young woman

Presented by Dr J. Disney. Apparently acquired in Italy in the mid eighteenth century. Inv.: GR.66.1850.

H. 0·151 m. Carrara marble.

The small, rectangular panel in low relief shows the draped bust of a young woman facing towards the right. Her hair is gathered towards the upper part of the back of the head in a somewhat imprecise imitation of the Greek 'melon-style'. See also **214** below.

Italian work of the eighteenth century A.D. (?).

J. Disney jr., *MS Cat.* 162; Marsden, *Cat. Disney Coll.* 86 no. 61; Michaelis, *Anc. Marbles* 267 no. 97; Chapman, *Handbook* (2nd ed.) 56.

214 Relief with the bust of a young man

Presented by Dr J. Disney. Apparently acquired in Italy in the mid eighteenth century. Inv.: GR.65.1850.

H. 0·144 m. Carrara marble. Repaired at the top right corner. Mounted on slate at the back.

In this case the small, rectangular panel in low relief shows the draped bust of a young man facing towards the left. It has been carved by the same hand as was responsible for **213** above and seems to have been intended as a companion-piece to it.

Italian work of the eighteenth century A.D. (?).

J. Disney jr., *MS Cat.* 162; Marsden, *Cat. Disney Coll.* 86 no. 63; Michaelis, *Anc. Marbles* 267 no. 96 (where the reference to Disney's *Museum Disneianum* actually belongs to his no. 98); Chapman, *Handbook* (2nd ed.) 56.

215 Relief showing Agamemnon rejecting the plea of Chryses

Presented by Dr J. Disney. Bought from Vescovali in Rome. Reputedly found in Perugia in 1826. Inv.: GR.35.1850.

H. 0·334 m., W. 0·625 m. Carrara (?) marble. The thin relief panel has been mounted on a larger slab of marble. Both relief and backing-slab have been repaired at the top left corner. Minor chips missing elsewhere. The surface has a yellowish false-patina.

The scene depicted in delicate, shallow relief on the rectangular panel is one described in the first book of the *Iliad*. Agamemnon, in the presence of Menelaos, Odysseus and other leaders of the Achaeans, is shown rejecting the plea of Chryses to ransom his daughter and sending him forth from the camp. The figures stand on a projecting base-line and the scene is framed with a profiled moulding. In *AA* 1864 169 f. Conze has suggested attributing this rather fine piece of neo-classical work to the Neapolitan sculptor, Vincenzo Monti, who executed numerous forgeries for the dealer, Vescovali.

Italian work of the early nineteenth century A.D.

J. Disney jr., *Museum Disneianum* 81 f., pl. 39; *AZ* V (1847) 159; *GGA* 1849 455 f.; Marsden, *Cat. Disney Coll.* 86 no. 53; Overbeck, *Bildwerke* pl. 16. 11; *AA* 1864 169 f., 1866 301; Michaelis, *Anc. Marbles* 260 no. 66; Chapman, *Handbook* (2nd ed.) 42.

216 Relief showing a female figure

Presented by Dr J. Disney. Provenance unknown. Inv.: GR.70.1850.

P.H. 0·233 m. Carrara marble. Deliberately broken away all around the edges with the aid of the hammer and point.

A young woman is shown seated on the ground and with her right hand outstretched. She is naked to below the waist, the lower part of her body being loosely draped. Her hair is gathered into a knot at the back of her head.

Neo-classical work of the late eighteenth or first half of the nineteenth centuries A.D.

Marsden, *Cat. Disney Coll.* 86 no. 59; Michaelis, *Anc. Marbles* 267 no. 101; Chapman, *Handbook* (2nd ed.) 38.

(C) ARCHITECTURAL

217 Pilaster-base

Presented by Dr J. Disney. Apparently acquired in Italy in the mid eighteenth century. Inv.: GR.44.1850.

H. 0·404 m., W. 0·312 m. Carrara marble. Much chipped. Anathyrosis on underside. Sides bevelled back at 45° to take marble panels continuing the dado on both sides of the pilaster. Clamps for their attachment were fitted in holes at the top of the base. However, the return on the right side is only 0·106 m. deep as against 0·136 m. on the left side—i.e. this pilaster was set at the edge of a shallow projection or recess, 3 cm. deep. The top shows anathyrosis to receive the pilaster-shaft. Rough-hewn with the point at the back. Surface weather-worn and with pitch-like scales of black at some points.

The base has elaborate foot and crowning mouldings and is decorated on three sides with reliefs. That on the front shows a nude female torso with the arms and legs developing into acanthus leaves, flanked to either side by convolutions of acanthus with large flowers. The relief-panel on the left side is occupied with a convoluted stem of acanthus, that to the right with a plant of rather similar kind growing vertically. This base was first recognized as of Renaissance workmanship by Dr D. E. Strong of the British Museum. The foliate decoration has already developed to an ornate stage and the closest parallels seem to be found in northern Italy in the late fifteenth and first half of the sixteenth centuries A.D. It is closely modelled on Imperial Roman decorative art, but contains elements that are foreign to the style of antiquity.

Italian work of the late fifteenth–first half of the sixteenth centuries A.D.

J. Disney sr., *Cat. Hyde* 3 no. 13; J. Disney jr., *MS Cat.* 248; Marsden, *Cat. Disney Coll.* 84 no. 23; Michaelis, *Anc. Marbles* 262 no. 75; Chapman, *Handbook* (2nd ed.) 52.

ADDENDA

After this Catalogue had been submitted to the press in 1962, the Museum's Greek and Roman Rooms were completely re-organized in order to improve their display facilities. In the course of this the sculptures were moved into new positions where they might be seen under better lighting conditions and so that inadequacies in their mounting, such as those noted under **81** and **161** above, might as far as possible be overcome. The availability of lifting equipment to shift the heavier marbles enabled surfaces that had not been accessible before to be examined closely. The most important of the new observations made as a consequence are given below, together with a certain amount of recent bibliographical information. These remarks are listed under the catalogue numbers of the individual sculptures. This book is being printed a little too soon for it to be possible also to include references to the new edition of the Museum's *Handbook* which is to appear early in 1964 and which will deal a little more specifically than its recent predecessors with the more important of the Greek and Roman sculptures.

17 In the new edition of G. M. A. Richter, *Kouroi*, the reference to the statuette cited in n. 4 becomes 57 no. 27, figs. 126–8.

49 For the Pan from Sparta, see now S. Meletzis and H. Papadakis, *National Museum of Archaeology, Athens* 10, pl. 46.

52 On the Sofia Eros, see now *Trésors des Musées Bulgares* (Paris exhibition, 1963) no. 66, with pl.

53 For a further copy, quite close to the Holkham Hall portrait, see now *Kunstwerke der Antike* (Museum of Classical Antiquities, Basle, 1963) no. A 10, with pl. facing.

54 On the Leconfield and Argos figures of Ganymedes, which show a limited typological resemblance to the Naples statue, see now *BCH* LXXXVII (1963) 165f.

55–7 For the latest discussion of the questions surrounding Bryaxis' Sarapis, see A. Adriani, *Repertorio d'arte dell'Egitto greco-romano*, ser. A, II 40f.

65–6 For examples of the statues of little girls from the Temple of Artemis at Brauron, see now S. Meletzis and H. Papadakis, *National Museum of Archaeology, Athens* 10, pls. 54–5.

81 There is a modern, almost horizontal, sawn surface underneath at the waist, pierced by a large modern socket for a dowel. To be added to the bibliography is G. E. Mylonas, *Eleusis and the Eleusinian Mysteries* 11, 159, 204.

82 Add to the bibliography of the Caesar portraits *Mon. Piot* XLVII 131f.; V. Poulsen, *Glyptothèque Ny Carlsberg, Cat. des portraits romains* I 60f. under nos. 29f.

84 On the Nile-god type, see now A. Adriani, *Repertorio d'arte dell'Egitto greco-romano*, ser. A, II 55f. nos. 195–6, pls. 92–3.

85–6 For other statuettes of the same type, see A. Adriani, *Repertorio d'arte dell'Egitto greco-romano*, ser. A, II 20f. nos. 75, 78, 85, 87, 88, 95–8, 100, 101, pls. 52f.

93 For the frontal treatment, cf. *BCH* LXXXVII (1963) 356 fig. 48.

94 For the relief-medallion of Artemis from Side, see now Arif Müfid Mansel, *Die Ruinen von Side* 134, fig. 112.

98 Cf. now also the torso, *BCH* LXXXVII (1963) 49f.

101 A re-examination of the pattern of the folds suggests that *two* superimposed linen garments may possibly be represented instead of one—i.e. an under- and an over-chiton, as well as the himation.

106 This head has now been removed from its modern bust.

112 It should be placed on record that the authors felt some qualms as to the antiquity of this head, but that these doubts have not been able to be substantiated at all up to the present.

117 For the type, cf. also E. von Mercklin, *Antike Figuralkapitelle* 13f., pls. 8–9.

121 Cf. also the frieze- and architrave-block from Side with comic masks: Arif Müfid Mansel, *Die Ruinen von Side* 134, fig. 110. It is similar to that with tragic masks, *Türk Arkeoloji Dergisi* VIII. I pl. 12.

125 Cf. also E. Mandowsky and C. Mitchell, *Pirro Ligorio's Roman Antiquities* pls. 14, 16–18.

145–155 It may avoid puzzlement to point out that the ablative, rather than the accusative, has been supplied in these inscriptions and in **190–1** to indicate the duration of a completed life (or military service) simply because this is the more usual form met with on funerary inscriptions of this kind from Italy where the expression is not abbreviated.

155 The authors are indebted to Mr P. R. C. Weaver for help with the bibliography of this inscription, particularly in connection with its double entry in *CIL*. Mr Weaver considers that the reading of the second line given on p. 95 raises considerable onomastic difficulties and feels more inclined to treat the whole group of letters, TḞLVERO, as representing a single personal name, perhaps mis-spelled.

160 The floor of the cist is worked in the form of a low pillow at the right end. This pillow has a shallow depression in the middle, shaped to receive a child's head. Immediately below the pillow a small rectangular drainage-hole pierces the floor of the cist.

161 The cist has been filled in almost solid in the modern restoration of the sarcophagus and this circumstance has prevented any investigation of its internal arrangements.

162, 163 The floors of both cists are carved in the form of a low pillow at the right end.

169, 170 Cf. *Annuaire du Musée National de Varsovie* VII (1963) 240f. nos. 8f. On Roman Corinthian capitals from Augustan to Antonine times see *BSR* XXX (1962) 12f.

171 On the type, cf. also E. von Mercklin, *Antike Figuralkapitelle* 135f., pls. 88–9.

193 Dr Nezih Fıratlı has recently informed the authors of the existence of certain unpublished fragments also from Dorylaion in the reserve of the Archaeological Museum in Istanbul. These are described as being in the same style and as suggesting the possibility that these sculptures as a whole, whose authenticity has been somewhat questioned, may in fact be of about Late Roman date. Other such pieces from the same site are reported to be in Ankara.

PLATES 1–62

1

3 4

8 2 7 6 5

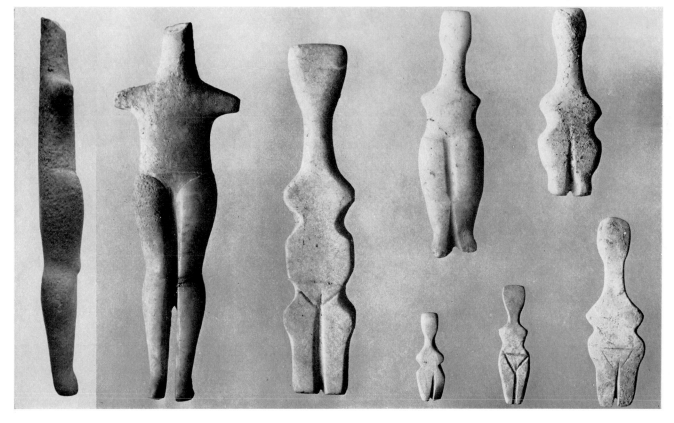

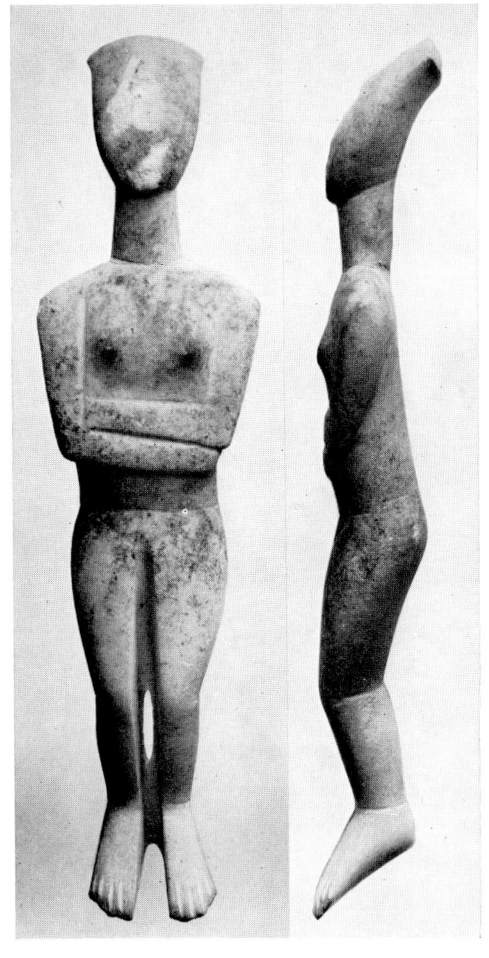

10

11

12

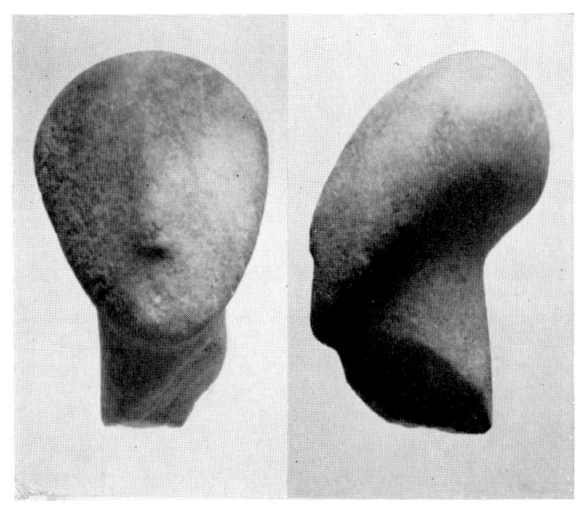

9

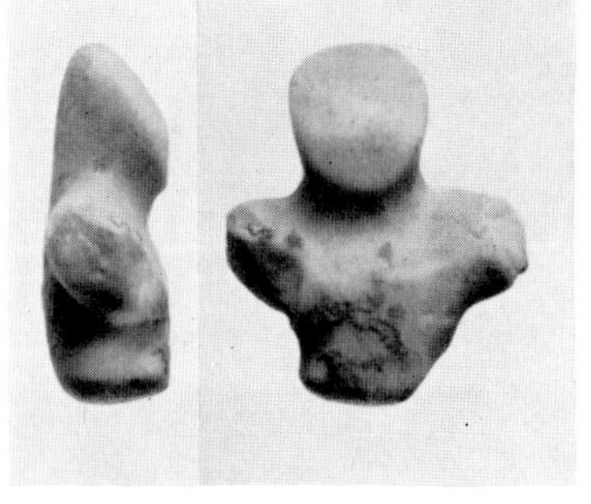

14

13

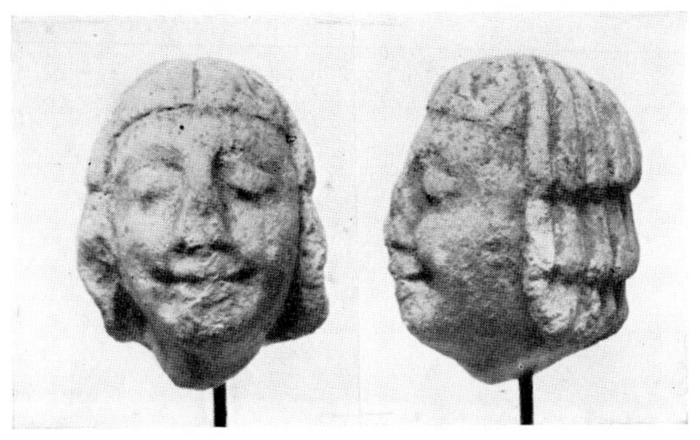

15

16

21

20

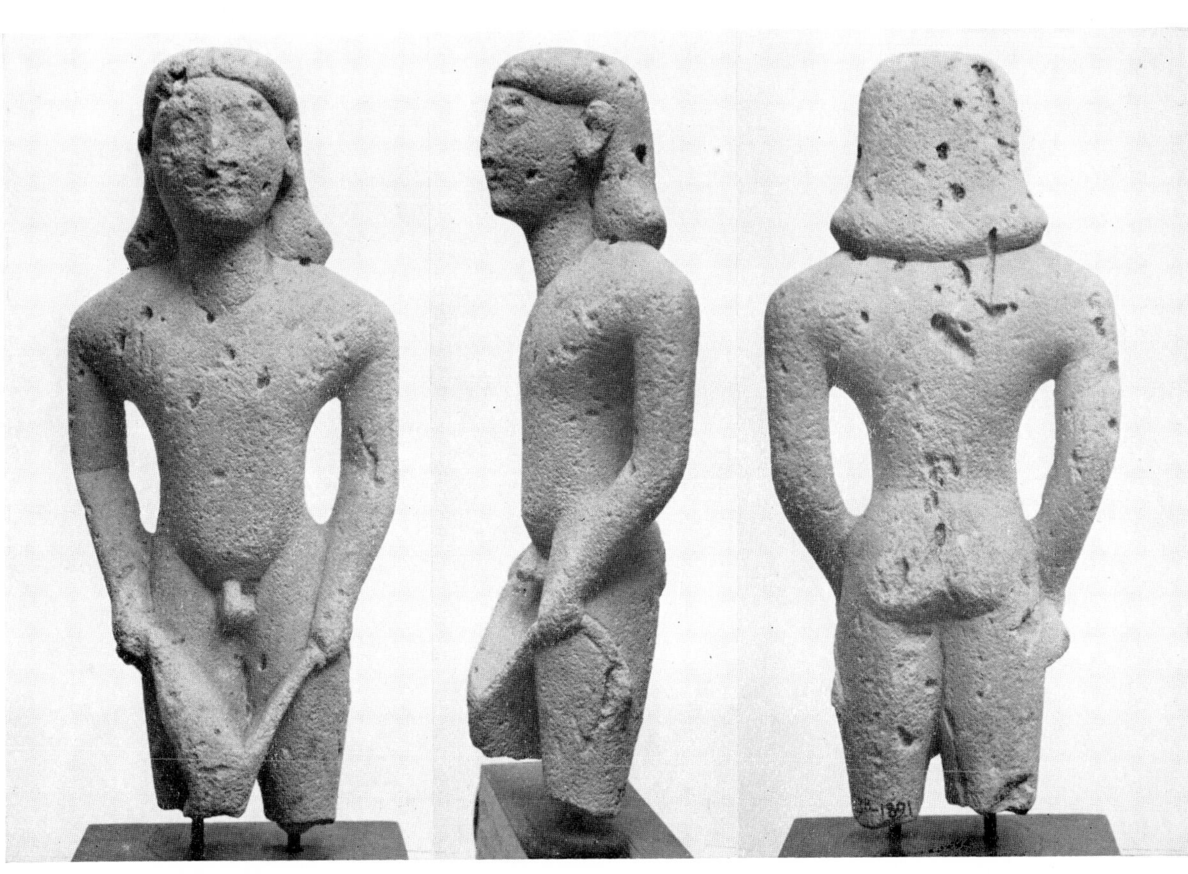

17

18

23

19

22

24

25

27

26

28

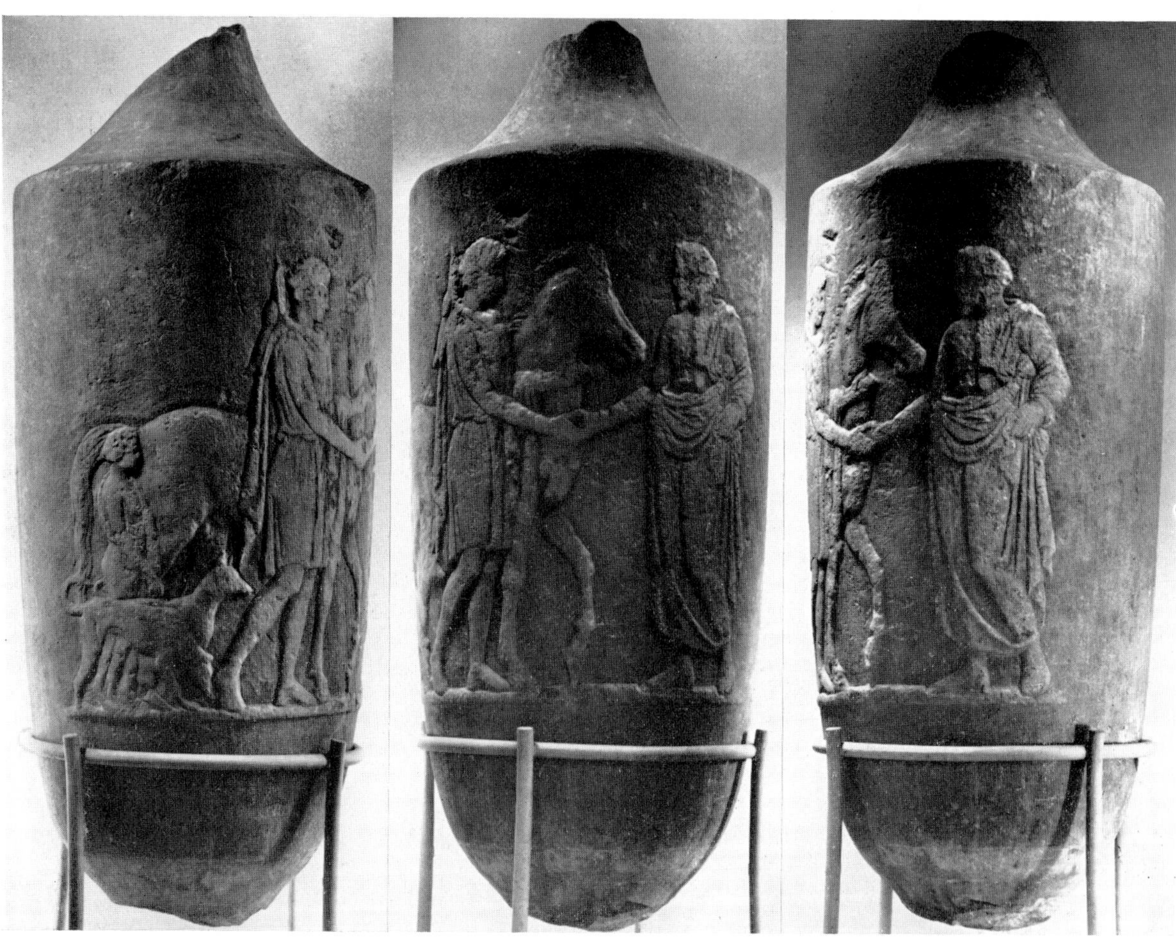

29

31

32

30

34

35

36

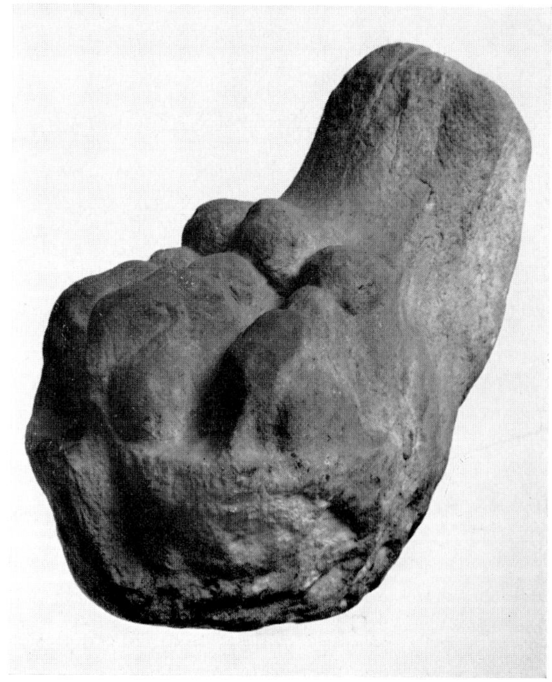

33

37

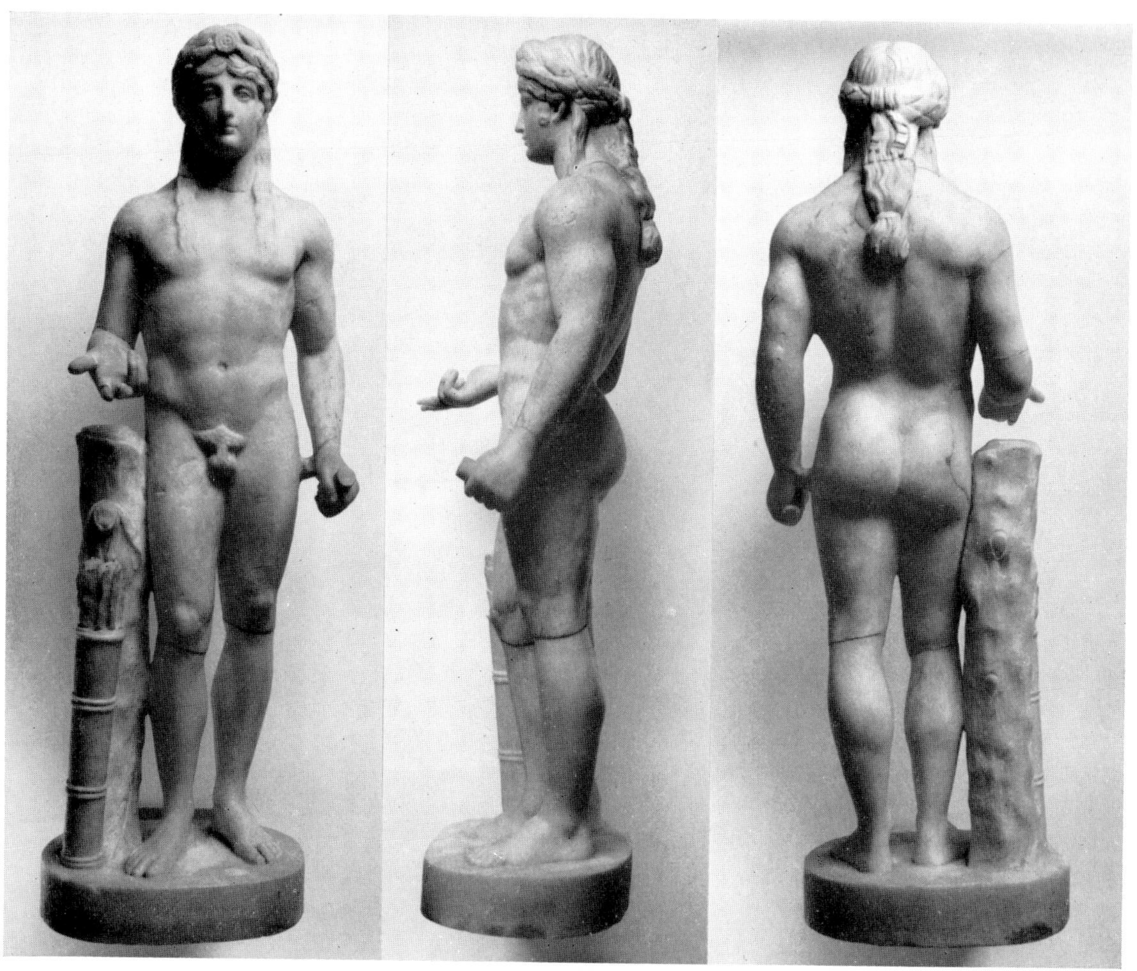

39

41

40

46

45

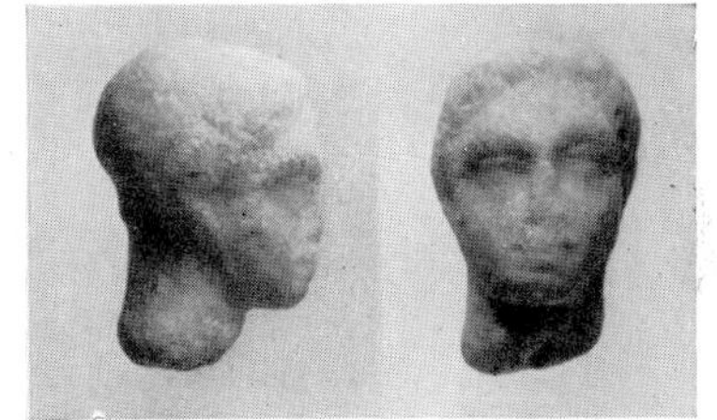

43

38

44

49

47

42

42

48

50

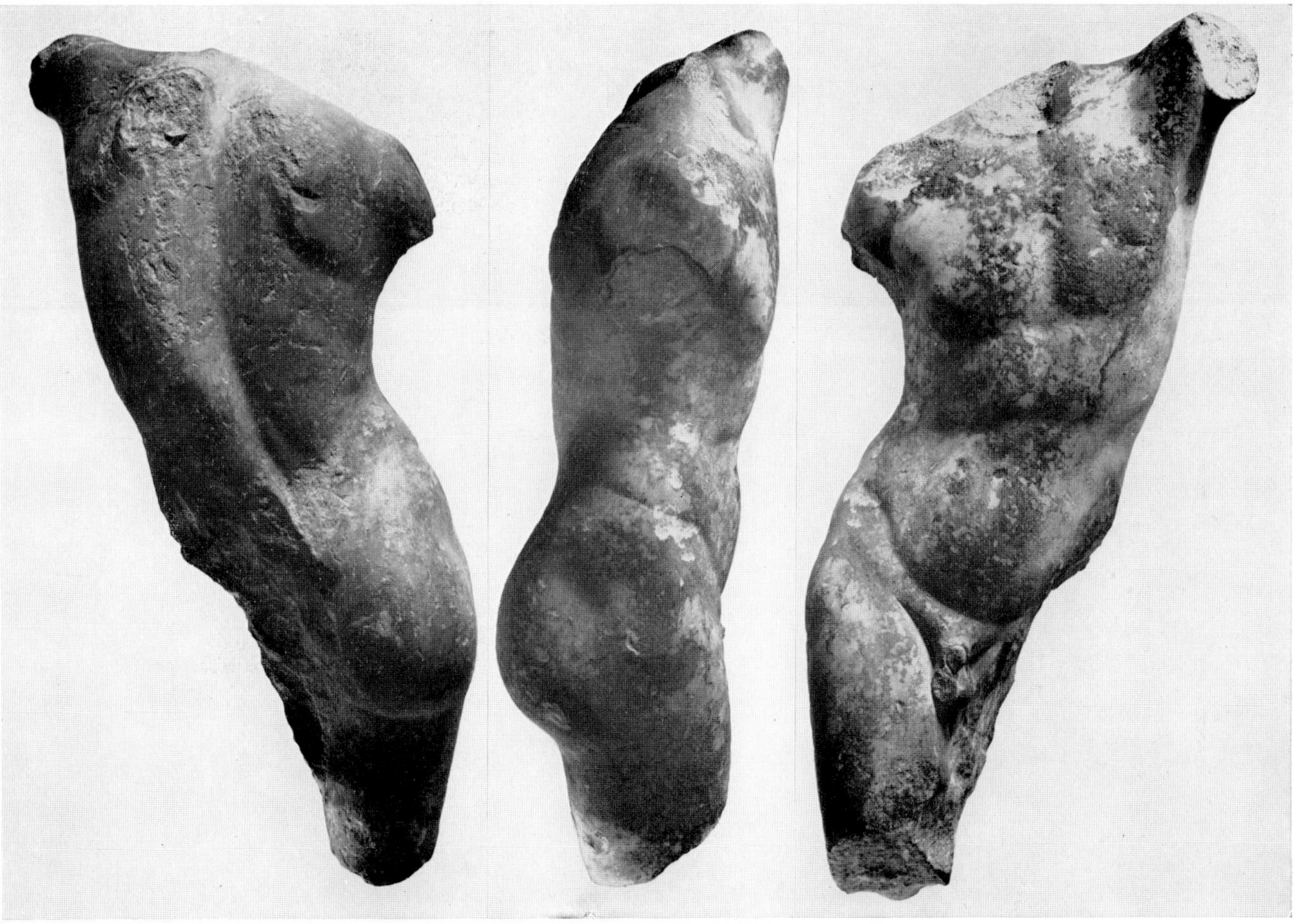

51

53

54

58

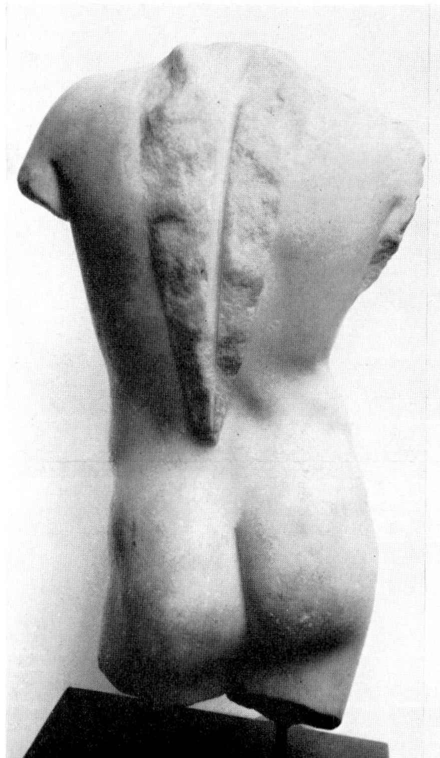

52

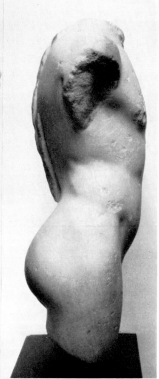

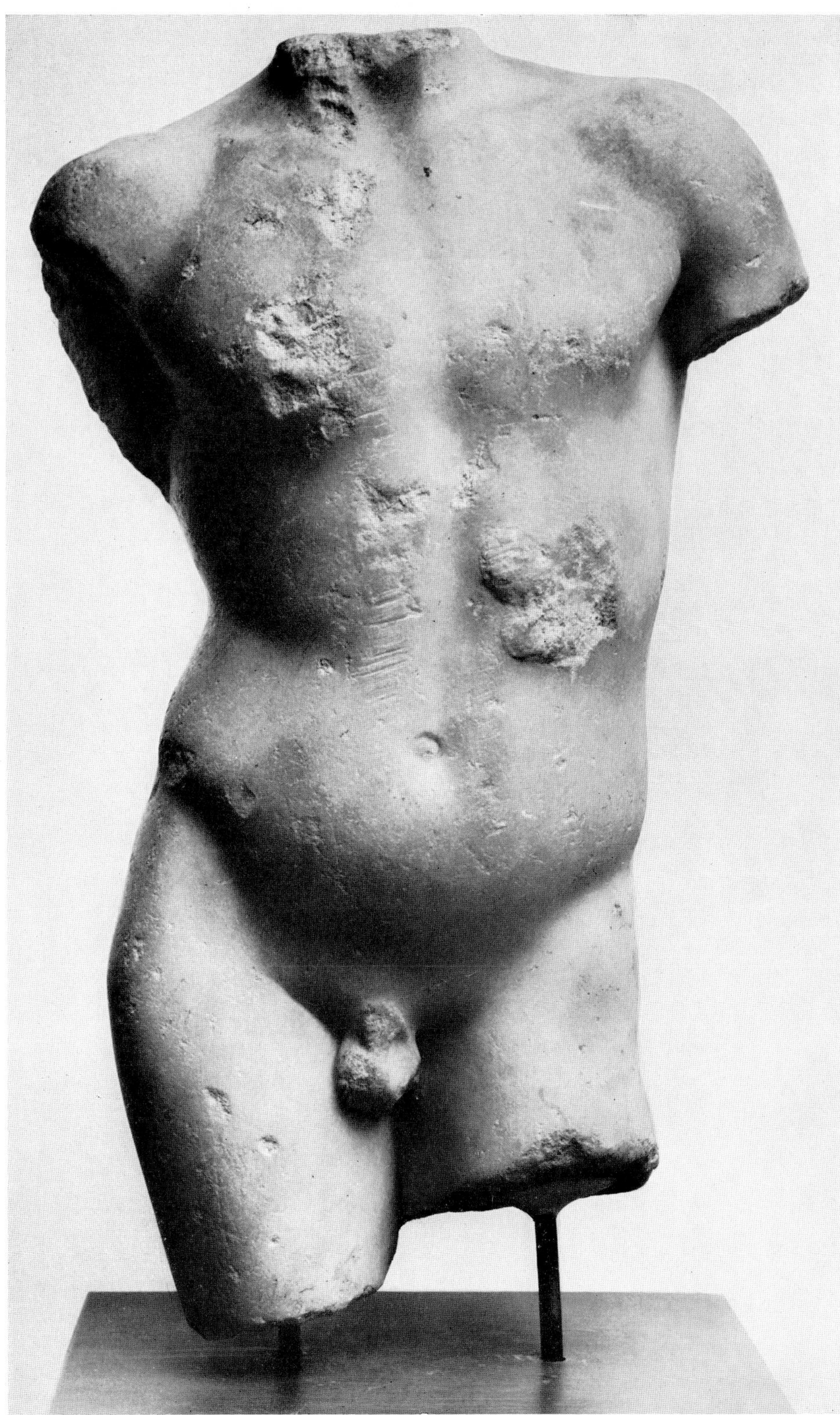

55

56

57

Plate 19

59

60

61

62

63

64

65

66

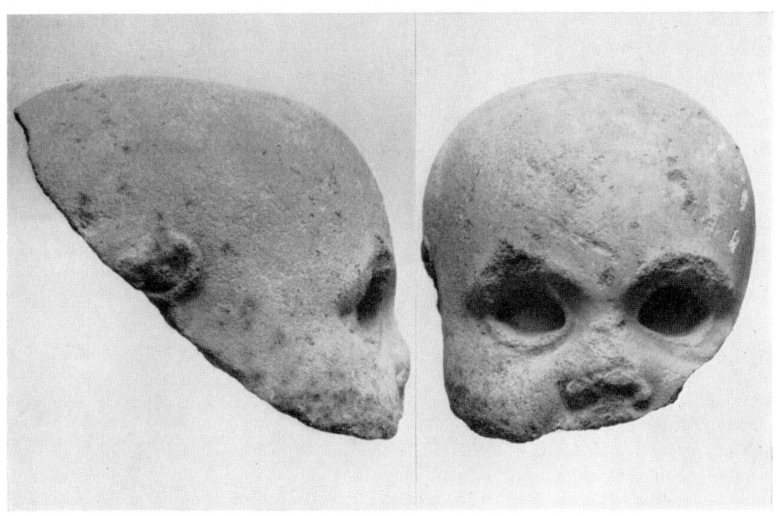

67

68

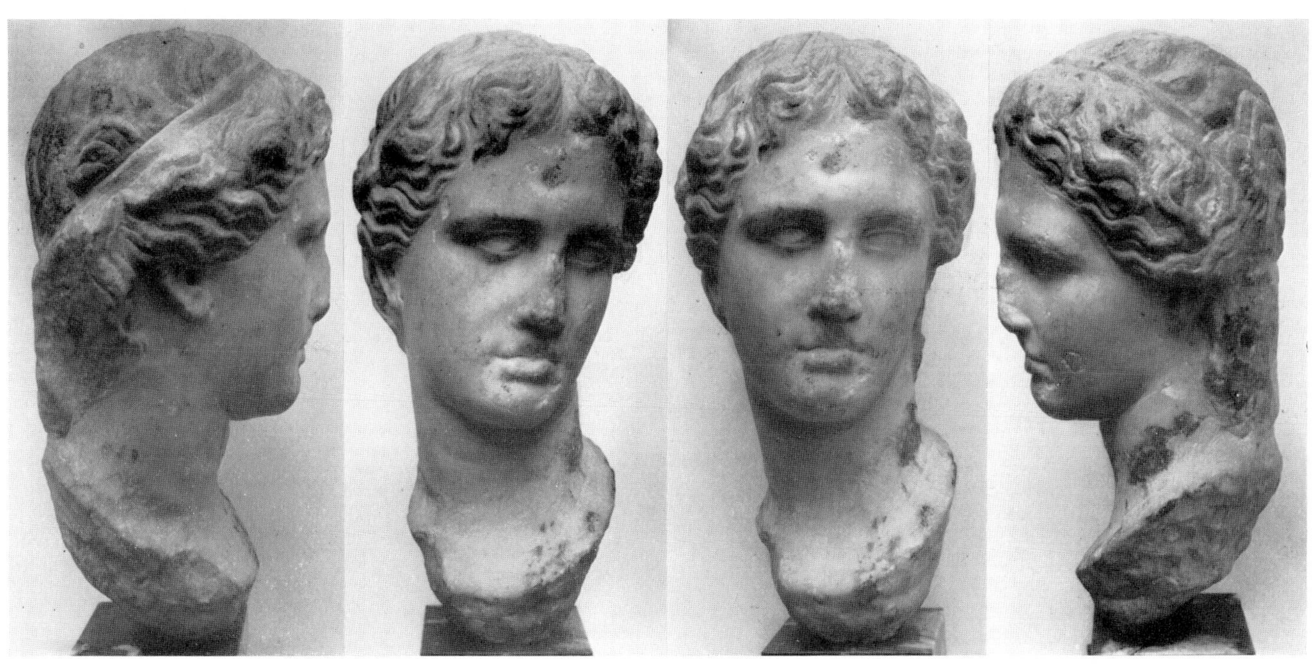

69

71

72

72

73

74

70

77

76

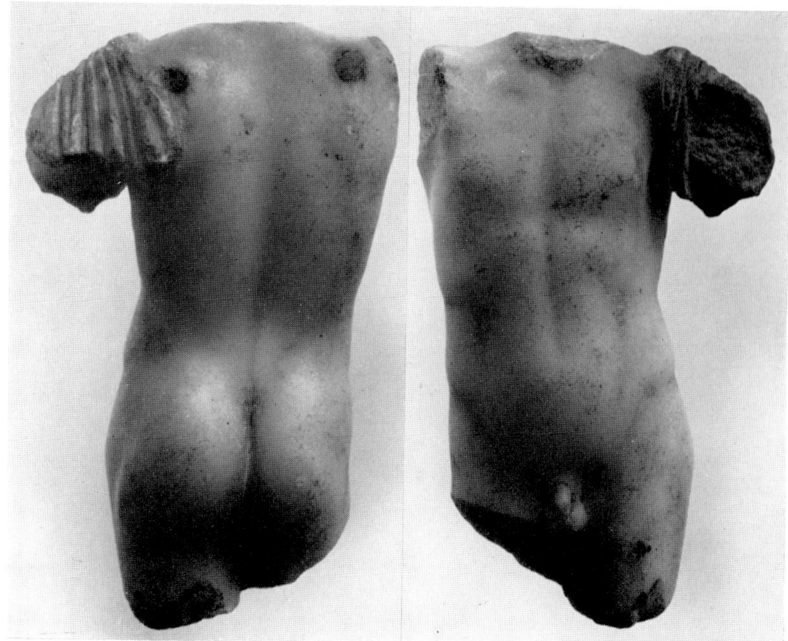

78

81

79

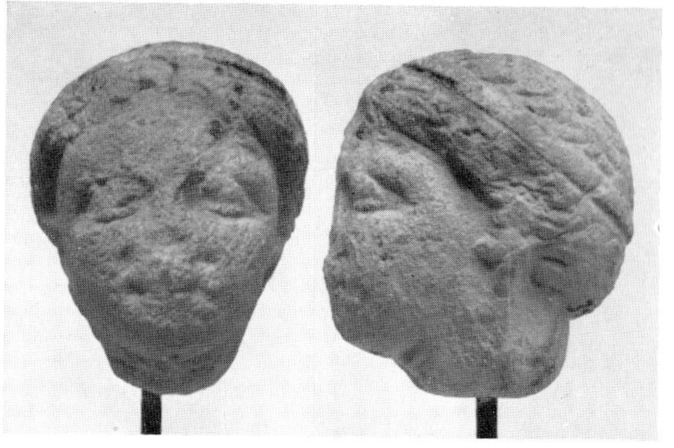

80

75

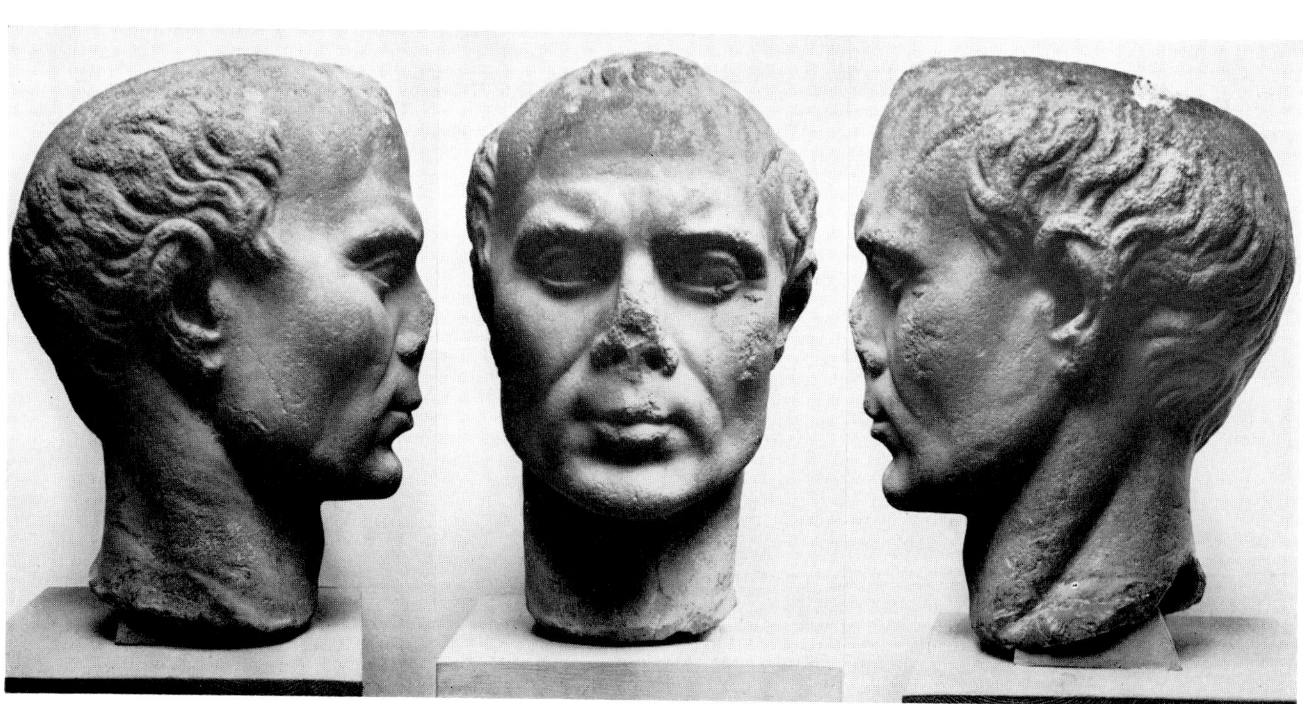

82

84

85

86

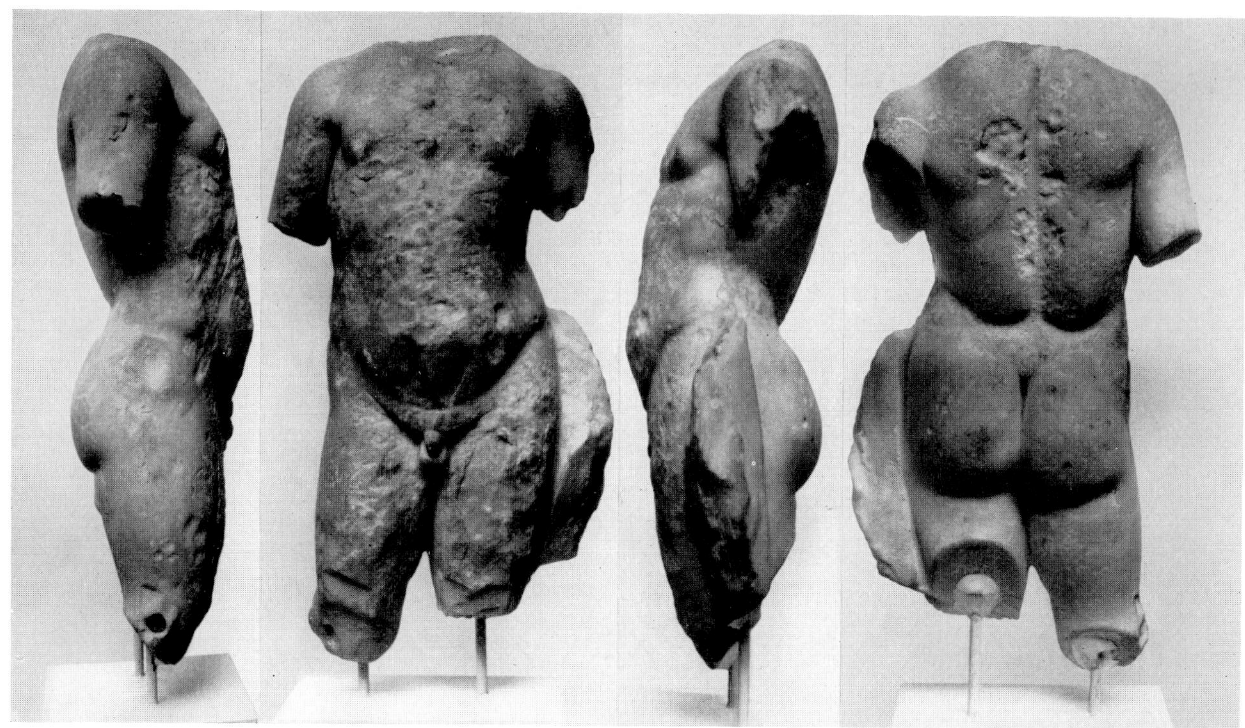

87

83

88

89

90

91

92

93

94

95

96

97

98

99

100

a

b

101

103

102

104

105

106

107

109

108

110

111

113

a

b

c

112

114

a

b

115

116

117

118

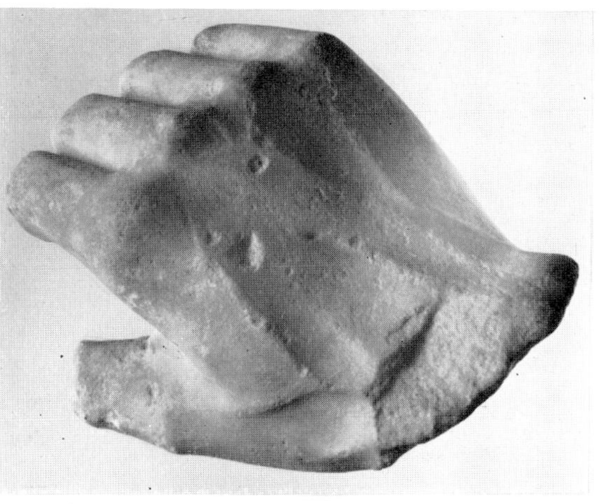

119

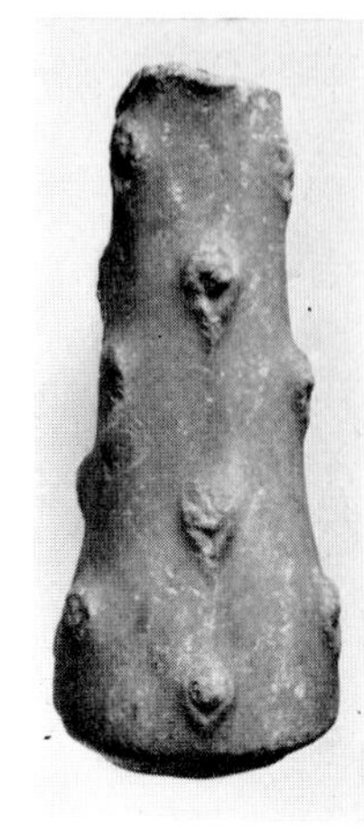

120

121

122

123

124

125

126

127

128

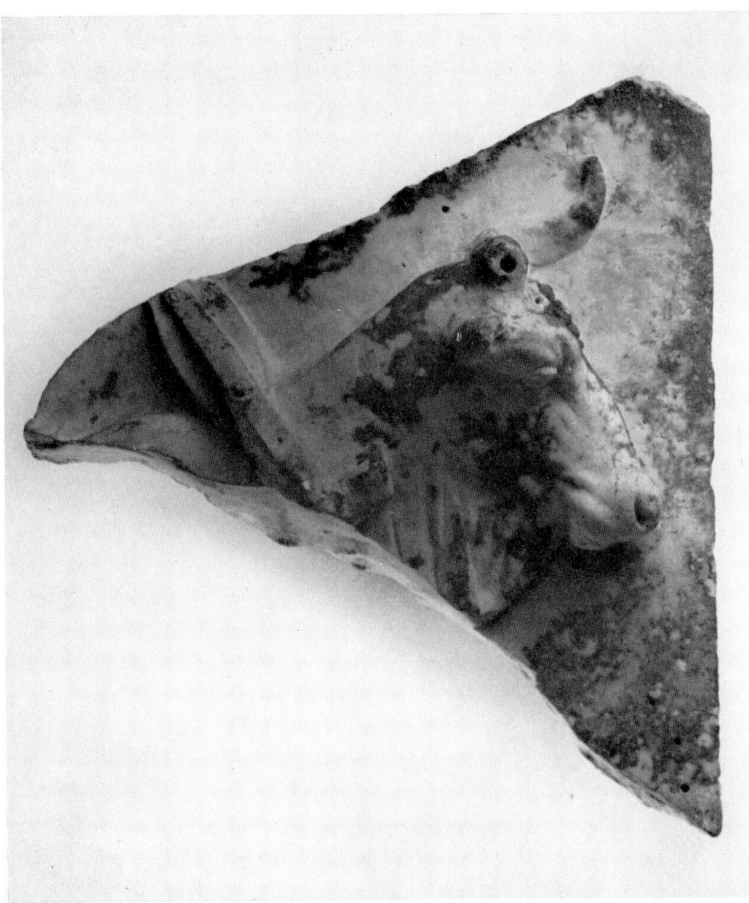

129

132

130

131

134

135

133

144

136

138

137

139

140

140

141

142

146

147

152

148

149

DIIS MANIBVS
SACRVM
T STATILIO HERMET
STATILIA PHILAENI
FECIT·CONIVGI
SVO·CARISSIMO
ET BENE
MERITO·DE·SE

143

145

CON QVO VIXIT AN XXIII B M

150

151

154

155

153

156

159

158

157

160

(*Detail*)

(*Impression*)

(*Impression*)

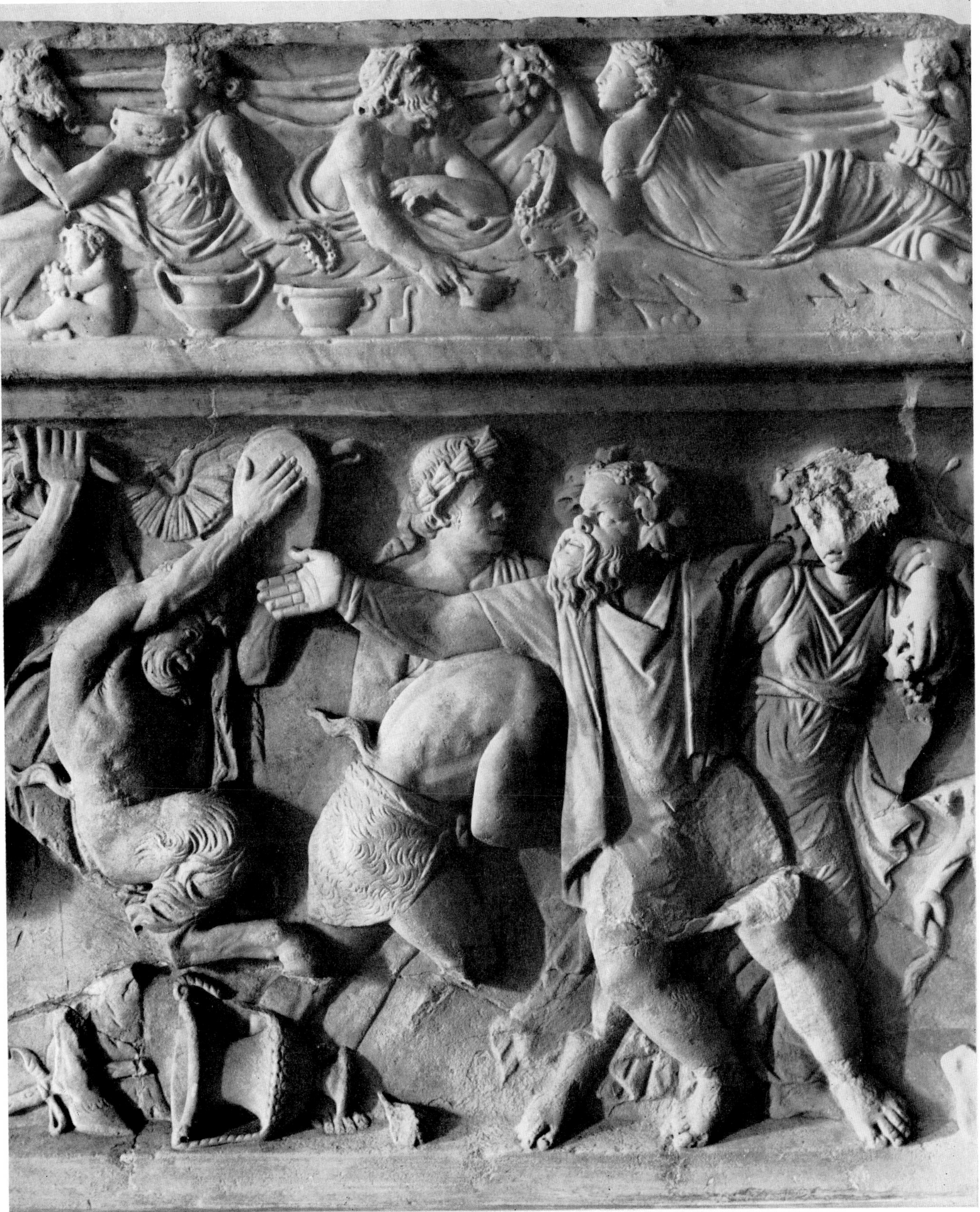

163

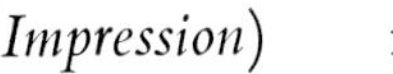

(*Impression*) 163

164

165

166

168

169

170

167

172

173

176

171

177

175

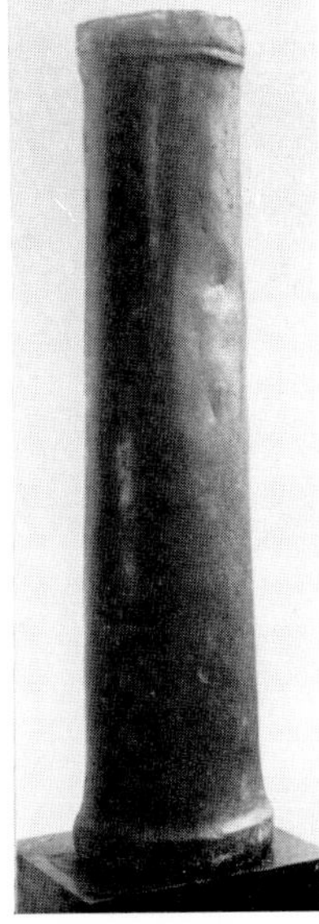

174

178

179

180

182

184

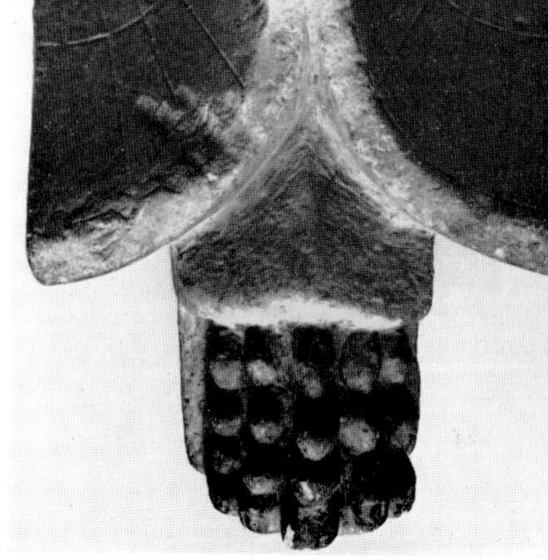

185

a *b* *d* *e*

183 *c*

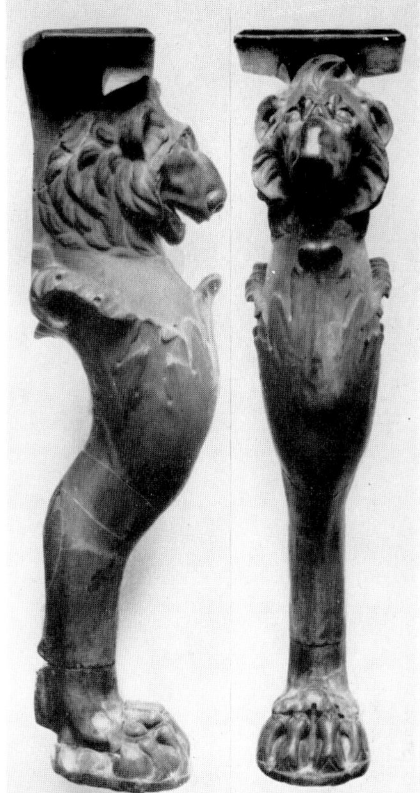

181

186

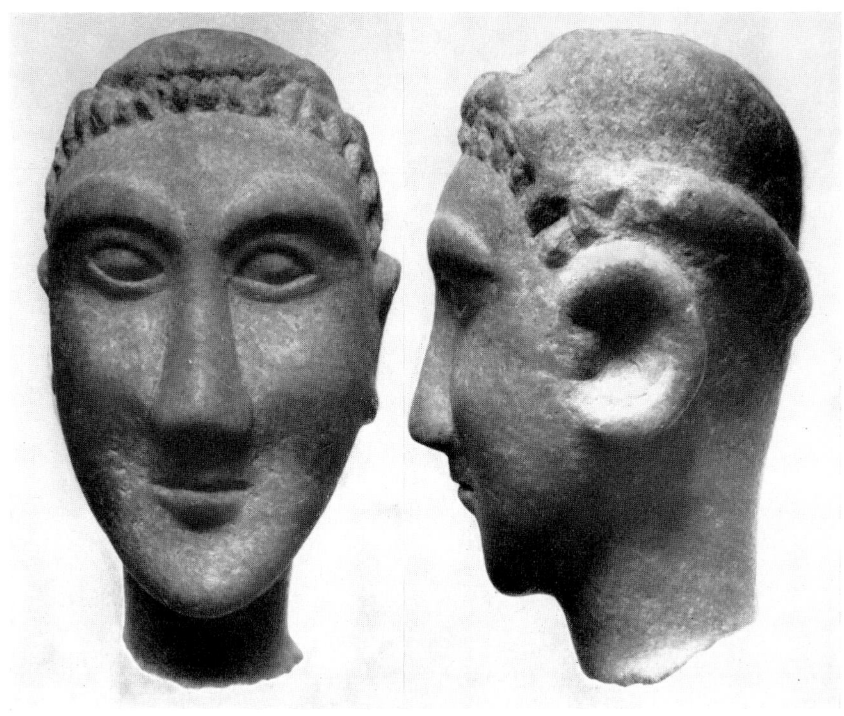

193

187

190

191

188

189

192

INDEX

(*a*) Concordance of inventory numbers

Inventory number	Catalogue number
GR.22.1899	**79**
GR.24.1899	**78**
GR.23.1901	**14**
GR.33.1901	**10**
GR.33*a*.1901	**12**
GR.33*b*.1901	**8**
GR.53.1902	**9**
GR.182.1902	**124**
GR.1.1906	**89**
GR.71.1906	**193**
GR.95*a*.1906	**130**
GR.95*b*.1906	**105**
GR.95*c*.1906	**159**
GR.100.1906	**185**
GR.87.1907	**55**
GR.113.1908	**26**
GR.157*b*.1909	**1**
GR.8.1912	**112**
GR.9.1912	**90**
GR.14.1917	**183a**
GR.15.1917	**183b**
GR.16.1917	**183c, e**
GR.17.1917	**183d**
GR.5.1919	**133**
GR.6.1919	**167**
GR.7.1920	**160**
GR.17.1924	**11**
GR.1.1926	**186**
GR.11.1931	**47**
GR.8*a*.1933	**3**
GR.8*b*.1933	**4**
GR.8*c*.1933	**2**
GR.8*d*.1933	**5**
GR.8*e*.1933	**6**
GR.8*f*.1933	**7**
GR.4.1934	**13**
GR.5.1934	**168**
GR.3.1936	**93**
GR.94.1937	**51**
GR.95.1937	**69**
GR.96.1937	**41**
GR.97.1937	**70**
GR.98.1937	**34**
GR.99.1937	**37**
GR.100.1937	**109**
GR.101.1937	**188**
GR.102.1937	**187**
GR.103.1937	**189**
GR.5.1938	**125**
GR.3.1948	**42**
GR.38.1952	**102**
GR.52.1952	**148**
GR.53.1952	**190**
GR.2.1954	**85**
GR.3.1954	**86**
GR.1.1960	**92**
GR.3.1961	**82**
GR.S.1	**43**
GR.S.2	**67**
GR.S.3	**88**
GR.S.4	**87**
GR.S.5	**118**
GR.S.6	**165**
GR.S.7	**195**
GR.S.8	**198**
E.189.1899	*see* **19**
E.1.1890	**176**
E.2.1890	**177**
E.87.1900	**104**
E.7.1906	*see* **185**
E.GA.3555.1943	**171**
E.SS.41	**175**

(*b*) Concordance to E. D. Clarke, *Greek Marbles Brought from the Shores of the Euxine, Archipelago, and Mediterranean, and Deposited in the Vestibule of the Public Library of the University of Cambridge* (1809)

Clarke number	Catalogue number
3	**174**
4	**138**
5	**136**
6	**137**
10	**62**
11	**49**
12	**132**
13	**135**
14	**81**
15	**123**
16	**91**
17	**107**
18	**28**
19	**121**
20	**75**
22	**122**
25	**71**
26	**94**
27	**36**
29	**27**
32	**58**
33	**120**
34	**99**
35, *lost before 1865*	
36	**45**
37	**33**
38	**119**

(*c*) Concordance to J. Disney, *Museum Disneianum* (1846–9)

Disney plate	Catalogue number
2	**113**
3	**114**
4	**201**
5	**196**
6	**54**
7	**108**
8	**57**
9	**103**
10	**106**
11	**40**
12	**50**
13	**95**
15	**200**
16	**48**
17	**53**

Disney plate	Catalogue number	Disney plate	Catalogue number	Disney plate	Catalogue number
18	**111**	32, 32*a*	**178**	50	**144**
19	**204**	33	**127**	51	**150, 192**
20	**203**	34	**207**	52	**191**
21	**205**	35	**59**	53	**153**
22	**116**	36	**131**	54, 54*a*	**145**
23	**38**	37	**128**	55	**146, 147**
24	**39**	38	**208**	56. 7	**149**
25	**97**	39	**215**	56. 13	**151, 152**
26	**83**	40	**210**	57, 58	**143**
27	**194**	41	**163**	85	**73, 74**
28	**202**	42, 42*a*	**162**	88, *lower*	**60**
29	**96**	48	**155**	94, *left*	**184**
30	**101**	49	**154**	94, *right*	**181, 182**
31	**206**				

(*d*) Concordance to A. Michaelis, *Ancient Marbles in Great Britain* (1882) (pp. 241 f.)

Michaelis number	Catalogue number	Michaelis number	Catalogue number	Michaelis number	Catalogue number
1	**81**	37	**46**	72	**127**
2	**91**	38	**96**	73	**212**
3	**45**	39	**199**	74	**156**
4	**49**	40	**113**	75	**217**
5	**99**	41	**114**	76	**162**
6	**58**	42	**201**	77	**163**
7	**119**	43	**196**	78	**131**
8	**107**	44	**54**	79	**164**
9	**94**	45	**108**	80	**73, 74**
10	**121**	46	**57**	81	**155**
11	**120**	47	**103**	82	**154**
12	**33**	48	**106**	83	**150, 192**
13	**25**	49	**40**	84	**191**
14	**126**	50	**50**	85	**144**
15	**27**	51	**95**	86	**153**
16	**123**	52	**200**	87	**145**
17	**62**	53	**48**	88	**146, 147**
18	**36**	54	**53**	89	**149**
19	**61**	55	**204**	90	**151, 152**
20	**28**	56	**203**	91	**143**
21	**132**	57	**205**	92	**206**
22	**29**	58	**116**	93	**178**
23	**63**	59	**38**	94	**207**
24	**135**	60	**197**	95	**208**
25	**136**	61	**100**	96	**214**
26	**138**	62	**44**	97	**213**
27	**137**	63	**110**	98	**210**
28	**122**	64	**115**	99	**209**
29	**71**	65 (?)	**111**	100	**211**
30	**75**	66	**215**	101	**216**
31	**161**	67	**59**	109	**64**
32	**97**	68	**60**	(p. 453)	
33	**83**	69	**35**	64	**109**
34	**194**	70	**128**	(p. 715)	
35	**202**	71	**128**	233	**82**
36	**101**				

(*e*) Concordance to C. Vermeule and D. von Bothmer, *Notes on a New Edition of Michaelis*, part III. 1 (*AJA* LXIII (1959) 142 f.)

Their number	Catalogue number	Their number	Catalogue number	Their number	Catalogue number
1	**42**	12	**77**	21	**56**
2	**183**	13	**52**	22	**98**
3	**129**	14	**39**	23	**31**
4	**30**	15	**159**	24	**133**
5	**166, 173**	16	**93**	25	**26**
7	**125**	17	**193**	26	**69**
8	**112**	18	**90**	27	**32**
9	**55**	19	**161**	28	**86**
10	**41**	20	**51**	29	**85**
11	**47**				

(*f*) Epigraphical index

PUBLICATIONS

GREEK PROPER NAMES

LATIN PROPER NAMES

PALMYRENE PROPER NAMES

(*g*) Index of donors, etc.

(*h*) General index

Index

(*i*) Glossary

This section is confined to the elucidation of those terms that the reader may not readily find explained in a classical dictionary. In general, only those meanings are cited which are appropriate to the present Catalogue.

ABACUS (*Lat. from Gk.*): flat uppermost member of a capital.

ACANTHUS (*Lat. from Gk.*): prickly plant whose spiky leaves are commonly found carved as architectural ornament.

ACROTERION (*Gk.*): decorative element set on top of the edge of a roof, either above the outer corner of a pediment (lateral acroterion) or above its top (crowning acroterion).

ALABASTRON (*Gk.*): tall, narrow jar, often of alabaster, used for holding unguents and perfumes.

ANATHYROSIS (*Gk.*): smooth marginal dressing of the outer part of a surface associated with the roughening and sinking of its centre in order to ensure a smooth join with an adjacent block.

ANAXYRIDES (*Gk.*): trouser-like garment worn by Eastern peoples such as the Scythians.

ANSATA, TABULA (*Lat.*): rectangular tablet, often inscribed, with projections to the sides, usually of dove-tail shape.

ANTA (*Lat.*): rectangular pilaster terminating the projecting end of the side-wall of a building and thereby flanking a kind of porch at its front.

ANTEFIX (*from Lat.*): ornamental feature set above the eaves of a building to mask the end of a lowermost cover-tile.

APOPTYGMA (*Gk.*): the large over-fold of material hanging down over the breast and back that is formed when the shoulder-pins fastening a peplos or chiton are inserted some way down from the upper edge of the garment.

ASPERGILLUM (*Lat.*): brush for sprinkling sacred water, commonly formed from the foot of a sacrificial animal.

ASTRAGAL (*from Gk.*): the bead-and-reel moulding common in architectural ornament.

BACELLATUS, SARCOPHAGUS (*Lat.*): coffin decorated with undulating fluting.

BAETYL (*from Gk.*): sacred meteoric stone.

BOUKRANIA (*Gk.*): representations of ox-skulls employed as a decorative feature in architecture and deriving from actual skulls nailed on sacred buildings as trophies of sacrifices performed.

CANALIS (*Lat.*): interior part of an Ionic volute, flanked to either side by half-round mouldings.

CARYATID (*from Gk.*): figure of a maiden taking the place of a column in supporting the entablature of a building.

CHITON (*Gk.*): Greek linen garment in the form of a tunic, seamed at the side and pinned, buttoned or stitched at the shoulders or sleeves. It was generally worn short by men and long by women. However, a ceremonial long chiton might be worn by kings, musicians, charioteers, etc., and women engaged in athletic pursuits adopted a short form of the garment.

CHLAMYS (*Gk.*): rectangular Greek woollen garment worn as a kind of short cloak by horsemen, soldiers and young men generally.

CINERARIUM (*Lat.*): box or urn designed to receive the ashes of the dead after cremation.

CISTA (*Lat. from Gk.*): container made of basket-work or of metal, etc., usually of a cylindrical or flaring shape and with a conical lid. CISTA MYSTICA: sacred cista employed to hold special cult utensils or emblems.

COLUMBARIUM (*Lat.*): burial place with 'dove-cote-like' niches in its walls to receive cinerary urns.

CORNUCOPIA (*Lat.*): horn of plenty.

DADOPHOROS (*Gk.*): torch-bearer in marriage or religious celebrations.

DEMOS (*Gk.*): personified populace of a Greek democratic state.

ECHINUS (*Lat. from Gk.*): the convex, 'sea-urchin-shaped' member under the abacus of a Doric capital; also that, usually with ovolo decoration, set under the cushion between the volutes of an Ionic capital.

GALLUS (*Lat. from Gk.*): emasculated priest of Cybele.

GANOSIS (*Gk.*): polishing of a marble surface with oil or wax.

GORGONEION (*Gk.*): representation of the head of the Gorgon, Medusa—an ornament believed to be capable of averting evil.

GUILLOCHE (*Fr.*): a continuous cable-pattern.

HEKATEION (*Gk.*): representation of the goddess Hekate, more especially in her three-fold form as first devised by Alkamenes and later interpreted as showing different aspects of the goddess as Artemis, the Moon, and goddess of the Underworld and witchcraft.

HERM (*from Gk.*): a statue, usually ithyphallic, in the form of a rectangular post surmounted by a human head and with projecting slabs for shoulders. Originally confined to representations of the god Hermes, and used as a boundary-marker, etc., it was later adapted to other deities, portraits of famous men, etc.

HIMATION (*Gk.*): a large Greek outer garment, generally of wool, worn swathed about the body or as a kind of heavy cloak. It was usually worn alone by men, whereas women normally draped it over the chiton, not infrequently carrying it up over the back of the head to serve as a veil.

JANIFORM (*from Lat.*): having a head with two faces looking in opposite directions, like the Roman god, Janus.

KANTHAROS (*Gk.*): form of drinking-cup with a deep bowl and two tall vertical handles.

KIONISKOS (*Gk.*): kind of miniature column which was the only form of grave-stone permitted in Attica in Hellenistic times following the sumptuary laws of Demetrios of Phaleron.

KISTE (*Gk.*): see CISTA (*Lat. from Gk.*).

KISTOPHOROS (*Gk.*): person carrying a cista (*q.v.*) especially in a religious ceremony or procession.

KOLPOS (*Gk.*): a kind of pouch of material over the waist formed when a peplos or chiton is deliberately worn over-long and the surplus cloth is tucked up over the girdle.

KOUROS (*Gk.*): a youth; in particular, the term applied to the nude statues of young men standing stiffly with their hands to their sides which were a favourite theme in archaic Greek art.

KRATER (*Gk.*): large and deep, wide-mouthed vessel used for mixing wine and water.

KYMATION (*Gk.*): 'wave-shaped' moulding employed in architectural decoration, etc. IONIC KYMATION: convex moulding—the ovolo (*q.v.*). LESBIAN KYMATION: moulding, partly concave and partly convex, which, where decorated, takes the form of the 'leaf-and-dart' ornament.

LAGOBOLON (*Gk.*): throwing-stick for catching hares, also used as a shepherd's crook and thus appropriate as an attribute of the shepherds' god, Pan.

LEBES (*Gk.*): a cauldron, used for heating water, or a vase in the shape of a cauldron, employed, like a krater, for mixing wine with water.

LEKYTHOS (*Gk.*): one-handled pottery bottle used to hold oil for anointing—especially frequent as an offering to the dead and, as a consequence, copied in marble as a grave-monument.

LIKNON (*Gk.*): winnowing-fan, usually of basket-work, employed for winnowing grain. It developed a special association with fertility aspects of the Dionysiac cult.

LITUUS (*Lat.*): spiral-shaped wand carried as an emblem of office by the Roman augurs—a priestly college concerned with divination; also a form of trumpet, curved at the end.

LOUTROPHOROS (*Gk.*): tall, long-necked, two-handled Greek vessel used to carry water for the bridal bath. Marble representations of the loutrophoros seem to have been set up over the graves of those who died unwed.

MELONENFRISUR (*Ger.*): Greek women's hair-style popular in late Classical and Hellenistic times and revived in the Imperial Roman period. The hair was carried back in parallel twisted braids to a coiled plait or 'bun' towards the back of the head.

MENISKOS (*Gk.*): metal spike carrying a small plate to protect the heads of statues set up out-of-doors.

MESOMPHALOS (*Gk.*): see PHIALE.

MITRA (*Gk.*): archaic belt or girdle (as in Homer); broad head-band worn by women, royalty, orientals and the god Dionysos.

MODIUS (*Lat.*): cylindrical or flaring head-dress in the shape of a corn-measure.

MYSTERIES (*from Gk.*): special sacred rites to which only the initiated (*mystai*) were admitted.

NAÏSKOS (*Gk.*): small temple or shrine; building in the form of a small temple.

OINOCHOE (*Gk.*): wine-jug.

OMPHALOS (*Gk.*): boss; at Delphi, a conical or hemispherical stone in the Temple of Apollo said to mark the centre of the world.

OSCILLUM (*Lat.*): disc, adorned with reliefs, which was hung as a decorative feature under the architrave between the columns of a colonnade.

OVOLO (*It.*): convex moulding with egg-and-dart decoration.

PALMETTE (*Fr.*): stylized flower of the palm-tree, usually surmounting volutes which represent its stylized leaves—a decorative motif adapted by the Greeks from oriental prototypes.

PEDUM (*Lat.*): form of shepherd's crook or throwing-stick, commonly carried by satyrs and by Pan—the equivalent of the Greek *lagobolon* (*q.v.*).

PELTA (*Lat. from Gk.*): light shield of Thracian type.

PEPLOS (*Gk.*): long, woollen outer garment worn by Greek women. It consisted, basically, of a simple rectangle of cloth of abundant width, folded about the body and pinned at the shoulders. See also APOPTYGMA, KOLPOS.

PETASOS (*Gk.*): low-crowned, broad-brimmed, felt hat worn by Greek men.

PHIALE (*Gk.*): shallow drinking-bowl without handles, used especially for pouring libations to the gods. PHIALE MESOMPHALOS (*Gk.*): phiale with a large projecting boss in the centre.

PILOS (*Gk.*): tall, conical felt hat with practically no brim worn by Greek men, more especially by travellers, soldiers and workmen.

PLEMOCHOE (*Gk.*): 'top-shaped' Greek toilet vessel on a broad foot, also used in pouring certain libations in the Eleusinian Mysteries.

POLOS (*Gk.*): cylindrical head-dress worn by certain deities and, in some cases, by the 'heroized' dead.

PROTOME (*Gk.*): fore-part, bust or head of a human being or animal used as a decorative feature or as an art-form in itself.

PYXIS (*Gk.*): small lidded box or vase used to hold toilet articles, trinkets, etc.

RHYTON (*Gk.*): form of drinking-horn, open at the tip, which often took the shape of the head of an animal, etc., used for drinking, pouring libations, or as a funnel for filling other vessels.

SAKKOS (*Gk.*): form of head-scarf worn by women wound round the head in order to confine the hair.

SCRINIA (*Lat.*): boxes or containers for books written on papyrus rolls, etc.

SPHENDONE (*Gk.*): 'sling-shaped' head-scarf worn by women, confining the hair below and at the sides, but usually partly open at the top.

STEATOPYGY (*from Gk.*): an extreme fatness of the buttocks found amongst women of certain races.

STELE (*Gk.*): post or slab, commonly carrying a relief, painting or inscription.

STEPHANE (*Gk.*): crescent-shaped metal ornament worn in the hair over the brow.

SYRINX (*Gk.*): pan-pipe.

TAENIA (*Lat. from Gk.*): head-band or fillet; ribbon used, e.g., for fastening a garland.

THYMIATERION (*Gk.*): incense-burner.

THYRSOS (*Gk.*): staff, crowned with a pine-cone-shaped knot of leaves, carried by maenads and others in Dionysiac celebrations.

TOGA (*Lat.*): men's woollen outer garment worn swathed about the body in a complex pattern of folds and constituting the ordinary civil dress of a Roman citizen.

TORUS (*Lat.*): convex moulding of semicircular profile.

TOTENMAHLRELIEFS (*Ger.*): 'funerary-banquet-reliefs' associated with the cult of the 'heroized' dead. Originally votive in function, they gradually became no more than a variety of gravestone.

TUBA (*Lat.*): long, straight military trumpet.

TYMPANON (*Gk.*): a kind of tambourine especially prominent in the cult of Cybele.

URKUNDENRELIEFS (*Ger.*): reliefs adorning stelae inscribed with public documents such as decrees, treaties, laws, etc.

VANNUS (*Lat.*): winnowing-fan—the Greek *liknon* (*q.v.*).

VANTH (*Etr.*): Etruscan winged goddess associated with the dead.